Medico-Moral Problems

GERALD KELLY, S. J.

Medico-Moral Problems

The Catholic Hospital Association
OF THE UNITED STATES AND CANADA
ST. LOUIS 4, MISSOURI

Imprimi potest:

JOSEPH P. FISHER, S.J.

Provincial, Missouri Province

Imprimatur:

✠JOSEPH E. RITTER

Archbishop of St. Louis

December 18, 1957

R
724
K38
1958

131890

3.00

CONTENTS

Explanatory Preface - - - - - vii
1. Some Basic Notions and Principles - - 1
2. Introductory Directives - - - - 17
3. Non-Catholics and Catholic Codes - - 26
4. Consent of the Patient - - - - 36
5. Informing the Dying Patient - - - 42
6. Should the Cancer Patient be Told? - - 46
7. Medical Consultation - - - - 51
8. Doctor and Supervisor - - - - 59
9. Destruction or Risk of Life: the Principles - 62
10. Therapeutic Abortion - - - - 68
11. Ergot and Abortion - - - - - 84
12. Cesarean Section - - - - - 90
13. Operations on the Infant in Utero - - 96
14. The Morality of Ectopic Operations - - 105
15. Abdominal Pregnancy - - - - 111
16. Euthanasia - - - - - - 115
17. Preserving Life - - - - - 128
18. Elective Induction of Labor - - - 142
19. Catholic Teaching on Contraception and Sterilization 149
20. The Morality of Rhythm - - - 168
21. The Doctor and Rhythm - - - - 176
22. Procedures Causing Sterility - - - 183
23. Vasectomy with Prostatectomy - - - 190
24. Castration for Cancer - - - - 199

v

25.	Hysterectomy	-	-	-	-	-	-	206
26.	Moral Aspects of Sterility Tests	-		-	-		218
27.	Artificial Insemination	-	-		-	-	228
28.	Mutilation: Some Particular Problems	-		-	245
29.	Experimentation on Human Beings		-	-	261
30.	Psychosurgery	-	-	-	-	-	270
31.	Narcoanalysis and Hypnoanalysis		-	-	282
32.	Hypnosis as Anesthesia	-	-	-	-	288
33.	Electro-Shock Therapy	-	-	-	-	294
34.	An Instruction on Baptism	-	-	-	-	298
35.	Baptism of Adults	-	-	-	-	-	304
36.	Calling a Non-Catholic Minister	-	-	-	320
37.	Disposal of Amputated Members	-	-	-	325
38.	Cooperation in Illicit Operations	-	-	-	332
Appendix: Statements of the Holy See	-	-	-	336
Index	-	-	-	-	-	-	-	340
Special Index of Directives	-	-	-	-	375

Explanatory Preface

Between 1949 and 1955, The Catholic Hospital Association of the United States and Canada published a series of five booklets entitled *Medico-Moral Problems*. As the booklets multiplied, there were many requests to put all the material under one cover. The present volume is an answer to these requests, with some important qualifications: (1) It does not contain all the material previously published in the booklets. It omits some discussions that are now obsolete (e.g., on the Eucharistic fast); and it reorganizes other materials so that everything about a given topic is treated in a single chapter (e.g., discussions of lobotomy and of hysterectomy). (2) It brings all the old material up to date, insofar as that was possible. (3) It contains much completely new material.

The content of this volume is arranged according to the sequence of topics in the second and revised edition of *Ethical and Religious Directives for Catholic Hospitals*. This revised edition contains sixty directives, numbered consecutively. Most, but not all, of these are explained in this book; and a few others are quoted in passing. To make it easy to recognize them, the directives that are explained are printed in bold type and slightly indented.

Ethical and Religious Directives for Catholic Hospitals is not an official code in any diocese unless the bishop adopts it as such. It is, however, the basis for the *Moral Code (Code de Morale)*, which was officially adopted by the entire Canadian Hierarchy in 1954, and for the *Code of Medical Ethics for Catholic Hospitals*, which was prepared in 1954 at the request of many bishops' representatives and is the official code in many dioceses of the United States. Whenever feasible, I give cross references to these official codes, using the expressions, "Canadian Code," and "U.S. Code."

Some further observations about references: Pertinent information about books and magazines referred to in my text is usually given in footnotes. In some instances, however, I have incorporated this data into the text itself because it seemed that this method would be more helpful to the reader. Finally, in referring to statements of the Holy See, I often give merely the date. The reason for this is that a complete list of all the statements cited, with information concerning the content, circumstances, official sources, translations, and so forth, is given in chronological order in the Appendix.

Some Basic Notions
and Principles

THE PURPOSE of this chapter is to explain briefly some of the concepts and principles that are basic to an understanding of medical morality. Many of these points, and others too, are more fully explained in subsequent chapters; but it seems desirable to give here at least a concise exposition of some of the more important notions and principles.

I. DIVINE LAWS

Speaking generally, we may say with the great jurist, Sir William Blackstone, that a law is a "rule of action dictated by some superior being."[1] In this general sense, there are laws that govern even inanimate things: plants, animals, and so forth. For example, there are the laws of gravitation, of nutrition, and of instinctive response.

In a more particular sense—and this is what concerns us— a law is a rule of human conduct established either by God

---

[1] My quotations from Sir William Blackstone are taken from the eighth edition of his *Commentaries on the Laws of England* (Oxford: The Clarendon Press, 1778), Introduction, pp. 39-42. Blackstone's *Commentaries,* like our own Declaration of Independence, is based on the firm conviction that man is a creature, entirely dependent on God, his Creator, and that the will of God is the supreme rule of all human conduct. In the quotations, I have naturally preserved the original spelling, even though archaic: e.g., "it's" for "its."

1

Himself or by some person or society that has authority from God. A law made by God Himself is called a *divine* law; a law made by others (e.g., the proper authorities in the Church or state) is a *human* law. Divine laws are of two kinds:

a) *The Natural Law:* In creating human beings, God necessarily wishes them to live in conformity with the nature He gives them. This will of God, imprinted in human nature itself, is the *natural law.* It binds all men. It concerns our essential relationships to God, to our individual neighbors, to society, and to ourselves. Absolutely speaking, the natural law can be known clearly, without any external help, by any man with sufficiently developed reason; practically, however, in the present order of things, men need the help of divine revelation in order to have a clear and adequate knowledge of the natural law.

b) *The Divine Positive Law:* Precepts given by God through revelation make up what are called *divine positive laws.* These precepts are of two kinds. Some (e.g., laws concerning the reception of sacraments) impose duties not contained in the natural law. Others express obligations already contained in the natural law: e.g., the inviolability of innocent human life, the prohibition of onanism, and, in general, the Ten Commandments. The revelation of these natural-law precepts adds no new obligation; it merely confirms the natural law and makes it easier to know it. There will be many references in subsequent chapters to certain precepts of natural law that are also an explicit part of divine revelation. When speaking of these, the popes often use the expression, "natural and divine law." Obviously, this does not mean that the natural law is not a divine law; it is merely a technical expression which means "the natural law and the divine positive law."

Today, especially among jurists who have no sound religious background, there is a tendency to ignore the notion of divine laws and even to deny their existence. Fortunately, this tendency seems to be waning; there are many signs of a return

2

to the kind of thinking that characterized Sir William Blackstone and the jurists of his time. Concerning the natural law, Blackstone wrote:

This law of nature, being coeval with mankind and dictated by God himself, is of course superior in obligation to any other. It is binding over all the globe in all countries, and at all times; no human laws are of any validity, if contrary to this; and such of them as are valid derive all their force, and all their authority, mediately or immediately, from this original.

Blackstone also recognized the difficulty of knowing the natural law and the need of divine help through revelation. Moreover, he was deeply conscious of the subordination of human laws to the divine. Here are some of his words on these points:

. . . And if our reason were always, as in our first ancestor before his transgression, clear and perfect, unruffled by passions, unclouded by prejudice, unimpaired by disease or intemperance, the task [of knowing the natural law] would be pleasant and easy; we should need no other guide but this. But every man now finds the contrary in his own experience; that his reason is corrupt, and his understanding full of ignorance and error.

This has given manifold occasion for the benign interposition of divine providence; which, in compassion to the frailty, the imperfection, and the blindness of human reason, hath been pleased, at sundry times and in divers manners, to discover and enforce it's laws by an immediate and direct revelation. The doctrines thus delivered we call the revealed or divine law, and they are to be found only in the holy scriptures. . . .

Upon these two foundations, the law of nature and law of revelation, depend all human laws; that is to say, no human laws should be suffered to contradict these.

In these words of one of the most renowned jurists, we have a description of the divine law that must be taken as the foundation of all sound morality. The one point on which the Catholic moralist would correct Blackstone is his statement that the revealed divine laws are found only in Holy Scripture; we would say that these laws are found also in apostolic tradition.

3

II. ON "DOING GOOD" AND "AVOIDING EVIL."

The two most general precepts of the natural law are: "do good," and "avoid evil." The former is called an *affirmative* law; the latter, a *negative* law. To the theologian, this distinction is of supreme importance. Moral evil must always be avoided, no matter what the cost. But there is a limit to the duty of doing good. Because of this distinction, we absolutely condemn such things as euthanasia and contraception; these are violations of negative natural law (i.e., of the precept of avoiding evil). On the other hand, we admit that there is a reasonable limit to a man's duty to care for his health, of a doctor's duty to care for his patient, of married people's duty to have children, and so forth. Practical applications of these limits to the duty of doing good will be found particularly in the chapters concerning the means of preserving health and life, and on the practice of rhythm.

The mention of the negative natural law prompts me to discuss a principle of great importance in morality in general and in medical morality in particular. I refer to the principle that a good end cannot justify the use of an evil means. This principle, so simple in itself, can be very complicated in its explanation. It does not mean that no evil may be done in order to obtain good. It refers primarily to *moral* evil; and in this respect it is absolute, because *moral* evil may never be done to obtain any kind of good. The principle is not absolute as regards *physical* evil, because there are some physical evils that we have a right to cause in order to obtain a good effect. An example of this latter that is very common in medicine is mutilation. Mutilation is certainly a physical evil; yet, as we shall see, there are some circumstances in which man has a right to mutilate himself or to authorize such mutilation.

The principle that a good end does not justify an evil means is not only a truth of reason; it is also stated in revelation. The Scripture text usually cited in this matter is Romans 3:8, which in the translation by Msgr. Ronald Knox runs as

4

follows: "If so, why should we not do evil so that good may come of it? *That is what we are accused of preaching by some of our detractors;* and their condemnation of it is just." Incidentally, the words I have italicized might have been a prophecy concerning the Jesuits!

It must be admitted that those who are not soundly trained in the science of morality are much inclined to judge things as if a good end did justify an evil means. Thus there are sincere defenders of such things as therapeutic abortion, masturbation to obtain semen for analysis, donor insemination, and so forth. Our objection to these and similar things is that, though the ultimate purposes are certainly good (e.g., to save a mother's life, to promote fertility), the means used to attain these purposes are morally evil and never permitted.

III. HUMAN LIFE AND BODILY INTEGRITY

Every living thing has within it some force, some principle, that makes it live. In the human being, this principle of life is the soul. Since the human soul is spiritual and immortal, it must come directly from God. It follows from this that no man is his own master, in the full sense of the word. God is the master; and man is only the steward of his life, of his bodily members, and of his spiritual and corporeal functions.

A steward can use things or destroy them only according to the will of his master. God gives to no one the power to directly destroy innocent human life. This applies to one's own life and to the life of others. On the other hand, there are some circumstances in which man has a right to do things which entail risk to life and even the indirect loss of life.

Over the members of his body, man has a somewhat wider "power of attorney"—if I may use the expression. By this I mean that there are circumstances which allow him, as the administrator of his body, to dispose directly of members of his body, even to the point of destroying them or suppressing their function. This will be explained more fully in nn. V and

5

VI of this chapter. For the time being, I should merely like to call attention to the fact that man's direct power to destroy members and to suppress functions depends on the nature, or purpose, of the members and functions.

As regards the purpose of the members and functions of the human body, an important distinction must be made between reproductive and non-reproductive organs. The latter exist precisely (that is, primarily, if not exclusively) for the good of the individual. They are simply parts of the whole. For example, the gall bladder, the kidneys, the legs, the eyes, and so forth, are certainly destined by God primarily for the good of the person; they are supposed to be aids to his total well-being. For this reason he can destroy or remove them when they become harmful.

As for the reproductive system, some qualifications must be made. The *reproductive power* (i.e., the function itself) is primarily for the good of the species, not for the individual; and this function is not directly subordinated to the individual's well-being. On the other hand, the endocrine functions of ovaries and testicles are certainly for the good of the individual; and all the reproductive organs are supposed to serve the individual, at least in the general sense of preserving his health. Hence, if the endocrine function becomes harmful or if one of the organs becomes diseased or a source of harm, suppression of the internal secretions or removal of the organs themselves can be justified.

IV. MUTILATION

Anyone who has studied dictionaries, encyclopedias, and more lengthy discussions of mutilation must know that this term has various meanings. As Dr. Austin O'Malley remarks:
The term Mutilation as applied to the human body has various meanings. In civil law mutilation of a person is called Mayhem, an old form of the word Maim, and is defined by Blackstone as "such hurt of any part of a man's body as renders him less able in fighting to defend himself or annoy his adversary." By statute in the United

6

States and Great Britain the scope of the offense has been so extended as to include injuries to a person which merely disfigure or disable.[2]

Dr. O'Malley then proceeds to discuss mutilation from the point of view of canon law and moral theology. As a partial conclusion of his discussion he has the following:

> To blind a man without removing the eye, to cut out his spleen in the treatment of Banti's disease, to remove a woman's ovary or uterus, to cut off part of the point of a finger, to crop the top of an auricle, to knock out a tooth, and any other permanent marring of the body, even to cause an unsightly scar across the face, are all mutilations in the moral sense of the term.[3]

Dr. O'Malley's is a good summary of the matter, yet it could be more complete. Generally speaking, moral theologians define mutilation as the removal of a bodily member or the suppression of a bodily function. Many, however, add that this definition refers only to mutilation in the strict sense of the word. They admit that in a broader sense the term includes such things as lacerations and disfigurement. Fr. B. J. Cunningham, C.M., who has published the most thorough discussion of this topic in recent times, defines mutilation as any injury, even temporary, to the corporal integrity of a person; and he divides mutilations into *major* and *minor*. Concerning this division, he writes:

> Major and minor mutilations are distinguished from one another quantitatively, that is, they are determined according to the amount of harm done to the body. A mutilation is said to be *major* or *grave* when corporal integrity is gravely injured, for example in the removal of a member, or in the total inhibition of an organic function. A mutilation is said to be *minor* when, although corporal integrity is violated, a member is not removed, nor is its function seriously impaired. Such, for example, would be the mutilation involved in face-lifting, or in the piercing of an ear-lobe.[4]

---

[2] Austin O'Malley, M.D., *The Ethics of Medical Homicide and Mutilation* (New York: The Devin-Adair Company, 1919), p. 23.

[3] *Ibid.*, p. 25.

[4] Bert J. Cunningham, C.M., *The Morality of Organic Transplantation* (Washington: The Catholic University of America Press, 1944), pp. 14-15.

Fr. Cunningham's discussion brings out other interesting points. For instance, he rightly calls attention to the fact that mutilation need not be by surgery, but that it can be accomplished by other means such as x-ray. (Similarly, I might add, the means might be merely chemical, such as a drug that inhibits a function.) Also, he includes under the concept of mutilation such things as blood transfusions and skin grafts.

I have given the foregoing data mainly for information. Certainly my purpose has not been to confuse. Rather, I wish to avoid confusion; and it seems to me that the best way of doing this is to use a very broad definition of mutilation: namely, any procedure which interferes, even temporarily, with the complete integrity of the human body. This general description refers to surgery, irradiation, or any other treatment, such as the use of drugs and chemicals. It includes serious things like the excision of a kidney, as well as minor procedures such as blood transfusions and skin grafts. It is not limited to the removal of organs or the suppression of functions; it extends also to such things as circumcision, exploratory operations, cosmetic surgery, and so forth.

From the point of view of civil and canon law, mutilation usually connotes some kind of wrongdoing. This is not the case in either medicine or moral theology. As we conceive them here, therefore, mutilations may be either justifiable or unjustifiable. They are justifiable if they are in accordance with sound principles; unjustifiable, if they are contrary to principles. The concluding sections of this introductory chapter will deal briefly with the pertinent moral principles.

V. THE PRINCIPLE OF TOTALITY

One principle that is frequently used to determine the morality of mutilating procedures was explained by St. Thomas Aquinas many centuries ago when he wrote:

Since any member is a part of the whole human body, it exists for the sake of the whole as the imperfect for the sake of the perfect.

8

Hence, a member of the human body is to be disposed of according as it may profit the whole. *Per se,* the member of the human body is useful for the welfare of the whole body. . . . If, however, a member, by reason of its diseased condition, should endanger the well-being of the whole body, it is permissible, with the consent of him whose member it is, to remove this diseased member for the well-being of the whole body.

St. Thomas spoke only of a "diseased" member. This should be understood as merely one example, and not as a necessary limitation, of the principle of the part-for-the-whole. Through the centuries eminent moralists have discussed three typical cases in which the principle might be applicable. The first of these concerns the diseased organ, as in the example given by St. Thomas. The second is illustrated by the case of the man whose foot is caught in a railroad track and who can save his life only by amputating the foot. The third concerns the perfectly healthy man who is ordered by a tyrant, "Cut off your hand or I'll cut off your head!" In all cases the sacrifice of the part would be permitted as a necessary means of preserving life.

The third case may sound fantastic (although, as a matter of fact, examples in which it is equivalently verified are not rare even in our modern and "advanced" civilization); but both it and the second case illustrate the point that a destructive procedure can be justified even though an organ is not diseased in the technical sense. The main point is not so much the diseased or nondiseased condition of an organ, but rather the fact that its presence or its functioning would be a real source of harm to the whole body.

In all the typical cases, the organ is sacrificed in order to ward off the danger of death. This extreme is not necessary. Bodily members and functions exist not merely for survival but also for maintaining a reasonable state of well-being. The sacrifice of a part is permitted, therefore, when this is necessary for alleviating great pain or removing or avoiding a pathological condition. But the benefit to be reaped in terms

9

of total well-being should be proportionate to the destruction involved. Good morality demands this, and good medicine concurs.

Pope Pius XII has often used and explained the principle of the part-for-the-whole, and has generally referred to it as "the principle of totality."[5] As far as I have been able to trace it, his first public use of this expression was in his important address on the moral limits of medical research and experimentation given to delegates to the First International Congress on the Histopathology of the Nervous System, Sept., 13, 1952.

In this discourse to the histopathologists, the Pope discussed the three reasons frequently alleged as justifications for experimentation on human beings. The first of these, the advancement of science, he admitted to be valid within properly defined limits. Speaking of the second alleged reason, the good of the patient himself, the Pope brought out three points: first, that the patient's consent is always required, even when an experimental or research procedure is for his own good; secondly, since he is not the owner of his body, but only the administrator, the patient's right to dispose of his members and functions is limited; and thirdly, as a good administrator, the patient may dispose of members and functions insofar as this is required for the good of the whole. The exact words of the Pope on these last two points are worth recalling:

. . . Because he is a user and not a proprietor, he does not have unlimited power to destroy or mutilate his body and its functions. Nevertheless, by virtue of the principle of totality, by virtue of his right to use the services of his organism as a whole, the patient can allow individual parts to be destroyed or mutilated when and to the extent necessary for the good of his being as a whole. He may do so to ensure his being's existence and to avoid or, naturally, to repair

---

[5] For an extended treatment of this topic, see "Pope Pius XII and the Principle of Totality," *Theological Studies,* Sept., 1955, pp. 373-396. For a more synoptic treatment, see *The Linacre Quarterly,* Aug., 1956, pp. 70-76.

serious and lasting damage which cannot otherwise be avoided or repaired.

A year later (Oct. 8, 1953), the Pope explicitly covered the case—apparently troubling some—of destroying or removing a healthy organ for the good of the whole. On this occasion he said:

> The decisive point here is not that the organ which is removed or rendered inoperative be itself diseased, but that its preservation or its functioning entails directly or indirectly a serious threat to the whole body. It is quite possible that, by its normal function, a healthy organ may exercise on a diseased one so harmful an effect as to aggravate the disease and its repercussions on the whole body. It can also happen that the removal of a healthy organ and the suppression of its normal function may remove from a disease, cancer for example, its area for development or, in any case, essentially alter its conditions of existence. If no other remedy is available, surgical intervention is permissible in both cases.

The principle of totality can be used to justify a mutilation only when and to the extent that its basic supposition is verified: namely, that a part exists for the good of the whole. It cannot, therefore, be used to justify harmful experimentation, with or without the consent of the subject, when the experimentation is "for the advancement of medicine or the good of society." The reason for this is that the individual is not a part of society in the same sense in which a bodily member is a part of the human body. Nor can the principle be used to justify organic transplantation (e.g., a renal transplant from one identical twin to another), because no human being is subordinated to another as part to whole. For the same reason, the principle of totality cannot of itself justify a mutilating procedure on a mother which entails the loss of a fetus. Nor, finally, can this principle afford complete moral justification for any procedure which induces sterility, because, as we have seen, the reproductive function is not directly subordinated to the individual.

11

VI. THE PRINCIPLE OF THE DOUBLE EFFECT

The possible justification of organic transplantation and harmful experimentation for the good of others will be sufficiently discussed in chapters 28 and 29. At this point, I wish to concentrate on the other problems mentioned in the last paragraph: namely, mutilating procedures which entail the loss of fetal life or which induce sterility. It is clear from the *Directives* that such procedures are sometimes permissible. For instance, in directive 20 it is stated that in an ectopic pregnancy a dangerously affected fallopian tube may be removed, even though fetal life is thus indirectly terminated. And directive 32 allows bilateral oophorectomy in the treatment of cancer of the breast, even though this procedure necessarily renders the woman sterile.[6] On what principle are these and similar procedures justified? The theologians' answer is, "the principle of the double effect."

The principle of the double effect, as the name itself implies, supposes that an action produces two effects. One of these effects is something good which may be legitimately intended; the other is an evil that may not be intended. Thus, in the examples mentioned in the preceding paragraph, the good effect of removing the dangerously affected fallopian tube is the saving of the mother's life, and the evil effect is the loss of fetal life; in the oophorectomy, the good effect is prevention of metastasis or at least palliation, and the evil effect is steriliza-

---

[6] In his address to urologists, Oct. 8, 1953, Pope Pius XII solved the problem of castration in the treatment of cancer of the prostate in terms of the principle of totality. This might be taken to mean that no other principle is needed, even when an operation induces sterility. However, if the papal teaching on this point is understood in the context of his general teaching about sterilization, it seems very clear that the principle of the double effect is required. According to the Pope's general teaching, a *direct* sterilization is never permitted; hence, any justifiable sterilization must be *indirect*. This clearly implies the need of the principle of the double effect. For further discussion of this topic, see *Theological Studies*, Sept., 1955, pp. 382-385.

tion. The main point in this presupposition is that some good effect is produced, because, if an action produces *only* an evil effect, that effect is necessarily intended.

Granted the presupposition of good and evil effects, an action is permitted, according to the principle, if these conditions are fulfilled:

1) *The action, considered by itself and independently of its effects, must not be morally evil.* There are some actions, as we know, that are intrinsically evil: e.g., blasphemy, perjury, masturbation, and murder. Such actions are always forbidden, no matter what beneficial consequences they might have. Consequently, if we can determine that a given action falls into this category, we know immediately that no principle can justify it.

I should add here, I think, that in many, if not most, surgical procedures and their equivalents, it is not possible to judge the morality of the action independently of its effects. When this is the case, it may be taken as a practical rule that the principle of the double effect is applicable if the next three conditions are verified.

2) *The evil effect must not be the means of producing the good effect.* The principle underlying this condition is that a good end cannot justify the use of an evil means. This principle has been sufficiently explained in n. II above. Here, I shall simply call attention to the fact that this condition is verified in both the typical cases we are considering. When the dangerously affected tube is removed, the mother is saved precisely by this operation and not by the killing of the fetus. And, when the oophorectomy is performed, the growth of cancer is impeded by the suppression of hormone activity and not by the sterilization. In both these cases, therefore, the evil effects (loss of fetal life and sterilization) are simply unavoidable by-products of operations designed to produce the good effects.

13

3) *The evil effect is sincerely not intended, but merely tolerated.* This is simply a repetition of our presupposition that we are dealing with evil effects that lie outside the scope of our rights and which, therefore, may not be *intentionally* caused. In the cases we are considering, therefore, neither the patient nor the physician may intend the loss of fetal life or the sterilization. The attitude toward these effects must be one of mere tolerance.

4) *There must be a proportionate reason for performing the action, in spite of its evil consequences.* In practice, this means that there must be a sort of balance between the total good and the total evil produced by an action. Or, to put it another way, it means that, according to a sound prudential estimate, the good to be obtained is of sufficient value to compensate for the evil that must be tolerated.

In some cases the difficulty of estimating the proportionate reason is so great that even the most eminent theologians may disagree in their solutions. It seems, however, that in the sphere of medicine, this condition presents no entirely unusual difficulty. The condition requires just what doctors often have to do in deciding what is good medicine. They have to weigh all the factors, favorable and unfavorable; and they thus reach a decision that, in view of all the factors, good medicine calls for this or that procedure. Thus, before removing a pregnant tube, one must consider the possibility of bringing the fetus to viability, the danger involved in delaying the operation, and so forth. And, before performing an oophorectomy in the treatment of cancer of the breast, one must consider not merely the organic condition of the patient, but also the probable psychological effects, the availability of other less serious curative procedures, and so forth. It is only by thus examining the total picture that one can make a correct appraisal of the proportionate reason for a procedure; and this is required not only by good morality but also by good medicine.

14

I have barely outlined the principle of the double effect. It is, as may be seen from my outline, a complicated principle— a practical formula for the application of many principles to an individual problem. And it is, as Fr. T. L. Bouscaren, S.J., remarks ". . . in its application, an extremely subtle principle. There are always some persons who are shocked by it, particularly when it is applied in difficult cases. Nevertheless, the principle is absolutely sound. It stands on its own feet, and justifies itself in the light of reason and conscience. . . . It is practically impossible to call that principle into question; and, as we have seen, it may at times be applied to justify the permission of even the gravest consequences, such as the death of innocent persons."[7]

Before I conclude this discussion, it may be well to note that, despite its complicated nature, the principle of the double effect contains the solution to many of life's practical problems, both great and small; and conscientious people often use the principle without any actual knowledge of the conditions. The aviator who bombs an important military target, foreseeing but not desiring the deaths of some civilians, is, perhaps unwittingly, applying the principle. The student who must read a treatise on sex, foreseeing but not desiring temptations against chastity, is also using the principle, although he too may have no training in its use. And all of us, whether we realize it or not, are following the same principle when we perform some good and necessary action, realizing that, despite our best intentions, some others will misunderstand and will be led to rash judgments and criticisms. The deaths of the civilians, the sexual temptations, and the harsh thoughts and criticisms are all simply unavoidable and unwanted by-products of actions that are good in themselves and of sufficient importance to be performed despite the evil effects that accompany them. Hence,

---

[7] T. Lincoln Bouscaren, S.J., *Ethics of Ectopic Operations,* 2nd ed. (Milwaukee: The Bruce Publishing Company, 1944), pp. 37-38.

these and similar actions are really examples of the legitimate use of the principle of the double effect, even though the persons performing the actions would not be able to formulate the principle itself.

chapter 2

Introductory Directives

1. **Catholic hospitals exist to render medical and spiritual care to the sick.** The patient adequately considered, and inclusive of his spiritual status and his claim to the helps of the Catholic religion, is the primary concern of those entrusted with the management of Catholic hospitals. Trustees and administrators of Catholic hospitals understand that this responsibility extends to every patient and that it is seriously binding in conscience. A partial statement of this basic obligation is contained in these Ethical and Religious Directives. All who associate themselves with a Catholic hospital, and particularly the members of the medical and nursing staffs, must understand the moral and religious obligations binding on those responsible for the management and operation of the hospital and must realize that they are allowed to perform only such acts and to carry out only such procedures as will enable the owners and administrators to fulfill their obligations.

2. The principles underlying or expressed in these Directives are not subject to change. But in the application of principles the Directives can and should grow and change as theological investigation and the progress of medical science open up new problems or throw new light on old ones.

3. As now formulated, the Directives prohibit only those procedures which, according to present knowledge of facts, seem certainly wrong. In questions legitimately debated by theologians, liberty is left to physicians to follow the opinions which seem to them more in conformity with the principles of sound medicine.

4. Cases can arise in which the morality of some procedure is doubtful, either because the Directives do not seem to

17

cover the case or because their application is not clear. In such cases, consultation is obligatory, if possible; and the hospital reserves the right to insist on this and to choose or to approve the consultants. In urgent cases that allow no time for consultation, the physician in charge should do what seems most proper to his own conscience. Having done what he honestly judges best in such an emergency, the physician has no just cause for anxiety of conscience; but he should refer the matter to the hospital authorities to obtain guidance for future emergencies of the same nature.

THESE DIRECTIVES are sufficiently clear, I believe, to any-one who is familiar with medical morality; hence, I shall limit my comments to a few practical suggestions that may be of use in further explaining these introductory topics, especially to those who have had no formal training in medical ethics.

DUTY OF AUTHORITIES

No attempt is made in the first directive to give a complete statement of the responsibilities of hospital authorities. But the directive does state clearly what is perhaps the primary *specific* duty of authorities in *Catholic* hospitals: namely, to see that the sick are cared for in accordance with Catholic principles. This means that the law of God must be observed in the care of every patient and that the laws of the Church pertinent to the duties, rights, and privileges of the sick must be observed by all who are subject to these laws.

It is very important, it seems to me, to see clearly the point of view expressed in this directive. It emphasizes the fact that in making certain demands on the staff and personnel the hospital authorities are not acting arbitrarily, but are merely carrying out a seriously-binding duty which they assume, at least implicitly, with their office. In other words, the observance of these ethical and religious directives is a matter of conscience for them, and not a matter of impulse or even of personal preference.

18

VITALITY OF DIRECTIVES

When people who do not understand the Catholic position hear that Catholic hospitals are revising their medico-moral codes, they are inclined to conclude that the Church is changing her principles. In fact, not a few have either openly said this or at least have asked about it. A brief answer to this problem is contained in the second directive. Moral principles do not change; and the Church makes no claim to the power of changing them. But our understanding of these principles and their implications can grow; and through this deepened understanding we can learn to formulate our principles more precisely. As for concrete cases, certainly the applications of principles can change from time to time, and even from case to case, according to the changing facts upon which the applications depend.

A somewhat more detailed explanation of the foregoing general statements seems in order. In the section of the ethical directives dealing with specific procedures (nn. 12-48), each group of directives is divided into "Principles" and "Particular Applications." If we were to publish a new medico-moral code every year, we would certainly make no substantial change in the statement of the principles. We might, it is true, learn through experience how to formulate some of these principles more clearly and precisely; and we might introduce this clearer formulation into subsequent codes. As a matter of fact, in the composition of both the first and second editions of the *Directives,* the compilers (who certainly did not disagree on principles) worked very hard to achieve an apt formulation of the principles; and, though there was general satisfaction with the final statement, no one would deny that a more perfect formulation might be possible. To strive for and to use such an improved formulation is certainly not the same as changing our principles.

I mentioned above that we can grow in our knowledge of the implications of principles. As a good example of this I

19

might point to the first part of directive 40: "Any procedure harmful to the patient is morally justified only insofar as it is designed to produce a proportionate good." In its present formulation the validity of the principle is unquestionable. But if we were to attempt to phrase the principle more precisely by including some absolute statement of what constitutes the proportionate good, we might endanger the validity of the principle. For—as is mentioned in the same directive 40—theologians are now confronted with the problem of organic transplantation; and, until they have weighed all the moral implications of this problem, they cannot say definitely whether the proportionate good legitimately includes the donation of a part of a living human body for use in another body. In the sense, then, of our achieving a deeper understanding of its implications, this principle certainly admits of reformulation.

I trust that from the foregoing it is clear that a statement of principles can admit of only accidental differences in subsequent editions of the *Directives,* as well as in various editions of hospital codes. And what is said of principles is also true of some of the particular applications contained in the *Directives.* For instance, there can be no question of any kind of notable change in what is said about direct abortion, direct attacks on fetal life, euthanasia, contraceptive sterilization, immoral sterility tests, and so forth. In these points the application of the general principle is so immediate and so logical that a change in the morality of the procedures is inconceivable. In fact, some of these directives are actually nothing more than restatements of the general principles.

But in those particular applications which involve merely a question of sufficient reason, changes are not only possible, but very probable, if not inevitable. For instance, we can at present allow certain drastic measures such as castration in the treatment of carcinoma, lobotomy in the treatment of mental illness and intractable pain, and so forth. The discovery of new remedies and the development of new techniques could render

20

such drastic measures unnecessary, useless, and even relatively harmful; and in that case they would cease to be morally justifiable just as they would no longer be good medicine. It is true that the statements in the *Directives* even now carefully qualify the justifiable use of severe remedies; but, once the value of simpler, available remedies has been clearly established, these statements can be omitted from future editions of the *Directives* or other medico-moral codes. In this sense, codes can and must change: they must always preserve a certain freshness and practicality by eliminating material that has become obsolete and by incorporating new material that solves the problems of the moment.

DEBATABLE QUESTIONS

The provisions of directive 3 are but concrete applications of the sound general principle that obligations (i.e., precepts and prohibitions) are not to be imposed unless they are certain. The compilers of the *Directives* tried to follow this principle with the utmost fairness. Even though in some cases their own opinions might incline to stricter views, they consistently made allowance for sound reason or sound authorities to the contrary.

An example of the conservative use of prohibitions is the directive concerning sterility tests (n. 38): only procedures already established as immoral are forbidden. And the same principle of liberty underlies many of the positive concessions made by the *Directives*. For instance, the provisions made for ectopic operations (n. 20), suppression of ovarian function for carcinoma of the breast (n. 32), and hysterectomy for prolapse of the uterus (n. 34) are perhaps not beyond controversy, either medical or moral; yet the reasons or authorities (or both) that can be cited in favor of these concessions are so strong that it would not be in keeping with sound principles to deny patients and their physicians the right to follow these procedures, granted the conditions outlined in the *Directives*.

21

I cannot say whether this is generally true—and I hope it is not—but I have noticed that some physicians are much less tolerant of other physicans' opinions than are moralists of the views of other moralists. This may be a digression, but I think it has a point here. It is not entirely uncommon that physicians adopt a certain procedure to attain a given purpose and that they wish the moralists to outlaw different procedures as unethical, despite the fact that these other procedures are apparently backed by reputable and conscientious medical authorities. The compilers of the *Directives* had regard not only for diversity of views among theologians (as is explicitly stated) but also for conflicting views of competent physicians. It would be neither possible, nor wise, nor just to compose a medico-moral code with specifications so rigid as to rule out all recognition of wholesome differences of opinion.

Before I leave directive 3, I should like to point out that the principle that obligations are not to be imposed unless they are certain is not exactly the same as saying "in doubt there is liberty." There are doubts and doubts; and not all of them can be immediately resolved into freedom from definite obligation. For example, it is stated in directive 27: "In all cases in which the presence of pregnancy would render some procedure illicit (e.g., curettage), the physician must make use of such pregnancy tests and consultation as may be needed in order to be reasonably certain that the patient is not pregnant." The reason for this directive is that a sound suspicion of pregnancy constitutes what is called a "doubt of fact"; and the standard rule for such doubts is that reasonable means to solve them must be taken before any potentially harmful procedure is employed.

UNFORESEEN DOUBTS

Directive 4 covers a number of very important points. In the first place, it is inevitable that in the course of hospital practice puzzling cases will arise that are not specifically solved by even a very up-to-date code. For instance, within a short time after the revised edition of the *Directives* was published, we had literally a stream of requests about the morality of hypnosis as an anesthetic. At the time these requests were made it was impossible to give a definite, general answer to the problem, because the answer would depend on the medical status of this particular use of hypnotism, and we were not certain as to its status. When a case like that arises, the individual hospitals and physicians must try to solve the problem as best they can by consultation on the local level. Factors to be considered in such consultation would naturally be the competence of the hypnotist, the emotional stability of the patient, the possibility of exposing the patient to uncontrollable dangers, the reason for using hypnotism rather than some other anesthetic, etc.

Again, there is the problem concerning the "ordinary and extraordinary means of preserving life." Directive 22 is very generic on the point; and with reason. For, to some extent the determination of what is ordinary and extraordinary must depend on the facilities of the hospital, the condition of the patient, and so forth. Doubts concerning such matters must be prudently considered in consultation. In saying this I do not wish to infer that theologians might not be a bit more helpful by using some more "modern" examples in their texts and articles; yet, even with such helpful examples, consultation would often be necessary.

The cases to which I have just referred concern doubts that do not arise suddenly; and which, therefore, allow time for consultation. But it might happen to any physician that an urgent case would arise in which he must make up his own mind, without consultation, about some delicate matter. For instance, Fr. Edwin F. Healy, S.J., proposes this question: "What should a surgeon do in an emergency case where in his opinion he will probably be doing wrong if he operates and probably be doing wrong if he does not operate? He must do one or the other at once."[1]

Cases like this can occur. They are treated by moralists under the title, "The Perplexed Conscience"; and all moralists would solve them as Fr. Healy does: "In such cases as this the surgeon should do what he thinks best; i.e., operate if that seems better, or refrain from operating if that appears preferable. In the event that both appear equally bad, he may choose either way of acting, and he will not sin."[2] The principle underlying this solution is that a man cannot sin without freedom; and one who must choose between two courses of action, each of which seems morally wrong, is not free to choose good or evil. Hence, the only reasonable solution is that he choose what he conscientiously judges the less evil, insofar as he can determine which apparent evil might be less.

I have chosen this case merely as an example. The essential point is that when a physician must quickly decide a delicate point, without the help of consultation, he must make up his mind according to his own conscience. When he does that, he has done all that God expects of him. Later he may decide that some other course of action should have been followed, but that cannot affect the morality of the action that he has already placed. None of us is infallible; all can and very likely do make some mistakes, even rather costly ones.

But all of us, too, must be willing to profit by our mistakes and to take reasonable precautions to avoid their recurrence. Hence, directive 4 closes with the provision that physicians who have been forced to solve emergency doubts without consultation should later obtain the necessary guidance for meeting future emergencies of the same nature.

---

[1] *Moral Guidance* (Chicago: Loyola University Press, 1942), p. 309, n. 6.

[2] *Teacher's Manual for Moral Guidance* (Chicago: Loyola University Press, 1942), p. 79.

In this brief commentary on the introductory directives, I have frequently referred to some of the specific provisions contained in other directives. The use of this other material was merely for the sake of illustration; it was not intended as a commentary on these specific provisions.

chapter $\boxed{3}$

Non-Catholics and Catholic Codes

A T TIMES I have written and stated in discussions with doctors and nurses that the ethical directives in the medico-moral codes of Catholic hospitals cannot admit of a double standard, one for Catholics, the other for non-Catholics. This is the meaning of **directive 5**, which reads:

These Ethical Directives concern all patients, regardless of religion, and they must be observed by all physicians, nurses, and others who work in the hospital.

Non-Catholics who hear or read this might ask for an explanation; and they are certainly entitled to it. The present discussion is an attempt to give the explanation, not in the manner of argumentation, but simply by way of information.

The *Directives* and the medico-moral codes of Catholic hospitals that I have seen consist mainly of three classes of regulations:

1. *Provisions for the religious care of patients.* These include directives concerning the administration of the sacraments, the religious care of the dying, Christian burial, and so forth.

2. *A statement of some moral principles and practical applications.* A moral principle would be, for example, that the direct killing of an innocent person is never permitted; and a practical application of this is the forbidding of destruc-

tive craniotomy on a living child. Another moral principle is that the unnatural use of the sex faculty is never permitted, even for a laudable purpose; and a practical application of this is the forbidding of masturbation as a means of semen sampling. Still another moral principle is that mutilation of the human body, even though it entails indirect sterilization, is permitted when required for the well-being of the patient; and a practical application of this is the allowing of orchiectomy in the treatment of carcinoma of the prostate.

3. *Certain precautionary regulations.* Under this heading would be such provisions as these: that excised organs be sent to the pathologist; that surgeons give notice of the operations they intend to perform; that there be adequate medical consultation before certain procedures are carried out; and so forth.

The first class of regulations generally pertain to specifically Catholic teaching. The cooperation of non-Catholic personnel is of course highly desirable in these matters; but I think I can safely say that Church authorities would not insist on the observance of these prescriptions by non-Catholics who could not render such assistance without violating their own religious convictions. However, in such a case of conscientious objection, the non-Catholics would be expected to notify the hospital authorities so that due provision could be made for the religious care of the patients.

The regulations of the third class are "ethical directives" in the sense that they are wise prescriptions made to prevent abuses and carelessness. They are not specifically religious; nor are they in themselves moral principles or direct applications of such principles. Although we are now considering these regulations as embodied in Catholic codes, it is well to remember that similar regulations are often made by civil authorities, medical societies, or by the staffs of non-Catholic hospitals. As I said, such regulations are not in themselves moral principles; but they can usually be reduced to the general principle that all reasonable means should be taken to protect

27

the rights of patients and the reputation of the medical profession. Because they are of this nature, such regulations must obviously be observed by the entire staff and hospital personnel.

From the foregoing, it seems clear that any inquiry about double standards in our hospitals is really limited to the regulations of the second class. To explain to our non-Catholic inquirers just why these prescriptions cannot admit of a double standard, we must discuss these two points: the meaning of natural law; and the authority of the Catholic Church to declare what is and what is not against the natural law. And to make this explanation complete, I think it is necessary to discuss a third point: namely, how the Church exercises its teaching authority. Before explaining these points, I should like to repeat the observation already made in my first paragraph: I am writing this merely to impart information and not to try to convince by argumentation.

THE NATURAL LAW

A rather time-worn, but still instructive, analogy may help to explain the meaning of the natural law.

Suppose that an inventor-mechanic would construct a new type of machine, e.g., a special type of automobile; and suppose that he would then sell it to me and would present me with a book of instructions concerning its correct and incorrect use. Granted that the mechanic acted reasonably, these instructions would not be a merely arbitrary afterthought without any reference to the nature of the machine. Rather, they would be a written formulation of "do's and don'ts" based upon his own intimate knowledge of the machine. He planned it for a certain purpose; he chose the materials and arranged them according to a certain design; he knows what is in it; and his instructions express this knowledge in a practical way. Another talented mechanic might examine this same machine and, by perceiving its materials, its arrangement, and its purpose, he could reach substantially the same conclusions as the inventor had expressed in his book of instructions. In other words, both the inventor and the examining mechanic would know that the very nature of the machine requires that it be operated in a certain way, or in certain ways, in order to accomplish its purpose.

Something similar, but in a much higher order, took place when God created human nature. He had a plan for this new being. He endowed it with certain powers and functions. When the nature is used according to its inherent design, it will accomplish its purpose; when it is used contrary to this design, its purpose is defeated. Obviously, in creating it with this particular design, God expressed His will that it be used in accordance with the design.

When God gave Moses the Ten Commandments, He gave him what might be called a book of instructions containing the main points concerning the right and wrong use of human nature. These Commandments were not merely arbitrary afterthought, not something "added" to human nature; they were, except for the detail concerning the Sabbath, a divine formulation of something already existing in that nature. In a word, human nature itself demands that human beings do some things and avoid others. And these requirements, these rules of conduct, existed, and will always exist, independently of any written or oral formulation. In giving the Ten Commandments, God merely helped man to know himself better by giving him a brief statement of the main requirements of his nature. As I have already noted and shall later explain more fully,[1] this kind of divine help is a practical necessity for most men. Nevertheless, a man with sufficiently developed reasoning powers and with sufficient opportunity could discover the truths expressed by the Ten Commandments, and even some more detailed ones, by an intense study of his own nature.

These requirements of human nature, these rules of con-

---

[1] *Cf.* Chapters 1 and 19.

duct existing in nature itself, constitute the *natural* law. This is called a *divine* law, to indicate that it originated directly from God, not from man. It is sometimes referred to as the natural *moral* law, to distinguish it from the laws that express the nature and properties of irrational things (e.g. the law that certain things will burn under certain conditions). It is often said to be "written in the heart of man," to signify that God expressed His will in the very creation of human nature, and that this will exists and can be known independently of any written or oral formulation—also to show that it binds all men, not just a certain group.

Like other analogies, this one may limp and may be inadequate to express the full truth; yet I trust that it sufficiently explains what is meant by the natural law. And I hope that it also makes clear why a double standard cannot be admitted when there is question of the principles of natural law and of their application to medical cases. For, since this law is the same for all human nature, it holds equally for non-Catholic patients and Catholic patients, for Catholic doctors and non-Catholic doctors.

COMPETENCE OF CHURCH

I believe that all who really understand the meaning of natural law will readily concede that its basic principles are the same for all men, regardless of creed. But non-Catholics may legitimately ask: "By what authority does the Catholic Church claim to have the only correct expression of the natural law? The Church may be erroneous in its statement of principles, and it may thus be imposing an unjust burden on those who consider that the natural law allows certain things (e.g., contraceptive sterilization) which the Church claims to be wrong."

An important observation should be made before I give the Catholic's answer to this question. I think the question might be misunderstood as implying that in matters of medical morality the Catholic Church is on one side and the rest of the world on the other. This, of course, is not true. Many who are not Catholics accept and rigidly adhere to most, if not all, the moral principles and applications contained in our codes. Hence, though the Church claims to possess the only correct interpretation of the natural law, it does not claim to be the sole possessor of this knowledge. With this observation, let me now explain the Catholic viewpoint regarding the authority of the Church to teach the natural law.

The Church, as Catholics conceive it, is a perfect society founded by Christ (whom we believe to be the Son of God). The Church can make laws for its own subjects, just as civil governments can legislate for their subjects. Laws made by the Church (e.g., fast and abstinence) are *human* laws; and as such they bind only the subjects of the Church. It should be carefully noted that, contrary to the impression that some people have, the Church does not claim the power to make laws for those who are not baptized.

But the Church does claim that, besides lawmaking power, it also has *teaching* authority from Christ. It claims further that, by His will, this teaching authority extends to the whole of divine revelation. Since revelation contains the natural moral law, it follows that the Church has the power, not to make, but to interpret, to teach, to declare the true meaning and extent of, that law. In interpreting it, the Church is explaining the demands of human nature itself—of that human nature which is the same in all men and at all times. Therefore, the Church cannot admit one interpretation of natural law as valid for Catholics only and another as valid for non-Catholics. Rather frequently, circumstances have made it necessary for the Holy See to explain the natural law as it applies to medical problems. Many examples of this teaching, especially as given by Pius XI and Pius XII, are given in this book.

It should be added here that the Church not only claims

31

divine authorization to interpret the moral law; it also claims that its teaching is a practical necessity for a clear and adequate knowledge of this law. A rather detailed explanation of this point is given later in Chapter 19.

The foregoing is merely to give information. Those who may be interested in the arguments for the Catholic contentions will find them explained in a treatise on apologetics. For my purpose, it suffices to state our position, without argumentation. As I have indicated, however, I think it will make for completeness if I add something on the way the Church teaches.

HOW THE CHURCH TEACHES

The Church has several ways of teaching. One way is what is called an *ex cathedra* pronouncement of a pope. This is had when the pope, speaking in his capacity as Vicar of Christ and using the fullness of his teaching power, infallibly pronounces on some matter of faith or morals. This is a *solemn* and *extraordinary* way of teaching. Also solemn and extraordinary are the infallible decrees and declarations made by the bishops of the world united with the pope in a general council.

Besides these solemn and extraordinary methods of teaching, the Church has many *ordinary* ways. First among these latter is the united teaching of the bishops in their respective dioceses throughout the world. This teaching may be expressed in many different ways; but in general we may say that it is substantially contained in approved catechisms. And still another ordinary way in which the teaching of the Church is expressed is in the doctrine on faith and morals contained in the common teaching of theologians. This teaching is found in approved theological manuals. Moreover, the Church also teaches through the liturgy, through traditional prayers, and so forth.

Besides the foregoing, the pope also has official, but not technically extraordinary, ways of conducting the business of the Church and of teaching Catholic doctrine. Among these are his own statements and declarations as contained in letters addressed to the Church, official discourses, and so forth. Moreover, he conducts the business of the Church, even that of teaching, not personally, but through the various Roman Congregations and Tribunals. An American might understand the meaning of a "Roman Congregation" better if we were to say that they are somewhat similar to the departments represented in our president's Cabinet. Each Congregation is composed of a committee of cardinals with authority to conduct the official business of the Church in a certain sphere. Most important of these Congregations is the Sacred Congregation of the Holy Office, which has authority to pronounce on matters of faith and morals. The pope himself is the head of this Congregation, though he does not always attend its meetings. Like the other Congregations, the Holy Office has attached to it eminent theologians called "consultors," whose task it is to study the various matters referred to the Congregation and report their conclusions.

I mentioned that the common teaching of theologians is one of the ordinary ways of expressing Catholic doctrine. I might add that, as regards medical questions, the study and united teaching of the moral theologians has usually preceded official declarations of the Holy See, so that these declarations were rather a religious confirmation of the moralists' teaching than a guide to such teaching. Moreover, official declarations on moral questions were comparatively infrequent before the time of Pope Pius XII. The usual procedure of the Church was rather to allow the moralists to discuss and clarify questions of morality and to sanction their conclusions more by "quiet acceptance" than by official pronouncements. One reason why official pronouncements have multiplied during the reign of Pope Pius XII is that he has had frequent requests from medical societies to speak on various moral topics.

A final word about moral theologians. It would be well, I think, for both Catholics and non-Catholics to know more about their *scientific* competence. What do I mean by scientific competence? I certainly do not mean that they are experts in the science of medicine. An occasional moralist may also be a physician and may have acquired a profound knowledge of medicine; but, as a group, the moralists neither are nor claim to be medical experts. They are not judges of good and bad medicine (except in obvious cases that should be apparent to anyone: e.g., that a pathological condition of a fetus is not remedied by destructive craniotomy); they leave such judgments to competent medical men.

But the Catholic moralists do have a just claim to special competence in the *science of ethics,* the science of moral right and wrong, the science of applying the moral law to the problems of human living. They are highly trained and experienced men in this particular field. Their preparation for this professional capacity is intense and comprehensive; they usually teach the science of morality over a number of years; and they are constantly dealing with practical applications of this science. Aside from any question of religion, the Catholic moralists represent by far the world's largest group of specialists in the science of ethics. And they have a tradition of scientific study that extends over centuries.

When such men agree on the statement of a principle of the natural law or on the application of a principle to a definite type of ethical problem, their unanimity is worthy of at least the same intellectual respect that is accorded the agreement of expert mechanics, physicians, lawyers, chemists, and so forth, in their respective fields. Their united opinion can reasonably be challenged only by those who have made a penetrating study of the natural law and who can offer sound reasons for their dissent.

(I have insisted here on "agreement" among the moralists. Such agreement gives a sound scientific argument for the correctness of principles and of many applications. As a matter of fact, there are many points of ethics, and particularly of medical ethics, in which the issues are not yet clearly defined and in which, therefore, there is a legitimate difference of opinion. In these cases, as stated in directive 3, our codes do not force either opinion on physicians.)

To this brief discussion of the moralists' scientific competence, I might add one observation, which many non-Catholic medical men have no doubt already noted. Catholic moralists are not dour individuals who are bent on projecting their own frustrations on other people by trying to make life hard for them. Physicians surely experience no morbid satisfaction when the sound principles of their own science force them to tell some disconsolate patient that he can save his life only by means of a serious operation or by a heroic diet. Nor are moralists without sympathy when they must give similar "hard answers" because the law of God, expressed in human nature, demands such answers.

chapter 4

Consent of the Patient

Even the procedures listed in this section as permissible require the consent, at least reasonably presumed, of the patient
or his guardians. This condition is to be understood in all
cases. **Directive 6.** (See also the Canadian Code, art. 6.)

THE FUNDAMENTAL reason for this directive is the principle of the natural law that each individual is constituted
by Almighty God as the administrator of his own life and
health. He has the right (and generally the duty) of self-
preservation and the right to take legitimate means to this end.
When a doctor applies some therapeutic measure, he is acting
for his patient; in other words, the patient is really exercising
his right through the doctor. When a parent or guardian gives
consent for a child or ward the same principle is applicable.
The parents or guardians are not the owners or administrators
of their charges; they too simply act for their charges, who
cannot in the circumstances directly exercise their own natural
right.

Consent is a free, rational act. Of its nature, therefore, it
supposes knowledge of the thing to which consent is given.
This knowledge need not always be precise, but it ought to be
substantially correct. For example, when two people marry
they need not be aware of all the duties that married life will
entail, but they must know the minimum essentials of the
marriage contract. Analogously, the patient need not know all

the minutiae involved in his cure; but his consent cannot be called free and rational when it is based on ignorance of the essential nature and consequences of a treatment or operation.

The fact that consent supposes knowledge sometimes poses delicate problems for the medical profession. In some cases it would be practically impossible to give a patient a correct understanding of the nature of a treatment. In other cases patients would obviously prefer not to know certain disagreeable things. And in still other cases, an explanation might prove harmful to the patients by stimulating irrational fears and perhaps even preventing them from submitting to a very beneficial procedure. In the following paragraphs I shall indicate some of these problems and suggest solutions that are consonant with the natural right of the patient. At times I shall refer to the provisions of the civil law; but let it be understood from the outset that I am interested primarily in the conditions required by the natural law. The civil law might occasionally go beyond these requisites, for example, by demanding that consent be written. Such provisions of the civil law should by all means be observed, not only in the interests of the patient, but also as a protection for the hospitals and members of the medical profession.

It may be taken for granted that a patient who presents himself to a physician for treatment implicitly consents to the customary diagnostic and therapeutic measures that are used by doctors and hospitals. It is true that the patient may have no detailed knowledge of these things; but he does know in general that his diagnosis and cure will entail many tedious procedures, and his very request for a cure would include the willingness to submit to these customary procedures. Generally speaking, therefore, it is not necessary to explain each of these measures in order to obtain his explicit consent.

Sometimes patients want to know the meaning of some of these procedures. It seems to me that their request for such knowledge is reasonable, and it is not right to tell them that it is none of their business or that they would not understand it anyway. A physician ought at least to try to distinguish between idle curiosity and a reasonable desire for legitimate knowledge.

When a treatment or operation would involve especially serious consequences such as long hospitalization, loss of a function, danger to life, or when it offers only slight hope of success, the patient should ordinarily be informed of these consequences. One reason for this is that the patient's duty of self-preservation does not normally extend to such measures; he has the right to refuse them. Also, as regards a dangerous procedure, the patient has a special right to the knowledge so that he can make the necessary spiritual preparation.

I have heard it said that, even with respect to the very serious procedures just mentioned, the patient's consent is sufficiently expressed by the fact that he voluntarily submits to the treatment or operation. I agree with this statement; but I would say that the patient's acquiescence cannot justly be called *voluntary* unless he has been made aware of the serious nature of the procedure.

Obviously, there are times when even these serious measures may be performed without any kind of expression of consent on the part of the patient. This is true in all cases in which the doctor must make an immediate decision and the patient is in no condition to be consulted: for example, when a patient is brought to the hospital in an unconscious or delirious condition. In this case the consent is said to be reasonably presumed: that is, the physician judges that, if the patient could be consulted, he would give his consent.

Another case in which the patient's consent is reasonably presumed is had when, in the course of an operation, the doctor discovers unexpected conditions that call for an extension of the originally-scheduled surgery. In fact, some might say that in this case the consent is more than presumed, and they might prefer to explain it as implicitly contained in the consent to the original operation.

Certain psychiatric treatments, like hypnoanalysis and narco-analysis, present special problems with reference to the consent of the patient because such treatments involve not merely the patient's right of administration over his health, but also his natural right to preserve his secrets. There is a special reason, therefore, for requiring that he be informed of the nature of the treatment before it is used.

But what of the case in which the psychiatrist is certainly competent and convinced that narcoanalysis would be a great benefit for his patient, yet he judges that if the patient were explicitly consulted about the treatment he would refuse it because of irrational fear? In chapter 31, I suggest that this might be one case in which the patient's consent could be legitimately presumed. Fr. Payen makes the same suggestion regarding the use of hypnotism.[1]

Is a doctor ever justified in acting against the express will of his patient, e.g., by operating when the patient has refused an operation? Fr. Payen (n. 357, II, 5) refers to two cases in which this might be done. In the first case, before losing consciousness, a man who has been badly hurt in an explosion tells the doctor to do everything necessary to save his life, but by all means to save his hand. As a matter of fact, the doctor finds that he cannot save the patient's life without amputating the hand. He is justified in doing the amputation because the man's general will to save his life nullifies his request to save the hand. In other words, his refusal of the amputation is more apparent than real.

Fr. Payen's second case concerns a person who is brought to the hospital after an unsuccessful attempt at suicide. The man

---

[1] P. G. Payen, S.J., *Déontologie médicale* (Zi-Ka-Wei, China: La Mission Catholique, 1935), n. 248. Subsequent references to Fr. Payen will be to numbers in this same work.

still has a suicidal intent; hence, he refuses to submit to the reparatory surgery. Since this refusal is manifestly against the natural law, the doctor may and should ignore it. Another way of solving this problem consists in analyzing the possible alternative explanations of the patient's state of mind. If he is insane, his refusal is clearly not a rational act; and the doctor may proceed on the presumption that a sane man would want the damage repaired. If he is sane, the civil law may justly require him to submit to the reparatory operation just as civil authorities might justly have tried to prevent his suicidal act.

In the practical cases I have reviewed here I have always referred to the consent of the patient. The same principles would apply to cases in which parents or guardians are empowered to give consent for the patients. The consent of parents or guardians must be given freely, and with adequate knowledge of the nature and effects of the procedures to which they consent. It may be considered as implied or reasonably presumed in the same conditions as the consent of the patient would be implied or reasonably presumed.

One final reference to Fr. Payen. He proposes the case in which a 15-year old boy wants an operation and the parents unreasonably refuse (n. 357, footnote 1). Fr. Payen thinks that the natural law would allow the doctor to perform the operation, because the boy in this case is able to give intelligent consent and, since there is question of his personal right to self-preservation, his consent would over-rule the unreasonable refusal of his parents. I agree with this; and it is my impression that in some states, if not in all, the civil law would uphold the boy's right.

Earlier in this chapter I mentioned that I am dealing primarily with the natural law, not the civil law. I also mentioned that in some cases the civil law might demand more than the natural law, e.g., by ruling that consent must be in writing. I should like to conclude by suggesting that occasionally the civil law seems to be fulfilled by something which is obviously against the natural law. For example, I have seen forms prepared for the signature of a patient which are couched in such general terms that they grant permission to the physician to do just about anything he judges to be necessary or advisable for the health of the patient. It may be that the patient's signature on such a form would secure legal protection for the doctor who would perform an immoral operation, e.g., tying off tubes to prevent pregnancy. In fact, I have heard of cases in which doctors seem to have taken advantage of Catholic patients by having them sign such forms. Obviously, this kind of unsuspecting consent, even though it might in some cases afford legal protection, is no consent at all according to the natural law.[2]

---

[2] On this same topic of consent, I highly recommend the article, "Fewer Malpractice Claims—Via Our American Way: Consent for Treatment," by T. Raber Taylor, A.B., LL.B., *The Linacre Quarterly,* Nov., 1955, pp. 131-136. Although primarily from the legal point of view, Mr. Taylor's article also explains the natural right of the patient which the laws generally presume. Pope Pius XII has often stressed the importance and necessity of the patient's consent. See especially his address of Sept. 13, 1952.

chapter 5

Informing the Dying Patient

DOCTORS OFTEN ask me whether they are morally bound to tell a patient he is dying so that he may prepare properly for death. The answer to this question is given in the Canadian Code, art. 7, the U.S. Code, general section, n. 4, and in directive 7. Since all of these are substantially the same, it will suffice here to quote **directive 7**:

> **Everyone has the right and the duty to prepare for the solemn moment of death. Unless it is clear, therefore, that a dying patient is already well-prepared for death as regards both temporal and spiritual affairs, it is the physician's duty to inform him of his critical condition or to have some other responsible person impart this information.**

Proper understanding of this directive requires the consideration of many factors. First, it should be noted that the directive concerns a real moral duty, binding in conscience. That duty belongs primarily to the physician because it flows naturally from the physician-patient relationship. But, as the directive clearly indicates, the doctor can fulfill this duty by having someone else communicate the required information, e.g., the chaplain, a special friend of the patient, etc. It seems to me, however, that it is seldom advisable for the doctor to use an intermediary. Doctors often have a special facility for giving this information—call it the "bedside manner," if you wish, or call it the grace of office. Moreover, when the proper physician-patient relationship exists, the patient usually expects to receive such information from his doctor; and the very fact that the doctor himself gives the information tends to increase the confidence of the patient in the doctor.

Secondly, the directive refers to both *spiritual* and *temporal* preparation for death. By temporal preparation is meant the paying of one's debts, arranging one's business affairs, making a will, etc. Obviously, it is not the physician's business to advise his patients in these matters. But it is the physician's duty to see that the patient has sufficient information to take care of these affairs of his own volition.

For a Catholic, the main spiritual preparation for death is the reception of the sacrament of extreme unction. This sacrament can and should be given not only to patients in *imminent* danger, but also to those who are in the *probable* danger of death from illness: that is, their condition is such that they are likely to die, even though it may be more likely that they will recover. When dealing with a Catholic patient, therefore, a doctor certainly has the duty to let the patient know that his condition is sufficiently critical to warrant the reception of extreme unction. But, supposing that the patient receives extreme unction, is there any obligation to give him more definite information, e.g., that there is no hope of recovery, that he very likely has only a month or two to live? It seems to me that, if the patient sincerely wants such information, the doctor is strictly obliged to give it. Whether it would be advisable to volunteer such definite information would depend on many circumstances, especially on the judgment of what would help the patient to make a better preparation for death; and I doubt that any general rule can be given on this point.

What about non-Catholic patients, patients with no religious convictions, and so forth? Even these patients, as the directive indicates, have the duty to prepare for death; and it is rare indeed that a man has no realization of this. Moreover, all have the right to know that the time has come to make this preparation; hence, whatever be his patients' religious convictions or lack of them, the doctor should see that they have the information. In fact, those who seem to be most callous spiritually are most in need of the information that their condition is critical.

Neither the doctors' question nor the wording of the directive is precisely concerned with telling the dying patient the *nature* of his illness. There is a special problem, it seems, regarding cancer patients. This problem, as well as some other important aspects of the question of notifying a patient about his condition, is discussed in the next chapter.

I mentioned that in the case of the Catholic patient the main spiritual preparation for death is the reception of extreme unction. This recalls another question that is often asked: who is to decide when extreme unction is to be administered, the doctor or the chaplain? The answer is that the chaplain is to make the decision—or the pastor of the parish, in case he is to confer the sacrament—but his decision must normally be based on the doctor's judgment that the patient is sufficiently ill to be in the probable danger of death. The proper way of handling this matter, therefore, is for the doctor to talk over the case with the chaplain or pastor. The doctor gives the medical information and the priest makes the decision as to the best time for the anointing. This conference between the doctor and priest may also bring to light any psychological problems, such as unfounded fears of the patient or relatives, and will help towards adopting a method of acting that will eliminate these problems.

In the previous paragraph I have taken for granted that there is time for a conference between the priest and the doctor. In cases in which a patient becomes suddenly critical, a priest could easily make the decision—and sometimes might have to do so—even before the arrival of the doctor.

Before concluding, I should like to refer to a practical point concerning the relationship of the physician to the nurses and hospital authorities. I am often asked by chaplains, nurses, and supervisors what they are to do when they know that a patient is dying and the doctor insists on withholding the information from the patient. The answer that I usually give to this question includes the following points: *(a)* discuss the matter with the doctor, pointing out to him what our code requires; *(b)* if he admits that the patient is dying, but still refuses to communicate the necessary information, the relatives or guardians should be informed of this; and *(c)* if both the doctor and the relatives or guardians refuse to let the patient be told of his true condition, the hospital authorities should get legal advice concerning the possibility of adverse action in case they act against the wishes of the doctor and relatives or guardians. I insist on this last point because, despite the great importance of the spiritual welfare of the patient, we cannot risk the greater spiritual good of our apostolate by getting involved in an adverse lawsuit.

Another rather practical question concerns the case in which a physician refers a patient to a specialist, e.g., a surgeon. Relatives are sometimes confused as to who should give them pertinent information. I am not sure of the professional etiquette in this matter; but I should think that, as long as the referring physician remains in charge of the case, it is his duty and privilege to give the information both to the relatives and to the patient.

chapter 6

Should the Cancer Patient be Told?

"YOUR PATIENT has a malignancy. Should you tell him, or not?" Some years ago the Office of Cancer Teaching and Research of Marquette University School of Medicine sponsored a symposium including the legal, psychiatric, and moral aspects of this question. Anyone who follows medical literature will immediately note that interest in the question is by no means limited to the time or place of the symposium. Because of the widespread and intense interest, it may be helpful to give here some of the points brought out in the symposium. This will entail some repetition of matters already treated in the preceding chapter; but it will also bring out some further practical points.

On the legal side, as I recall the Marquette discussion, the point particularly stressed was that a physician could be held legally liable if his failure to inform the patient of the nature of his disease would be a cause of damage to the patient. An interesting case was cited of a man who had made a large investment and who later sued his physician on the grounds that, if the physician had revealed to him his true condition, he would not have embarked on the perilous business venture. Another rather obvious case of legal liability concerned costly deception of a patient by holding out false hopes of recovery and thus inducing the patient to undergo expensive treatments which the physician should have recognized to be useless.

Psychiatrists stressed the need of estimating the probable reaction of the patient before telling him he has cancer, and they insisted that the physician must avoid an approach and the use of terms that might create anxiety. It was pointed out that the very word, cancer, fills many people with dread and that the discovery that they have cancer might be the occasion of a severe depression for such people. The psychiatrists would be in favor of a general educational policy which would help people to view the prospect of having cancer with more calm; but they believe that at present, when the danger of creating harmful anxiety is so great, the problem of notifying the patient defies general rules and must be looked upon as a decidedly individualistic one.

The moralist's view of this problem can be summarized along the lines, legal and psychiatric, already indicated. In the first place, the moralist would certainly agree with the lawyer that to damage a patient through deceit is wrong. It is not merely a juridical (legal) fault but also a moral fault to take money under false pretenses or to conceal the true state of affairs from a patient, with the knowledge that he will be led by his false hopes to damage himself financially. But the moralist would not limit the consideration of "damage to the patient" to the merely material, or pecuniary, sphere. He would think equally, even primarily, in terms of *spiritual* damage.

In chapter 5, I quoted and briefly explained directive 7, which enunciates the moral principle about informing the dying. At Marquette it was pointed out that, as regards cancer, the obvious application of this principle concerns incurable cases. It is definitely contrary to the principle to feed an incurable patient on false hopes of recovery to the extent that he neglects to take care of his temporal affairs (e.g., by making his will) and, above all, fails to prepare his soul to meet his Judge. A Catholic patient must be notified of his critical condition in plenty of time to allow for the fruitful reception of

47

the Last Sacraments; others must be allowed to make whatever preparation their consciences might demand.

That is the minimum; it is not everything. I know of an alarming number of devout people who expressed deep regret at the time of receiving the Last Sacraments that they had not been previously notified that their condition was incurable so that they could have spent their time more profitably and accumulated richer merits for heaven. Perhaps these people were indulging in vain regrets; perhaps they would not have used the time so well. But on the other hand, their complaint may be well founded. The last years, months, and especially weeks, of life are very precious. Certainly no patient should be deprived of the opportunity of reaping a rich harvest merely because of a false optimism—or perhaps I should say, a false standard of optimism.

The duty of informing the patient of his critical condition so that he can prepare well for death does not necessarily include the obligation of telling him the precise nature of his illness. For instance, I recall the case of a devout Catholic mother who died of cancer, apparently without ever having suspected the character of the disease. But she expected to die, and she was always prepared to go, as she put it, "when the Lord wanted to take her." Since she did not ask what was wrong with her, her physician and her family agreed to say nothing about the precise nature of the ailment because they thought this information might induce an unfavorable psychological reaction by creating an uneasy anticipation of pain. They came to this decision only after they had made sure that she was entertaining no false hopes of recovery.

In the case just cited, it seems that no real benefit could have been reaped by telling the patient she had cancer, and actual harm might have resulted. In such a case, there certainly could be no moral obligation to tell the patient she had cancer, and there might be a duty to withhold such knowledge.

THE CURABLE PATIENT

What about curable cases, i.e., cancer patients for whom there is at least some hope of recovery? The principle governing these cases, as was brought out in the Marquette discussion, is this: the patient should be given whatever information is necessary for him to cooperate intelligently with the physician. This principle is easily formulated; yet its application to individual cases is rendered difficult by the existence of complicating psychological factors. For one patient, the knowledge that he has cancer may be just what is needed to induce him to cooperate faithfully with treatment; for another, the horror of cancer might be such as to make him look upon hope of recovery as a mere delusion. These factors were stressed by the psychiatrists. The physician must estimate them carefully before communicating information to his patients and must, perhaps, use considerable psychotherapy to obtain the necessary cooperation.

I might add that the consensus of medical opinion as expressed at Marquette was that patients of the curable class cooperate better when the nature of their disease and the possibility of recovery are reasonably explained to them. Moreover, the general trend of opinion was decidedly in favor of an educational policy that would reduce the dread of cancer and thus allow calm judgment to supplant fear.

CONCLUSION

Must the cancer patient be told? From a moral point of view, the principal ideas to be kept in mind in answering this question are these:

1. The incurable patient must be given whatever information is needed for him to prepare well for death. This does not necessarily mean that he must know he has cancer.

2. The curable patient must be told whatever is necessary to obtain his intelligent cooperation with the physician. No abso-

49

lutely general rule can be given; but it seems that patients usually cooperate better when their condition and their hope of cure are reasonably explained to them.[1]

[1] For another discussion of this topic, see "What Must the Cancer Patient Be Told?" by John J. Lynch, S.J., in *The Linacre Quarterly*, Nov., 1955, pp. 127-130.

chapter 7

Medical Consultation

Adequate consultation is required, not only when there is doubt concerning the morality of some procedure (as stated in n. 4), but also with regard to all procedures involving serious consequences, even though such procedures are listed here as permissible. The hospital reserves the right to insist on such consultation. **Directive 8.** (See also the Canadian Code, art. 9, and the U.S. Code, general section, n. 1.)

CONSULTATION WHICH is primarily *moral* has been explained in connection with directive 4. Directive 8 is mainly concerned with *medical* consultation, the purpose of which is to determine whether a procedure is good medicine or what procedure would, under the circumstances, be the best medicine. Indirectly, of course, this involves a judgment on the morality of a procedure, because if it is bad medicine it is also bad morality.

In general (with certain reservations to be indicated later), we are willing to accept the judgment of medical societies or hospital staffs regarding the cases that require medical consultation. As a matter of fact, when the present directive was first formulated, we had in mind the provisions on consultation made by the *Code of Ethics* approved and adopted in 1947 by the American Hospital Association and the American College of Hospital Administrators, and the *Principles of Medical Ethics* published by the American Medical Association. The AHA provision reads: "For the protection of the patient in all

51

serious or doubtful cases there should be adequate consultation." And the AMA statement is this: "In a case of serious illness, especially in doubtful or difficult conditions, the physician should request consultations."[1]

JOINT COMMISSION

Today, the standard for consultation more or less generally accepted by medical societies is the one formulated by the Joint Commission on Accreditation of Hospitals.[2] It may be useful to quote this standard, to indicate what we cannot accept as sound morality, what seems dubious, and what is entirely acceptable. The standard reads:

Except in emergency, consultation with another qualified physician shall be required in all first Caesarean sections and in all curettages or other procedures by which a known or suspected pregnancy may be interrupted. The same requirement shall apply to operations performed for the sole purpose of sterilization on both male and female patients. Included in consultations required under this Standard are all those which are required under the rules of the hospital staff.

In major surgical cases in which the patient is not a good risk, and in all cases in which the diagnosis is obscure, or when there is doubt as to the best therapeutic measures to be utilized, consultation is appropriate. Obviously, judgment as to the serious nature of the illness and the question of doubt as to diagnosis and treatment rests with the physician responsible for the care of the patient. It is the duty of the hospital staff through its chiefs of service and Executive Committee to see that members of the staff do not fail in the matter of calling consultants as needed. A consultant must be well qualified to give an opinion in the field in which his opinion is sought.

A satisfactory consultation includes examination of the patient and the record and a written opinion signed by the consultant which is made part of the record. When operative procedures are involved, the

---

[1] The abbreviated A.M.A. Code, adopted in June, 1957, has this statement on consultation: "A physician should seek consultation upon request; in doubtful cases; or whenever it appears that the quality of medical service may be enhanced thereby."

[2] *Standards for Hospital Accreditation*, Jan. 28, 1956, "II. Medical Staff" n. 6.

consultation note, except in emergency, shall be recorded prior to operation.

The provision that consultation is required for "operations performed for the sole purpose of sterilization on both male and female" is morally unacceptable. Since these operations are *direct* sterilizations, they are never permitted; hence, consultation regarding the so-called indications for them is entirely out of place. The requirement of consultation for "all curettages or other procedures by which a known or suspected pregnancy may be interrupted" is ambiguous. It might mean that even the *direct* interruption of pregnancy before viability is permitted, provided consultants agree that this is medically indicated. If that is its meaning, then we must reject it as morally unacceptable, because direct abortion is never permitted for any reason whatsoever. On the other hand, if this latter provision is restricted to procedures that might *indirectly* interrupt a pregnancy before viability, it is morally acceptable. In this case, the consultation would concern such points as these: whether a patient is pregnant, whether a fetus is still alive or has reached viability, and so forth. The provision might also mean that consultation is required to determine whether a premature induction of labor is medically indicated —in which case also it is unobjectionable.

Because the provision about direct sterilization is clearly unacceptable and because the provision about interruption of pregnancy is at best ambiguous, the "Guide for Preparation of Medical Staff By-Laws," prepared by the Council on Hospital Administration of The Catholic Hospital Association, does not literally follow the standard of the Joint Commission. Rather, the "Guide" recommends the following:

Except in emergency, consultation with a member of the consulting or active staff shall be required in all major cases in which the patient is not a good risk and in all primary sections. The consultant shall make and sign a record of his findings and recommendations in every such case. A roster of consultations shall be made available. The recommendations of consultants will not justify a violation of the

53

ethical code of the diocese or of the Catholic Hospital Association.[3]

Although this statement is actually not as extensive as directive 8, it may be taken as a practical interpretation of the directive. Individual hospitals or groups of hospitals may make more stringent rules; but care should be taken to have no rules for consultation which even by implication might allow immoral procedures if consultants approve of them.

MEANING OF CONSULTANT

Our rejection of the standard suggested by the Joint Commission certainly does not mean disapproval of the entire standard. With the exception of the provisions mentioned above, it is not only acceptable but worthy of sincere praise.

In explaining their standard on consultation, the Joint Commission described what is meant by a consultant. No doubt, members of the medical profession are already familiar with this description; but I feel sure that many readers of this book will not have had this opportunity. For the sake of these latter, I should like to quote this description, even though it is somewhat lengthy:

The question has been raised as to the definition of a consultant. A consultant is a second physician called by the attending doctor to examine and discuss his patient. In the sense in which we use the term, it does not necessarily imply seniority. If the chief of a service calls one of his junior men who may have been working in a special field—say, for instance, pulmonary physiology or hematology—the younger man in seeing the patient is the consultant and should write the consultation note. The members of the consulting staff are on that staff because they have qualifications that make them valuable as consultants; but, in a given instance, any physician who sees a patient with a colleague is the consultant on that case, no matter what his standing on the staff may be. Of course, it is common for physicians to aid each other at times, informally, but in all instances in which the second physician makes a careful study of the problem presented by the patient, the consultation should be formalized by a note on the record. Although as stated above a consultant is, by

---

[3] Cf. "Guide for Preparation of Medical Staff By-Laws," p. 20, n. 12.

definition, a second physician called to examine a patient, to satisfy the requirements of the Commission as stated in the standard, the consultant must be qualified by training and/or experience to give a competent opinion in the special phase of the patient's illness about which he has been called to examine the patient. The determination of the consultant's competence should be made by the hospital staff. As stated in the standard, a consultation is not complete or satisfactory unless it includes an examination of the patient and the patient's record and a written opinion signed by the consultant and attached to the record.

It is not practicable or proper to take the matter of board certification into consideration. Board certification is no more than a relative indication of proficiency. Furthermore, a physician's standing as chief of service, or any like position, should not exempt him from carrying out his moral obligations to his patient. A chief of service who has the degree of humility that should be an attribute of all physicians in treating illness will seek the aid and advice of his colleagues when the situation is sufficiently serious.[4]

This is an excellent clarification of a difficult question. Despite its excellence and completeness, however, I am tempted to add one small point from my personal experience as a writer. In the Society of Jesus, of which I am a member, we have very strict rules of censorship. Everything that we publish must have at least two, and often three, Jesuit censors. And besides this, there is a further requirement of diocesan censorship. Obviously, when the writer is a specialist in some field, it is seldom possible to get censors who are equally qualified as specialists. It has been my experience, however, that even when my censors were not specialists, they have not only noticed some points to which my own specialization had more or less blinded me but have also made many valuable suggestions. I would certainly rather know of these things before publishing something than have my attention called to them later. For my own protection, as well as for the good of the Church and my readers, I have always thanked God for our rules of censorship.

---

[4] *Bulletin of the American College of Surgeons,* March-April, 1955, p. 135.

I have mentioned my own experience merely because it might be helpful to doctors who are specialists. They may at times feel resentment that men less qualified than they are the only available consultants. But in their hearts they must feel the same as I do: these other men often notice certain angles of a case that might escape the specialist; and it is certainly better to know of such things before an operation or treatment than afterwards. Moreover, for the doctors as well as for writers, there is the obvious fact that, when consultants or censors approve of their opinion, they have greater peace of mind and a deeper sense of security.

DISAGREEMENT IN CONSULTATION

"Must a doctor always follow the advice of his consultants; and must the hospital authorities always forbid him to act against a majority opinion of consultants?" I have been asked this question frequently. Since I have not found an explicit answer in the regulations of medical societies, I have attempted to work out a reasonable answer for myself. In doing this, I was greatly helped by the advice of several other moral theologians, all of whom agreed with what is said in the following paragraphs.

As a basis for a prudent answer to the question, let me call attention to a provision of the Code of Canon Law (canon 105). The Church often demands that ecclesiastical and religious superiors take counsel before acting, but it does not demand that they always follow the advice of their counselors. In some cases the superiors are obliged to follow a majority vote, but in other cases they are permitted to act contrary to the advice of the consultors. In these latter cases the purpose of the consultation is to guarantee that the superiors will not act with imprudent haste.

By analogy, I would say that the requiring of medical consultation does not always or necessarily mean that the physician must follow the opinion of his consultants, even a majority

56

opinion. There are some cases in which he should not be allowed to act against a majority opinion; but this is certainly not an absolute and universal rule. In some cases it should be sufficient for the doctor to give prudent consideration to the views expressed by his consultants without being morally obliged to follow these views. In fact, he may not in conscience follow these views if he sincerely thinks they would be detrimental to his patient.

Before deciding whether or not they should permit physicians to act against the advice of their consultants, hospital authorities must consider many factors. For one thing, mere number is not always the best criterion; because the opinion of one eminent physician may be more valuable than the views of many less capable men. Also, differences of opinion among physicians are sometimes due to differences in training; and some allowance has to be made for this in appraising the results of consultation.

I mentioned that there are some cases in which a physician should not be allowed to act against a majority vote. How can we determine these cases? I would not attempt to state any absolute rules; but I can offer three suggestions which should help hospital administrators and staffs to formulate a policy which is adapted to their own circumstances.

1. *Protect the helpless.* I am thinking particularly of the unborn child and of the patient who is not *sui compos.* These are unable to protect themselves. It is true that parents and guardians have the duty of making decisions for them; but the parents and guardians are seldom able to make a proper appraisal of the medical facts and in some cases their own self-interests are contrary to the interests of their charges. Hence, administrators and staff should exercise special care to safeguard these helpless charges. I do not see how they can exercise this care unless their normal policy follows this line: when there is question of procedures that involve danger for an unborn child (e.g. radiation therapy of pregnant repro-

57

ductive organs) or for a patient who is not *sui compos* (e.g. lobotomy for mental illness), if a majority opinion favors a less dangerous procedure, the attending physician should not be allowed to act against this opinion.

2. *Do not unnecessarily interfere with the liberty of the individual physician.* We must remember that the attending physician is the man responsible for his patients; and we must credit him with competence and sincerity unless he gives evidence to the contrary. Hence, except for the cases mentioned in n. 1 and apart from conditions that indicate danger of abuse, a physician should not ordinarily be forbidden to act against even a majority opinion of consultants, provided that the patient, when properly informed of the difference of opinion, wishes to follow the opinion of his own physician.

3. *Prevent or check abuses as occasions call for it.* No doubt, there are abuses. Some doctors are too much inclined to surgery; some hold on to outmoded harmful procedures; some are given to experimentation or novelty; some may even look upon consultation as a mere formality; and so forth. One way to minimize such abuses is to have the policy that consultation cases involving differences of opinion should be reviewed by the staff. This might not prevent all unnecessary harmful procedures; but it would prevent their repetition. And it would very likely prevent most of them from taking place, because a doctor would hardly insist on following an opinion he thought would be censured by the staff.

I have been told of one hospital where the staff has the rule that female reproductive organs may not be excised without the approval of a consultant. If the attending physician disagrees with the first consultant, he may ask for another; but, if both consultants agree that an organ should not be excised, the operation is not permitted. The reason for this ruling was the fact that some younger physicians were inclined to do hysterectomies that more mature judgment considered unnecessary. This is an example of one local solution to the problem of abuse.

chapter 8

Doctor and Supervisor

SISTERS HAVE often asked me whether, as supervisors of operating rooms, they are obliged to forbid the performance of an illicit operation. Also, they sometimes ask whether the supervisor may presume that a doctor who has scheduled a licit operation has no intention of doing anything illicit.

I am simply stating the obvious when I say, as a prelude to answering these questions, that there ought to be a very friendly and cooperative spirit between the various supervisors and the members of the staff. Generally speaking, there is such a spirit; yet there are exceptions, some of which are personality problems, while others are simply misunderstandings. The following answers cannot solve personality problems, but they may help to eliminate misunderstandings.

One basis for mutual understanding consists in the consciousness of others' responsibilities and a willingness to help them to fulfill their responsibilities. A second basis consists in avoiding rash suspicions and in acting on the presumption that others mean well. Everyone should be given the benefit of this presumption unless there are good reasons to the contrary.

SUPERVISOR'S DUTY

The answer to the first question is that the supervisor does have a duty to see that the illicit operation is not performed. This is at least implied by **directive 9:**

59

The physician is required to state definitely to the supervisor of the department concerned the nature of the operation he intends to perform or of the treatment he intends to give in the hospital.

The same provision is made in article 10 of the Canadian Code and in number 2 of the general section of the U.S. Code.

One purpose of directive 9 is *practical*: to enable the supervisor to see that proper preparations are made for the operation or treatment. A second purpose is *legal*: to protect the hospital in matters that might involve prescriptions of civil law. A third is *moral*: to guarantee that the specific provisions of the *Directives* are observed. For instance, as regards this third aspect, some procedures are not permitted without previous consultation; other procedures are not permitted at all.

The very fact that the directive requires the previous statement to be made to the supervisor indicates that the supervisor has a responsibility in this matter. When she requests that the statement be made, or when, after having read the statement, she informs a doctor that consultation is necessary or that the procedure scheduled is not allowed, she is simply fulfilling her duty. No doctor should resent this. If there is resentment, it must be attributable to personality factors.

PRESUME GOOD WILL

The second question is directly concerned with my preliminary observation about presuming that others mean well. According to this rule, when a doctor has scheduled an operation that is licit, the supervisor should presume that he intends nothing illicit; and she should not question him further nor investigate the case unless she has some positive reason for suspecting that he really intends to do something unethical. But if she has such a positive reason (e.g., because of something which happens in preparing the patient or because she knows from experience that this particular doctor makes light of the hospital code), she should look into the matter, graciously, of course, and avoid offense as much as possible. Many doctors have told me that they can see no reasonable grounds for offense on the part of the physician if the supervisor asks questions in order to clarify a doubt.

I might add here that the mere fact that a physician would schedule an illicit operation would not indicate bad will on his part. Even a very conscientious doctor might not realize the illicitness of certain procedures. Many doctors have had no opportunity to study medical morality; and both their textbooks and their teachers held views contrary to good morals. Moreover—and this is very strange—when these doctors come to our hospitals, they are asked to promise that they will abide by our code, yet they are never given a copy of the code or any explanation of it until some unpleasant situation arises! We certainly have a right, and a duty, too, to presume that the doctors are conscientious as long as they give no positive contrary evidence; but we have no right to presume that all doctors have an instinctive knowledge of the fine points of medical morality.

In conclusion, it may be well to refer briefly to the case in which a physician who has scheduled a licit operation actually accompanies this operation with some illicit procedure, e.g., ligating fallopian tubes. It is difficult to presume "good will" in this case, because if the doctor had good will he would have scheduled the sterilization. Therefore, it seems rather obvious that he did not schedule it because he knew it would not be permitted. Some disciplinary action is called for here; but just what it should be depends on circumstances. Whatever the disciplinary action is, it seems that it should be taken by the superior of the hospital or by the chief of staff or by the chief of the department concerned. All that is required of the supervisor is that she report the violation of the code to the proper authority.

9

Destruction or Risk of Life: the Principles

T HE PRINCIPLES especially pertinent to this topic are stated in the U.S. Code under the heading, "Risk to, or Destruction of, Life," in article 12 of the Canadian Code, and in **directives 12-14**. These directives read as follows:

12. The direct killing of any innocent person, even at his own request, is always morally wrong. Any procedure whose sole immediate effect is the death of a human being is a direct killing.

13. Risk to life and even the indirect taking of life are morally justifiable for proportionate reasons. Life is taken indirectly when death is the unavoidable accompaniment or result of a procedure which is immediately directed to the attainment of some other purpose, e.g., to the removal of a diseased organ.

14. Every unborn child must be regarded as a human person, with all the rights of a human person, from the moment of conception.

DIRECT KILLING

Directive 12 is based on—or perhaps it would be better to say it is a restatement of—the principle already referred to as *the inviolability of innocent human life.* God is the creator and master of human life; and no one may take it without His authorization. In our ethics classes and textbooks, we give sound arguments for the authority of the state to punish criminals and for the right of private individuals to defend their

lives and precious possessions against unjust aggression, even
to the extent of killing the aggressor when that is necessary.
But neither the state nor private individuals can establish any
authorization to kill the innocent. Hence, the principle that
innocent human life is absolutely inviolable. By reason of
this principle, we exclude all *direct* killing of the innocent,
e.g., by destructive craniotomy of a living fetus, by "mercy"
killing, by all *direct* abortion, even for "therapeutic" reasons.

The meaning of this principle is strongly and clearly explained in a memorable passage in the address of Pope Pius
XII on the moral problems of married life (Oct. 29, 1951).
This passage should be familiar to all members of the medical
profession. Said the Pope:

Now the child, even the unborn child, is a human being in the same
degree and by the same title as its mother. Moreover, every human
being, even the child in its mother's womb, receives its right to life
directly from God, not from its parents, nor from any human society
or authority. Therefore there is no man, no human authority, no
science, no "indication," whether medical, eugenical, social, economic,
or moral, that can show or give a valid juridical title for a deliberate
and *direct* disposing of an innocent human life, that is to say, for an
action which aims at its destruction, whether such destruction be intended as an end or as a means towards some other end which may
itself be in no way illicit. So, for example, to save the life of the
mother is a most noble end, but the direct killing of the child as a
means to that end is not lawful. The direct destruction of the so-
called "valueless life," whether born or unborn, which was practised
a few years ago in numerous instances, can in no way be justified.
And therefore when this practice began the Church formally declared
that it is contrary to the natural law and to the positive law of God,
and consequently illicit—even under instruction from the public
authority—to kill those who, although innocent, are nevertheless by
reason of some physical or psychical taint useless to the nation and
even become a burden on the community. The life of an innocent
human being is inviolable, and any direct assault or attack on it
violates one of those fundamental laws without which it is impossible
for human beings to live safely in society. We have no need to teach
you the particular significance of this fundamental law and its bearing
upon your profession. But do not forget it: above any human law,

63

above any "indication" whatsoever, there stands the indefectible law of God.

About a month later (Nov. 26, 1951), in his address to the Family Front, Pope Pius XII again spoke of the inviolability of innocent human life, and added the following very pertinent and powerful remarks:

This principle holds good both for the life of the child as well as for that of the mother. Never and in no case has the Church taught that the life of the child must be preferred to that of the mother. It is erroneous to put the question with this alternative: either the life of the child or that of the mother. No, neither the life of the mother nor that of the child can be subjected to an act of direct suppression. In the one case as in the other, there can be but one obligation: to make every effort to save the lives of both, of the mother and of the child.

It is one of the finest and most noble aspirations of the medical profession to search for ever new ways of ensuring the life of both. But if, notwithstanding all the progress of science, there still remain, and will remain in the future, cases in which one must reckon with the death of the mother, when it is the mother's wish to bring to birth the life that is within her, and not to destroy it in violation of the command of God: Thou shalt not kill!—nothing else remains for the man, [i.e., the doctor], who will make every effort right up to the last moment to help and save, but to bow respectfully before the laws of nature and the dispositions of Divine Providence.

But—it is objected—the life of the mother, especially the mother of a large family, is of incomparably greater value than that of a child not yet born. The application of the theory of the equivalation of values to the case which occupies Us has already been accepted in juridical discussions. The reply to this harrowing objection is not difficult. The inviolability of the life of an innocent human being does not depend on its greater or lesser value. It is already more than ten years since the Church formally condemned the killing of life considered to be "without value"; and whosoever knows the sad events that preceded and provoked that condemnation, whosoever is able to weigh up the direful consequences that would result, if one were to try to measure the inviolability of innocent life according to its value, knows well how to appreciate the motives that determine that disposition.

The Pope's words are obviously directed against those who

think that in certain situations there are good reasons (they call them "indications") for the direct killing of an unborn child. He defends the right of the child, but he does not limit his words to the child; he defends the mother, too, and all innocent life. In doing this he alludes to crimes that filled the whole civilized world with abhorrence: the execution of masses of innocent human beings because they were "useless" or a "burden to the state."

INDIRECT KILLING

From the foregoing it should be clear that the direct (i.e., the intentional) taking of innocent life is never permissible. Any procedure which would result in death for either the mother or the child (or for any other innocent person) can be justified only when the death is an unintended and unavoidable by-product of the procedure. This latter is called *indirect* killing. It has already been explained briefly in chapter 1. Since directive 13 is but a brief restatement of some of this material, it will suffice here merely to indicate the meaning of the main expressions used in the directive.

"Risk to life" refers to procedures which would probably, but not certainly, result in death. This would be verified in almost any operation that physicians would classify as very dangerous. The "indirect taking of life" means more than this. It implies that a procedure will certainly result in loss of life: e.g., the removal of a cancerous uterus in early pregnancy is certain to result in the death of the fetus. This is indirect killing, in the full sense of the expression. The directive states that even this and similarly drastic procedures are permitted, provided all the conditions for the application of the principle of the double effect are fulfilled. This point has also been clearly explained by Pope Pius XII. It seems that his statement on the inviolability of human life made on Oct. 29, 1951, was misrepresented; hence, in his discourse to the Family Front he said:

On purpose We have always used the expression "direct attempt on the life of an innocent person," "direct killing." Because if, for example, the saving of the life of the future mother, independently of her pregnant state, should urgently require a surgical act or other therapeutic treatment which would have as an accessory consequence, in no way desired or intended but inevitable, the death of the fetus, such an act could no longer be called a direct attempt on innocent life. Under these conditions the operation can be licit, like other similar medical interventions, granted always that a good of high worth is concerned, such as life, and that it is not possible to postpone the operation until after the birth of the child, or to have recourse to other efficacious remedies.

UNBORN CHILD A PERSON

With reference to the subject-matter of directive 14, I am often asked what is the teaching of the Church regarding the time the human soul is infused into the body. In answering this question, one has to distinguish between the *speculative* and the *practical*: that is, between speculative thinking and practical rules. In the sphere of speculation, there are two theories, each backed by representative Catholic philosophers and theologians. St. Thomas Aquinas, for instance, was of the opinion that the rational soul is not infused into the body until the fertilized ovum has reached a certain stage of development. Just what this stage is, is not clear. For a long time this theory was very commonly held by philosophers and theologians; then it was more or less abandoned. Today, however, the general idea of this theory—namely, that there must be some development of the material before the infusion of the rational soul—is proposed as the more acceptable explanation of the beginning of human life by many philosophers and theologians. The other view, also with many sponsors, is that the rational soul is always infused at the moment of fertilization.

We have no divine revelation on this point, nor any official pronouncement of the Church which clearly condemns or approves either theory. Catholics are still free to speculate on the

66

matter. However, in the practical order, we must follow the safer course of action and always treat a living fertilized ovum, whatever be its stage of development, as a human person, with all the rights of a human being. Thus, for example, canon 747 of the Code of Canon Law orders that every aborted fetus, no matter when expelled, should be baptized absolutely if it is certainly alive and conditonally if the presence of life is dubious. Also, when theologians give doctors a practical rule on what may be done in the case of rape, they say the doctor may do anything medically possible to remove the aggressor's semen but may not do anything to remove or kill a fertilized ovum.

Since I have quoted liberally from Pope Pius XII in explaining directives 12 and 13, it seems advisable to cite a paragraph of his which is pertinent to the present topic. In his address of Nov. 26, 1951, he said:

Innocent human life, in whatsoever condition it is found, is withdrawn, from the very first moment of its existence, from any direct deliberate attack. This is a fundamental right of the human person, which is of general value in the Christian conception of life; hence as valid for the life still hidden within the womb of the mother as for the life already born and developing outside of her; as much opposed to direct abortion as to the direct killing of the child before, during or after its birth. Whatever foundation there may be for the distinction between these various phases of the development of life that is born or still unborn, in profane and ecclesiastical law, and as regards certain civil and penal consequences, all these cases involve a grave and unlawful attack upon the inviolability of human life.

I would not want to say that these words condemn the opinion that the rational soul is not infused at the moment of fertilization; but they certainly seem to favor the opposite view.

chapter 10

Therapeutic Abortion

THE NUMBER of questions that can be and actually are asked about therapeutic abortion is legion. Among them all, the most pertinent and important seems to me to be this: "Is the Catholic teaching on this subject different now from what it was fifty or seventy-five years ago?" A comprehensive answer to this question will really include replies to most of the other questions; hence, I shall use this as my approach in the present chapter.

The question could be answered by a simple, "no, it is not." A more complete answer, however, would distinguish between the official teaching of the Church and the opinions expressed by individual theologians. The official teaching of the Church has not suffered the slightest change; every official pronouncement from 1884, when the Holy See was first asked for a statement, to the present day has condemned therapeutic abortion. On the other hand, when the subject first became a burning issue, there was a small number of Catholic moralists who thought that therapeutic abortion could probably be justified.

The preceding paragraph really contains the answer to the question. However, I should like to use this occasion for outlining the official statement of the Holy See, as well as the views of Catholic moralists, on the subject of therapeutic abortion. To these I shall add a brief survey of pertinent and valuable medical opinions.

At the outset, let me say that much of the material I shall present is given more completely in the introductory chapters of Fr. T. L. Bouscaren's excellent study, *Ethics of Ectopic Operations,*[1] a book which should be in the library of every member of the medical profession.

Also at the outset, let me explain that I am using the expression, "therapeutic abortion," in its ordinary sense: namely, as a *direct* abortion which is deliberately induced for the purpose of saving the life of the mother. This is the procedure with which the U.S. Code ("Destruction of Life," n. 1), article 16 of the Canadian Code, and **directive 15** are especially concerned. The directive reads as follows:

Direct abortion is never permitted even when the ultimate purpose is to save the life of the mother. No condition of pregnancy constitutes an exception to this prohibition. Every procedure whose sole immediate effect is the termination of pregnancy before viability is a direct abortion.

I. OFFICIAL TEACHING

Between 1884 and 1930, the Holy See issued five pronouncements that are pertinent to our present topic.

1. On May 28, 1884, the Sacred Congregation of the Holy Office (then known as the Congregation of the Inquisition), in reply to a question sent by the Cardinal Archbishop of Lyons, stated that it cannot be safely taught in Catholic schools that a death-dealing craniotomy may be performed on the fetus, even in cases in which both mother and fetus would otherwise perish. The words, "It cannot be safely taught," were used in this reply because the Cardinal himself had used them in his query. The minimum meaning of the expression is that, if there was any opinion favoring the licitness of craniotomy, the opinion could not be considered sufficiently probable to be reduced to practice.

---

[1] Milwaukee: Bruce Publishing Company, 1944.

69

2. Some time after the first reply, the Archibishop of Cambrai sent a number of questions to the Holy Office. Under date of Aug. 19, 1889, the Holy Office answered these questions by repeating the reply of 1884 concerning craniotomy and by adding that the statement also applied to all operations which directly kill either the mother or the child. These last words should be carefully noted. They are a clear refutation of the calumny that the Church always prefers the life of the infant to that of the mother. From the very beginning the official Catholic position has been that each life is inviolable and that neither may be directly killed to save the other.

3. Readers may wonder why I have cited the preceding statements in a discussion of therapeutic abortion, because these replies refer to death-dealing surgical procedures. And it seems that some physicians of the Archdiocese of Cambrai also wondered about this. Hence, to settle the consciences of the physicians, the Archbishop soon sent another query to the Holy See, asking whether direct abortion to save the life of the mother could be considered licit. The reply of the Holy Office, given on July 24, 1895, and confirmed by Pope Leo XIII on the following day, stated that the answers of 1884 and 1889 also referred to direct abortion. It is because of this reply that I have listed these former statements among the decrees condemning therapeutic abortion.

4. Another pertinent reply of the Holy Office was given to the Bishop of Sinaloa, in Mexico. The Bishop had asked a number of questions, one of which concerned the licitness of inducing an abortion when it was judged impossible to wait for the viability of the fetus. In a response dated May 4, 1898, and confirmed by Pope Leo XIII on May 5, the Holy Office stated that this procedure is illicit and referred to its reply of 1895.

5. A further and most emphatic pronouncement was given by Pope Pius XI, in his encyclical on Christian Marriage, Dec. 31, 1930. After surveying the various modern attempts to

70

justify direct abortion, he singled out the medical justification for special attention.

As to the "medical and therapeutic indication" to which, using their own words, We have made reference, Venerable Brethren, however much We may pity the mother whose health and even life is gravely imperiled in the performance of the duty allotted to her by nature, nevertheless what could ever be a sufficient reason for excusing in any way the direct murder of the innocent? This is precisely what we are dealing with here. Whether inflicted upon the mother or upon the child it is against the precept of God and the law of nature: "Thou shalt not kill." The life of each is equally sacred, and no one has the power, not even the public authority, to destroy it.

To the foregoing official statements should be added the various strong pronouncements of Pope Pius XII, some of which I have quoted in chapter 9. From a consideration of all of them, it should be evident that the official teaching of the Church has unwaveringly condemned therapeutic abortion as being tantamount to the direct killing of the innocent.

II. THEOLOGIANS

Even before the decision of the Holy Office the vast majority of Catholic moralists held that therapeutic abortion is the direct killing of the innocent, and therefore never justifiable even in the most extreme case. Nevertheless, a small number, and among these a few eminent theologians, were not convinced of the necessity of this absolute position; and they suggested various solutions that were either a justification of direct abortion in very extreme cases or an avoidance of the difficulty by making the abortion seem to be a merely indirect killing of the fetus.

In a certain sense, it might be considered fortunate that some of the theologians involved in the early discussions of this topic were opposed to the more common absolute position. For, in suggesting some reasons why the fetus might be sacrificed to save the life of the mother, they discussed and brought forth

71

answers to most of the objections that are urged even today against the Catholic position.

One tentative solution to the problem was this: "In an extreme case, when the mother's life can be saved only by the termination of the pregnancy before viability, may we not say that the fetus is a *materially* unjust aggressor?" This solution is based on a suggested analogy between the infant *in utero* and a madman who is attacking an innocent person. The madman is called an "unjust aggressor" because he is violently attacking an innocent person; and he is said to be "materially" unjust because, being insane, he cannot be subjectively (formally) guilty in the attack.

If this analogy were correct, the infant could be licitly killed or aborted. But theologians were quick to point out that the analogy is not sound. For the infant is not carrying out an "aggression" in any reasonable interpretation of the word. As Fr. Aertnys, an eminent Redemptorist theologian, said very aptly: "But the child is making no attempt on its mother's life; it is only trying to be born, and it is only by a natural concourse of circumstances that this effort becomes a cause of death to the mother. The child, therefore, is not an aggressor, and much less an unjust aggressor."

It might be added that Fr. Aertnys was referring to an ectopic pregnancy; his words apply with much greater force to normal pregnancy.

Another suggestion, offered by Fr. A. Lehmkuhl, S.J., followed this line: "In a storm at sea a man may sacrifice his life for a friend by voluntarily yielding to the friend a plank which is not large enough to save both of them. By analogy, may we not say that in a crisis, when both mother and fetus would otherwise perish, the fetus would want to relinquish his right to remain in the uterus so that the mother's life would be preserved, and the fetus itself, though sure to die outside the uterus, would have a better chance of baptism?"

It should be noted that the man who allows his friend to have the life-saving plank does not kill himself. He merely permits his death by letting go of or not taking hold of an extrinsic thing which happens at that time to be necessary for his life. The death of the man, therefore, is an indirect result of his act of charity toward his friend. If therapeutic abortion could be reasonably explained as an action which only indirectly results in the death of the fetus, there would undoubtedly be a great similarity in the cases. It might be said that the fetus is merely giving up its place in the uterus just as the man gives up the plank for his friend—or that the mother is simply "letting go" the burden which she can no longer safely carry. But the same author who proposed this solution to the problem later pointed out the weakness of his own argument. He wrote: "To tear asunder violently the membranes and tissues which connect the fetus to the womb of the mother is nothing else than to inflict a fatal wound on him." In other words, it is a *direct* attack on the life of the fetus; and this cannot be justified, with or without the presumed consent of the fetus, even to save the life of the mother.

A few theologians thought that the killing or aborting of the fetus might be justified by appealing to the principle: "Where there is a conflict of rights, the stronger right should prevail." On this basis they argued that the mother had the prior and stronger right to life; therefore, when both could not be saved, the fetus might be sacrificed.

This argument won no favor with great moralists. They replied that an appeal to the principle of "conflict of rights" showed a complete misunderstanding of this principle. The valid application of the principle supposes that there is a dispute over the possession of something which any one of several persons could possess, and the dispute is finally settled in favor of the one who seems to have the best claim to the object. But an individual's life is not something alienable, like property; nor can any doubt arise concerning the rightful possessor.

Hence, in the crisis of pregnancy, in which there is question of the lives of two innocent persons, there simply is no question of a "conflict of rights." Each has an inalienable and clear right to life.

Rightly understood, a somewhat similar principle can have application to the *failure to save* a human life, but never to the direct killing of an innocent person. For instance, if two people are dying and a doctor has time to save only one of them, he should, if possible, save the one who has the greater claim on him (a relative in preference to a perfect stranger) or the one whose life is of special value to the state during a crisis (an eminent statesman in preference to a private citizen), and so forth. But in these cases, when he saves the one person, he does not kill the other. In a therapeutic abortion, he kills the child in order to save the mother.

The foregoing difficulties were suggested by theologians themselves in their early attempts to solve the problem of the "extreme case" in which both mother and child would die if the child were not sacrificed. The theologians' doubts were not common, and they were of short duration. But the difficulties they suggested are still brought up by those who are opposed to the Catholic position. And, besides these difficulties, other reasons for justifying therapeutic abortion are advanced.

For instance, it is frequently said: "Faced with two evils, the doctor must choose the less. But it is a less evil to sacrifice the child by a therapeutic abortion than to have both the mother and child die. Therefore, the doctor must perform the abortion." In my comments on directive 4, I explained one sense in which it is perfectly true that when a doctor is faced with two evils he should choose the less. But the one case in which this maxim is applicable to moral evil is that of the "perplexed conscience," in which case a man *thinks* he must choose evil. For example, if a doctor, while performing an emergency operation, thinks that he would do wrong by taking out a uterus and that he would fail in his duty by not taking

74

it out, he is said to have a "perplexed conscience," because it seems to him that he would sin no matter what he does. If he could ask advice, he should do so. But if he had to act immediately and could not get advice, then he should do what seems to be the less evil. In doing the best he can under the circumstances, he does not sin.

As a matter of fact, those who advocate therapeutic abortion as the less of two evils are not thinking of the "perplexed conscience" case. They are simply insisting that it is better to have one death than two deaths. And if it were merely a question of deaths, they would be right. But actually, it is a question of the *direct taking* of one innocent life or of merely *permitting* two deaths. In other words, there is question of one *murder* against two deaths; and, of these two evils, the moral evil of murdering the fetus is far greater than the merely physical evil involved in the unavoidable deaths of both mother and fetus.

Opponents of the Catholic position have not too much patience with our continued insistence on the principle that an innocent human being may not be directly killed even for a good purpose. They say that we are sacrificing lives for a principle. In this they are definitely wrong, for the principle that the life of both mother and child is inviolable is in reality a life-saving principle. It may mean that some lives are occasionally lost that might have been saved by a therapeutic abortion; but in the long run it saves many lives that would have been lost. Doctors who are convinced that they have no right to sacrifice either life are much more likely to find a means of saving both lives than are doctors who readily resort to therapeutic abortion to solve a critical case.

III. MEDICAL ASPECTS

In previous chapters I have made repeated references to the papal teaching on the inviolability of innocent human life. It is principally the question of therapeutic abortion that generates resistance to this teaching on the part of some members of the medical profession.

Underlying this resistance are several false or gratuitous assumptions. For instance, it is falsely assumed that Catholics prefer the child to the mother, so that the mother may be sacrificed for her child, but not vice versa. A step beyond this is the gratuitous assumption that the mother's life is of greater value than the life of the child. Thirdly, it is gratuitously (if not falsely) assumed that the mother's life is less safe in hospitals where therapeutic abortion is not performed than in hospitals where it is practiced. Finally, it is falsely assumed that therapeutic abortion is good medicine.

That the first assumption is false (and often malicious) is evident from the repeated papal statements to the effect that both lives, and all innocent lives, are inviolable. As for the claim that the mother's life is of greater value, it is irrelevant when there is question of directly killing one or the other; yet even if it were relevant, it would still be gratuitous. As Pius XII said so well in his address of Nov. 26, 1951: "Besides, who can judge with certainty which of the two lives is in fact the more precious? Who can know what path that child will follow and what heights of achievement and perfection he may reach? Two greatnesses are being compared here, one of them being an unknown quantity."

The assumption that conservatism costs more maternal lives than therapeutic abortion is also unfounded, and very likely completely false. At any rate, it would be interesting to see some statistical evidence that therapeutic abortion is more life-saving. Certainly the statistics I have seen do not bear this out. The following brief references will indicate what I mean:

In *The Linacre Quarterly,* July, 1941, p. 61, John F. Quinlan, M.D., cites a study of 2,005 cases of eclampsia, which reported a maternal death rate of 10 percent in Ireland against approximately 25 percent for England and Scotland. Yet conservatism was the rule in Ireland, whereas intervention was the accepted procedure in England and Scotland.

The *Catholic Medical Quarterly*, January, 1952, p. 62, presents a comparison between two representative Catholic hospitals in London during 1948-50 and the National Health Service Hospitals in England and Wales during 1949-50. The comparison covers stillbirths, neo-natal deaths, and maternal deaths; and it reveals that the Catholic hospitals were safer on all three counts.

Someone might suggest that the number of deliveries in the London Catholic hospitals was a mere handful compared to those in the national hospitals; and it might also be suggested that the cases calling for therapeutic abortion are not brought to the Catholic hospitals. In neither of these suggestions is there a real explanation of the difference; and certainly neither of them would apply to the statistics presented by the *Quarterly* in its April, 1952 number. These latter statistics were supplied by Dr. Samuel A. Cosgrove, and they concerned the Margaret Hague Maternity Hospital (which is not a specifically Catholic hospital) and two other large American hospitals. At the Margaret Hague Hospital, in 66,101 deliveries, without any therapeutic abortions, the maternal mortality rate was only 0.103 percent of the total deliveries; at the other two hospitals, where therapeutic abortion is not absolutely excluded, the maternal mortality was 0.12 percent in a series of 21,990 deliveries and 0.21 percent in a series of 20,679 deliveries.

By far the most impressive of all the statistical surveys is that presented by Roy J. Heffernan, M.D., F.A.C.S., and William A. Lynch, M.D., in their article "What is the Status of Therapeutic Abortion in Modern Obstetrics?"[2] They sent questionnaires to 367 hospitals in this country. 171 hospitals answered the questionnaires; and, of these, 152 were suffi-

---

[2] *American Journal of Obstetrics and Gynecology*, Aug., 1953, pp. 335-45.

ciently detailed to admit of analysis. The questionnaires covered two five-year periods: 1941-45; and 1946-50. In the hospitals where there were no therapeutic abortions, there were 1,680,989 deliveries during the ten-year period, with a total of 1,469 maternal deaths. In the hospitals where therapeutic abortions were performed, there were 1,574,717 deliveries, with 1,558 maternal deaths. Thus the percentage of maternal deaths in hospitals permitting therapeutic abortion was 0.98 whereas it was only 0.87 in the hospitals where therapeutic abortions were not allowed.

The mother who is told that her life is safer in a hospital that allows therapeutic abortion might reasonably ask for an explanation of statistics like these.

What about the final assumption: that therapeutic abortion is good medicine? Before I comment on this, I should like to note that, like the problem of the relative value of lives, this question is also irrelevant, as well as positively misleading, if it is taken to mean that conservatism is morally defensible only if it is good medicine. Even in the supposition that therapeutic abortion would be the best possible medicine, it would still be morally wrong. However, it is consoling to note that here, as in other matters, good morality is also good medicine. The statistics I have just cited indicate this; and many thoroughly scientific articles of the past decade or so either give an unqualified confirmation of our opposition to therapeutic abortion or at least show that there is a strong tendency away from the practice just on the basis of good medicine.

As far back as 1943, Edgar Hull, M.D., was able to show that modern medical research was gradually discrediting the various "indications for therapeutic abortion."[3] In 1944, Samuel A. Cosgrove, M.D. and Patricia A. Carter, M.D., reported that, in the course of 67,000 deliveries at the Margaret Hague Maternity Hospital, they had found it "necessary" to

---

[3] *The Linacre Quarterly,* April, 1943, pp. 31-35.

perform only four therapeutic abortions; and later they questioned the need of one of these.[4] Two years later, *Cahiers Laënnec*[5] carried an article by Dr. L. Portes, President of the National Council of the Society of Physicians (in France). The import of this article was the same as that of Dr. Hull: it showed how the progress of medicine was gradually eliminating all the so-called indications for therapeutic abortion.

Fr. James Pujiula, S.J., testified that the best physicians in Spain held that therapeutic abortion is never a necessary means of saving the mother.[6] Joseph L. McGoldrick, M.D., expressed a view similar to that of the Spanish physicians: namely, that therapeutic abortion is never a necessary means of saving the mother.[7] In long years of experience he had never encountered the mother-or-child dilemma; and he was confident it was merely a relic of the early days of obstetrics.

I have already mentioned the report of Dr. Samuel A. Cosgrove and Dr. Patricia A. Carter concerning the number of therapeutic abortions at the Margaret Hague Hospital in the twelve years previous to 1944. The total was four therapeutic abortions in 67,000 deliveries. Later, in a panel discussion on the indications for therapeutic abortion at the Clinical Congress of the American College of Surgeons held in San Francisco, Nov. 5-9, 1951, Dr. Cosgrove reported on 136,467 deliveries, still with only four therapeutic abortions. This means that, after 1944, in approximately 70,000 deliveries, there were no therapeutic abortions. It is easy to understand how

---

[4] "A Consideration of Therapeutic Abortion," *American Journal of Obstetrics and Gynecology*, Sept., 1944, pp. 299-314.

[5] Oct., 1946, pp. 3-12. *Cahiers Laënnec* is a quarterly published by Catholic physicians in France. It usually devotes a complete issue to one topic. Many of the discussions are now being published in English under the general title, *New Problems in Medical Ethics*. To date, three volumes have appeared in English. The publisher is The Newman Press, Westminster, Md.

[6] *De medicina pastorali* (Turin: Marietti, 1948), p. 108.

[7] *Hospital Progress*, May, 1948, pp. 181-184.

Dr. Cosgrove, who is not a Catholic, would make the simple declaration: "I believe the negation of abortion on the strict grounds of moral law is *good medicine*" (italics mine).

With Dr. Cosgrove in the panel discussion in San Francisco were Roy J. Heffernan, M.D., of Tufts College; Bernard J. Hanley, M.D., of the Los Angeles County Hospital; and John H. Morton, M.D., also of the Los Angeles County Hospital. Both Dr. Heffernan and Dr. Hanley agreed with Dr. Cosgrove that there are no indications for therapeutic abortion. Dr. Morton, though unwilling to take the absolute stand of the other members of the panel, frankly admitted that there are far too many therapeutic abortions.

During the panel discussion Dr. Heffernan said: "Anyone who performs a therapeutic abortion is either ignorant of modern medical methods of treating the complications of pregnancy or is unwilling to take the time to use them." The following year, with William A. Lynch, M.D., Dr. Heffernan published a scholarly article—"Is Therapeutic Abortion Scientifically Justified?"[8]—which musters the strongest kind of medical testimony against the so-called indications for therapeutic abortion. The merits of this article, according to a British physician, are "that it is by two distinguished American doctors, that it is heavily documented with recent medical work, and that it relates not only the most recent evidence on such old topics as tuberculosis, nephritis and heart disease, but also recent work on the possible effect of the Rhesus factor or virus diseases on the foetus. . . . Drs. Heffernan and Lynch's article clearly demonstrates that the scientific evidence against therapeutic abortion could scarcely be stronger."[9]

Dr. Heffernan and Dr. Lynch included the main points of this article in their subsequent article in the *American Journal*

---

[8] *The Linacre Quarterly,* Feb., 1952, pp. 11-27.
[9] Cf. *The Catholic Medical Quarterly,* July, 1952, p. 138.

of Obstetrics and Gynecology.[10] Less emphatic than their position, but still impressive, is a statement made by Nicholson J. Eastman, M.D.[11] He testified that the percentage of therapeutic abortions was steadily declining at Johns Hopkins Hospital; and he added that "the hard jolts of clinical experience have demonstrated to us rather clearly that therapeutic abortion is rarely necessary to achieve this objective [of saving maternal life and health]." It is clear from this statement that Dr. Eastman did not go the whole way of absolutely repudiating therapeutic abortion on medical grounds. Moreover, cheering though his article was, the very principle enunciated at the beginning is not sound morality and is at best questionable obstetrics. "The paramount aim of obstetrics," he wrote, " is the preservation of maternal life and health; and therapeutic abortion must find its sole justification (if it can be justified) in the degree to which it serves that end." One might reasonably ask why the paramount aim of obstetrics is not the preservation of maternal *and* fetal life and health. The mere fact that the fetus is completely helpless to speak for itself does not make it less the obstetrician's patient than is the mother.

Another impressive testimony to the trend against therapeutic abortion has been given by Keith P. Russell, M.D.[12] He records the experience at the Los Angeles County Hospital, and his main conclusions are as follows:

Whereas the average incidence of therapeutic abortion in the Los Angeles County Hospital 20 years ago was 1 in every 106 deliveries, during the past five years it has been 1 in 2,864 deliveries and in the past year, 1 in 8,383 deliveries. . . . No abortions have been per-

---

[10] See above, footnote 2.

[11] *Current Medical Digest,* May, 1953, pp. 85-88. A similar statement by Dr. Eastman concerning the trend away from therapeutic abortion is found in the "Obstetrical Foreword" to *Therapeutic Abortion,* edited by Harold Rosen, Ph.D., M.D. (New York: Julian Press, 1954).

[12] "Changing Indications for Therapeutic Abortion," *Journal of the American Medical Association,* Jan. 10, 1953, pp. 108-111.

formed for hyperemesis gravidarum since 1937. None has been performed for pyelitis since 1939. . . . No abortions have been performed for fetal indications in the past 20 years. . . . No abortions have been performed for mental or nervous system diseases since 1942. . . . Despite a greatly lowered incidence of therapeutic abortion, the maternal mortality rate in the hospital has not risen; rather, it has shown a progressive decline.

The foregoing survey is largely confined to articles that showed the general trend against therapeutic abortion. Besides these, many other articles have appeared that were concerned with showing that therapeutic abortion is medically unjustified in various specific maladies.[13] In view of all this literature, one wonders why some doctors can be so confident in asserting that therapeutic abortion is ever good medicine. And one wonders, too, why we who oppose the procedure must always defend our position. It is high time, it seems to me, that those who wish to take the lives of the innocent should show their credentials. Even on medical grounds alone, they have a very weak case; on moral grounds, they have no case at all. The whole matter is very aptly summarized by Dr. Heffernan and Dr. Lynch in the conclusion to their article in *The Linacre Quarterly*:

Therapeutic abortion is an unworthy and unwholesome paradox in modern medicine. The "unenlightened physician" of the pre-modern

---

[13] One of the specific diseases for which "therapeutic abortion" is sometimes recommended is rubella (German measles), when contracted by a mother in the first trimester of pregnancy. The reason for recommending the abortion is that the fetus will probably be born with some kind of defect, more or less serious. Is it necessary to point out that, even if therapeutic abortion could be justified, this case cannot really qualify as a therapeutic abortion? It is, purely and simply, euthanasia of the fetus—that is, a killing of the fetus to prevent it from being born with some defect. For a more lengthy development of this point, see "Rubella and Abortion," *Hospital Progress*, April, 1953, pp. 64-65. This article was reprinted in Part V of the former editions of *Medico-Moral Problems*; but it seemed to me unnecessary to incorporate it into this revision.

era with limited means, a faith in his Creator and an undying hope and optimism, challenged disease. Today, with so many of his dreams realized in the armamentarium of modern medicine, some of his successors would shrink from the challenge, face difficulties with pessimism and, bowing to expediency, would destroy life.

Therapeutic abortion is a deliberate destruction of innocent life, morally evil and scientifically unjustified. Therapeutic abortion is legalized murder.

Ergot and Abortion

IT USED to be almost a commonplace for me to receive questions concerning the morality of using ergot preparations to control hemorrhage in cases of threatened, inevitable, or incomplete abortion. Today, these specific questions are less frequent, although I still receive many others on the general subject of hemorrhage in early pregnancy. Whatever be the cause of the hemorrhage, the moral principle concerning treatment is the same; hence, in this chapter I shall explain the principle, but shall limit my application for the most part to the specific problem of controlling hemorrhage by means of ergot preparations.

THE PRINCIPLE

It should be noted that in the chapter on therapeutic abortion we were mainly concerned with cases in which there is no disturbance of the products of conception, but the pregnancy is a supposed threat to the life of the mother because of some strictly maternal illness such as hypertension, tuberculosis, renal insufficiency, and so forth. In these cases, therefore, the sole problem concerns what is frequently referred to as *voluntary*, or induced, abortion. The problems of hemorrhage in early pregnancy are slightly different. They usually refer to cases in which there is already some degree of *involuntary*, or spontaneous, abortion; and the moral problem is precisely concerned with procedures which might further this process and, in that sense, become induced abortions.

The practical principle concerning the treatment of hemorrhage is stated thus in **directive 17**:

> **Regarding the treatment of hemorrhage during pregnancy and before the fetus is viable: Procedures that are primarily designed to empty the uterus of a living fetus still attached to the mother are not permitted; procedures primarily designed to stop hemorrhage (as distinguished from those designed precisely to expel the living and attached fetus) are permitted insofar as necessary, even to the extent of risking an abortion. In this case the abortion would be indirect.**

For the sake of clear application in our discussion, I should like to break down that principle into briefer statements and suppositions:

a) If the physician has good reason to believe that the fetus is already dead, there is no moral objection to his emptying the uterus. He may follow any procedure which conforms with good obstetrics.

b) If he has good reason to believe that the placenta is already completely detached, there is no moral objection to emptying the uterus, even though the fetus might still be living. This would not be an induced abortion in the theological sense. (I might add here that, if this supposition were verified—namely, that the fetus were detached but still probably alive—the uterus ought to be emptied as soon as possible so that the fetus could be baptized.)

c) If the fetus, as far as the physician can judge, is still alive and still attached to the uterus, no procedure is permitted which has as its sole immediate purpose the emptying of the uterus. Such a procedure would constitute a direct abortion or a direct hastening of the death of the fetus.

d) In this last case—namely, when the fetus is still alive and still attached to the uterus—the physician may and should use some treatment which is precisely calculated to control the hemorrhage; but, if he has a choice of procedures, he should use that which best safeguards the lives of both mother and child. In those cases, however, in which he cannot successfully stop the hemorrhage without at the same time risking the expulsion of the fetus, he is justified in treating the hemorrhage. The expulsion of the fetus is then unavoidable and indirect.

OBSCURITY OF QUESTIONS

The principle and its explanation seem clear enough, and it ought to be easily applicable to cases in which the data is clearly presented. But in my experience the cases are seldom presented with sufficient clarity.

For instance, sometimes I am asked whether ergot may be used *to control hemorrhage;* at other times I am asked whether it may be used *to empty the uterus.* It may be that the questioners have the same thing in mind, but the wording certainly does not express it. And this distinction between treating hemorrhage and emptying a uterus is of the greatest importance when the case deals with a living, nonviable fetus that is still attached to the uterus.

Again, even when the first wording ("to control hemorrhage") is used, I am often confused by other aspects of the problems presented. This confusion has to do principally with the use of the terms, "threatened" and "inevitable" abortion. Some people seem to think that the terms are interchangeable; but, if the information I have gleaned from obstetricians and obstetrical manuals is correct, they should represent very different cases.

Perhaps it would clarify matters if I would indicate what I understand by the various kinds of involuntary abortions, with regard to the condition of the fetus. I take *complete* abortion to mean that the fetus and placenta are already expelled; *incomplete,* to mean that the placenta remains, but the fetus is dead and already partially or totally expelled; and *threatened* to refer to a case in which the nonviable fetus is still living, still attached to the mother, and not in imminent danger of being dislodged.

There seems to be great difficulty in determining the meaning of *inevitable* abortion. Some obstetricians who helped us in preparing the *Directives* stated that they do not like the term; they think that "inevitability" is too often merely in the mind of the physician. However, the term is used, and, insofar as I can estimate its ordinary meaning, it seems to refer to a case in which the products of conception are disturbed to such an extent that the mother's life is in danger and the fetus, if still alive, cannot be saved.

In explaining what I understand by these various terms, I am not trying to usurp the role of obstetrician. I am merely giving what I have gleaned from study and consultation. If others attach different meanings to these terms, it would be well to note the difference so that there would be no confusion in interpreting the answers concerning the morality of various treatments.

TYPICAL CASES

Granted that my estimate of these terms is at least substantially correct, there is no moral problem, as far as the fetus is concerned, in the use of ergot in either complete or incomplete abortion. Whether the use of ergot in such cases is good obstetrics is not for me to decide.

The problem concerns the so-called threatened and inevitable abortions. The solution can be given by outlining two typical cases.

First case: The mother is bleeding, but not so severely that either her life or the life of the fetus is in immediate danger. This is "threatened" abortion, as it has been described for me. Competent obstetricians tell me that the basic treatment for this condition is bed rest and sedatives. Ergot, they say, is not called for. In this event, there seems to be no problem.

87

Obstetricians I have consulted seem to be in agreement that ergot is not called for in this case. But there seems to be some disagreement concerning the effect ergot would have if it were used. I once had the impression that it would always create a danger for the fetus. But several obstetricians expressed the opinion that it would not disturb a firmly-attached pregnancy unless given in large doses. Sollmann seems to agree with this when he says: "Contrary to popular opinion it [ergot] is not an abortifacient unless dangerous doses are long continued."[1]

Second case: The hemorrhage is excessive, indicating that the mother's life is in imminent danger and that the fetus, though perhaps still alive and still at least partially attached to the uterus, cannot be saved. This, I think, represents one of the cases often described as an inevitable abortion.

I do not know whether obstetricians agree that ergot preparations are indicated in this case; but I do know that I have often been asked about their use by hospitals which presumably have competent obstetricians. Moreover, I believe that it is generally agreed that, if an ergot preparation is used, the resultant contracting of the uterus will not only seal off the blood vessels but will also very likely sheer off the placenta. The question is, therefore: may the ergot preparation be used to control the hemorrhage, even though it is foreseen that it will probably hasten the expulsion of the fetus?

The answer to the question is this: granted the condition assumed in the case, the use of ergot to control the hemorrhage is permissible. I base this answer first on the fact that ergot is an agent calculated to control hemorrhage. I have consulted several texts of pharmacology and each of them states that the *principal* use of ergot is to control *postpartum* hemorrhage. I infer from this that, independently of the presence or

---

[1] T. H. Sollmann, *Manual of Pharmacology* (Philadelphia: W. B. Saunders Co., 7th ed., 1948), p. 400.

absence of a fetus, ergot has an effect on hemorrhage. In other words, it does not stop the hemorrhage by means of the expulsion of the fetus.

The second basis for my answer is the supposition that there is no way of saving the fetus. If there were some way of stopping the dangerous hemorrhage *and* saving the fetus, the use of ergot would not be permitted.

SOME FURTHER OBSERVATIONS

In my brief discussion of inevitable abortion, I indicated that there is much confusion as to the precise meaning of the expression. Cunningham takes inevitable abortion to mean that the fetus is already detached, and the treatment he recommends is to empty the uterus.[2] Granted that his interpretation of inevitable abortion is correct, there is certainly no moral objection to the treatment recommended. I have always hesitated to give a blanket approval of this treatment because it is by no means clear that all doctors mean the same as Dr. Cunningham when they speak of inevitable abortion.

Another point worth re-stressing is the fact that directive 17 makes a clear distinction between cases in which the fetus is still alive and attached and cases in which it is either not alive or at least already detached. Obviously, the judgment of this condition rests with the doctor. Moreover, in a case of real emergency, when a mother is bleeding dangerously, a doctor cannot make this judgment with the same degree of certainty as he could when the course of the pregnancy is normal. The most that we can legitimately ask of doctors in this kind of crisis is a rough, practical estimate which might be put in words such as these: "In all likelihood the fetus is dead"— "most likely the fetus is dead or already detached." To demand more than this is to require what is often practically impossible.

---

[2] *Textbook of Obstetrics* (London: William Heinemann, 1954, 2nd ed.), pp. 189-192.

chapter 12

Cesarean Section

Cesarean section for the removal of a viable fetus is permitted, even with some risk to the life of the mother, when necessary for successful delivery. It is likewise permitted, even with some risk for the child, when necessary for the safety of the mother. Directive 18.

A DISCUSSION of cesarean section should make some distinction between a first section and repeat sections. For the moment, I shall confine my remarks to the morality of a primary section. Later, I shall add a word about repeat sections.

The Joint Commission for the Accreditation of Hospitals includes primary cesarean section as one of the cases in which there should be consultation. Although the Catholic Hospital Association does not recommend the complete standard for consultation proposed by the Joint Commission, it does retain the provision that, apart from emergencies, there ought to be consultation about primary sections.

The very fact that both the Joint Commission and the Catholic Hospital Association require consultation on primary sections indicates very clearly that this is a serious matter, not something to be taken lightly. And this certainly squares with what I have gathered from reading obstetrical literature and from consulting eminent obstetricians. It is true, compared with the medical picture of a number of years ago, cesarean section is now a relatively safe procedure. Nevertheless, apart from special considerations, it certainly does not yet approach the safety of vaginal delivery for either mother or child. And, besides the risk of the operation itself, primary section is the source of definitely undesirable consequences. It leaves a scar on the uterus which affects the power of that organ to function smoothly and safely in future pregnancies. It creates at least a high probability that future deliveries must be by cesarean section. It often causes troublesome adhesions in the peritoneal cavity. And, because of these various consequences, it frequently gives rise to vexing moral problems concerning sterilization.

From the foregoing, it is easy to see that primary cesarean section is not good medicine unless it is a real necessity, as when normal delivery is impossible, or at least when there is a sound reason which makes it the procedure of choice, even though vaginal delivery might be possible. In a word, as the U.S. Code puts it briefly, cesarean section is permitted "when medically indicated." (The wording of article 24 of the Canadian Code is practically the same as directive 18.) It is not for me to state what is good medicine in this matter; and I doubt that it would be feasible to draw up a set of indications so absolute as to cover all cases. Here, as in many matters, cases should be individualized; and this is the responsibility of the physician.

A word about the expressions of directive 18 that cesarean section is permitted "when necessary for successful delivery" and "when necessary for the safety of the mother." "Successful delivery" is not limited to a case in which vaginal delivery would be either impossible or entirely unsafe. The fact that a section would offer a genuinely better chance than vaginal delivery of having a healthy, normal infant sufficiently fulfills the notion of successful delivery. And the same idea underlies the expression "safety of the mother." It is not required that the section be the only means of safeguarding her life; it suffices that, according to competent medical judgment, the section would contribute better to her welfare than would vaginal delivery. But in each of these cases—that is, when the section is for the welfare of *either* the child *or* the mother— there must obviously be due consideration of the total picture: that is, for *both* mother and child. In a word, if the section is for the welfare of one, but a risk for the other, there must be a due proportion between the benefit for the one and the risk for the other. That is the meaning of the directive.

"THE MOTHER WANTS IT"

In my files of correspondence on medical morality, there are several letters that substantially come to this: "A woman who is having her first baby wants a cesarean section in order to avoid the inconvenience of normal labor. Her doctor resents the fact that the hospital will not allow the section. He says that, if the woman wants the operation, that's her privilege."

It is evident from what I have already written that the mere desire to avoid the inconvenience of normal labor is not a sufficient reason for a primary cesarean section. I mention the problem here, first, because it is not an isolated instance, and, secondly, because it brings out certain false attitudes that are occasionally found in both patients and doctors.

First, this exemplifies an entirely mistaken idea of the rights of the patient or of any other individual. As I have explained in chapter 1, an individual's right to mutilate himself or to consent to a mutilation is not absolute. The right is conditioned by the necessity or at least the proportionate utility of the mutilation. In the present case, there is neither necessity nor proportionate utility; hence, the woman has no right to ask for the section.

The second false attitude concerns the doctor-patient relationship. In this case, there are really two errors—one, moral; the other, professional—on the part of the doctor. The moral error is the assumption that he may do whatever the patient wants. The truth is that he may do only what the patient reasonably wants; his right to perform an operation is limited by the patient's right to have it. The professional error consists in letting the patient decide what medical or surgical treatment he is to have. This decision is the doctor's prerogative; he is to make the judgment according to recognized medical standards, and not according to the personal whims of patients.

REPEAT SECTION

There was a time when it was taken for granted that "once a cesarean, always a cesarean." In recent years there has been a trend away from this rule, at least to the extent of recommending vaginal delivery in some cases in which a previous delivery was by cesarean. In view of this trend, some hospital administrators and obstetrical supervisors have asked me whether they may still accept "previous section" as a sufficient indication for elective cesarean section.

Since this is primarily a medical problem, administrators and supervisors may and should allow their own doctors to decide whether there is to be a repeat section or a vaginal delivery. Disagreements among doctors should be amicably settled at staff meetings. From my own limited following of recent medical literature and from consultation with obstetricians, I get the impression that the majority of doctors still believe in following the dictum, "once a cesarean, always a cesarean."

For example, in their article, "One Thousand Cesarean Sections in the Modern Era of Obstetrics," Charles Leavitt Sullivan, M.D. and Elmore M. Campbell, M.D., say: "It is obvious that our staff practically always follows the dictate that once a cesarean section, always a cesarean, and in our opinion the proponents of delivery through the vagina following cesarean section in selective cases have not collected sufficient material to prove otherwise."[1]

---

[1] *The Linacre Quarterly,* Nov., 1955, p. 123.

Dr. J. P. Greenhill summarizes some recent reports on vaginal delivery after cesarean section and then comments as follows:

In my opinion a previous cesarean section is usually an indication for a repeat operation. If the indication for the first one is still present, such as a contracted pelvis, all normal-sized babies must be delivered by cesarean section. Even if the indication for the first section, such as placenta previa, is no longer present, it is best to deliver nearly all subsequent babies by elective cesarean section if the first was a classic section. If a cervical operation was performed, a test of labor is given by many obstetricians. However, I believe in the dictum "once a cesarean always a cesarean" for most women because at present the death rate from an elective operation is almost nil. Uterine rupture following cesarean section is always a danger; when it occurs the mother may die and the baby usually does. Furthermore, most ruptured uteri must be removed. In the few instances in which a patient goes into labor spontaneously, the cervix dilates rapidly and the head descends, labor should be permitted to continue, but only in a hospital. When the cervix is completely dilated the baby should be delivered with forceps. After expulsion of the placenta the uterine cavity must be carefully palpated to be certain the uterus is intact.[2]

Somewhat milder in his judgment of this matter is Dr. J. F. Cunningham. Relative to previous section as an indication for a repeat section, he says:

If the original indication is present, a repeat operation is necessary. If the original indication, such as placenta praevia, is now absent, but if the patient has not had a previous vaginal delivery and, if at the same time a Classical operation had been performed, a repeat operation is usually safer. If, on the other hand, she has had a previous vaginal delivery, or if the operation was through the lower segment, a vaginal delivery is attended with little danger of rupture of the uterine scar.[3]

The foregoing are merely samples of the literature. Verbal consultations with obstetricians give the same picture: namely, the majority of obstetricians still believe in the dictum that once a cesarean, always a cesarean. But this is not absolute.

---

[2] *Year Book of Obstetrics and Gynecology,* 1955-1956 series, p. 190.
[3] *Textbook of Obstetrics* (2nd ed., 1954), p. 435.

Even among the doctors who favor it, many admit there are exceptions to the rule. As a matter of practical prudence—as I have said above—administrators and supervisors should allow the staff to determine the policy of the hospital regarding the following of the dictum and the judgment of the exceptions.

13

Operations on the Infant in Utero

Cranial and other operations for the destruction of fetal life are forbidden. Procedures designed to preserve fetal life (e.g., aspiration for hydrocephalus) are permitted even before delivery when such procedures are medically indicated. Directive 19. (Cf. the Canadian Code, art. 15, and the U.S. Code, "Destruction of Life," n. 5.)

THE MAIN problem that I wish to discuss in connection with this directive is the delivery of the hydrocephalic infant. Before doing this, however, I should like to make some preliminary observations about the meaning of the directive and then say something about cleidotomy, an operation that seems to be too little known and, even when known, to be misunderstood.

I. PRELIMINARY OBSERVATIONS

The directive makes an explicit distinction between operations to destroy fetal life and operations to preserve it. The former are immoral because they are the direct killing of the innocent. This would refer principally to embryotomy and to destructive craniotomy. Fortunately, these operations are much less common than they used to be; nevertheless, if one may judge from the obstetrical manuals, they are still performed occasionally. For this reason, they are explicitly forbidden by the directive and the codes.

Attention should be called to the provision that operations to "preserve" fetal life are permitted. Here we have a change of wording from the old directive, which allowed such operations when designed to "increase" the infant's chance to live. This expression gave rise to a misunderstanding, as it seemed to imply that operations on the fetus could be permitted only when they gave the fetus a *greater* chance to survive than it would otherwise have, e.g., if delivered by cesarean section. This restriction was not intended. The main point of the directive was to distinguish clearly between operations which are designed to destroy fetal life and those which are not. It might be noted here also that the directive takes no stand on the purely medical question as to the better method of effecting a delivery, i.e., by cesarean section or by some operation on the fetus which makes vaginal delivery of a living fetus possible. Finally, the directive is concerned only with a living fetus. If a fetus has already died *in utero* there is no moral objection to such procedures as embryotomy or craniotomy when they are medically indicated.

II. CLEIDOTOMY

Sometimes, when the infant has died *in utero* it is necessary to cut or break the collar bone in order to effect a vaginal delivery. These procedures are known respectively as cleidotomy and osteoclasis. The morality of employing them on a dead infant is already covered by the preceding paragraph. I have also been asked, however, whether the same procedures may be used on a living baby in cases in which the head is already born but the size of the shoulders is an obstacle to complete delivery. The principle to be applied is the same as would govern any mutilation; and its particular application to the unborn infant is enunciated in directive 19: that is, the mutilation is permitted when necessary to effect a successful delivery. A moral judgment of the case, of course, calls for a knowledge of the facts. When I was first confronted with the problem, I knew nothing of the facts; hence, I checked available literature and consulted obstetricians. Much of the literature was not very helpful. It said almost nothing about intentional fracture of the clavicle, and it seemed to treat cleidotomy only as a death-dealing procedure or as a means of extracting a dead fetus. I received some help, however, from two brief passages in Stander, *Textbook of Obstetrics*, 3rd ed., 1945. He writes.

When excessive size of the shoulders prevents the delivery of the child after birth of the head, labor can often readily be terminated after diminishing the size of the shoulder girdle by osteoclasis or by cutting through the clavicles with a pair of heavy scissors—cleidotomy. (p. 918)

Occasionally, in head presentations, the excessive size of the shoulders may prove a serious obstacle to labor. In such cases *cleidotomy* renders excellent service. In this operation a pair of long curved scissors is introduced under the guidance of the hand and cuts through the clavicle on either side, after which the shoulder girdle collapses and delivery is readily effected. (p. 1122)

These passages are helpful because both fracture of the clavicles (osteoclasis) and cleidotomy are mentioned, and the procedures seem designed to effect the delivery of a living child. Nevertheless, I wanted a more explicit assurance of this, especially since cleidotomy is described in a general context of life-destroying operations. I found the following pertinent passage in Titus, *Management of Obstetrical Difficulties*, 4th ed., 1950:

This operation [cleidotomy] consists in dividing the clavicles in order to collapse a shoulder girdle, the girth of which is so great that the infant cannot be extracted although the head has been born. . . . Both clavicles are divided. This is not necessarily a fatal type of embryotomy nor mutilating beyond recovery. (pp. 785-86)

This same judgment is expressed in Willson's revision of Titus, published in 1955. (p. 566)

Here we have explicit testimony that cleidotomy can be a means of saving the child's life. Since noting this passage in Titus, I have also received verbal reassurance from unquestionably competent sources. As for fracture of the clavicle, which means breaking of the bone by direct or indirect pressure, very little is said in the literature, except that it occasionally happens accidentally and that the break readily heals after birth. Here again, however, I have the verbal assurance of competent sources that it is possible to break the bone intentionally without doing any permanent harm to the fetus, and that this is sometimes necessary in order to effect a delivery. The conclusion is that either procedure is permissible when necessary for safe delivery.

It is well to note that in *Moral Problems in Hospital Practice,* Father Finney said that cleidotomy is not permissible on a living child.[1] Fr. Finney's judgment was based on a statement in the then-current edition of De Lee's *Principles and Practice of Obstetrics* that cleidotomy is used when the child is already dead. Even some very recent textbooks give the same impression—namely, that this is an operation to be used only on a dead fetus. For example, this impression persisted in the tenth edition of De Lee by Greenhill, published in 1951. According to the information I have presented here, this is incorrect. Cleidotomy can also be used to effect the delivery of a living child. When necessary for this purpose, there can be no moral objection to it.

III. ASPIRATION FOR HYDROCEPHALUS

Directive 19 explicitly mentions aspiration as a legitimate method of delivering the hydrocephalic infant; and this same provision was included in the first edition of the *Directives.* Nevertheless, both before and after the publication of the *Directives,* questions were sent to The Catholic Hospital Association which showed that there was considerable misunderstanding regarding this topic. The following material was assembled in order to clarify the apparently obscure points.

---

[1] This has been changed in the revision of Fr. Finney's book made by Fr. Patrick O'Brien, C.M. (St. Louis: B. Herder Book Co., 1956), p. 93.

The Catholic Medical Guardian, April, 1928, p. 55, carried this significant statement by Dr. Louis Cassidy, F.R.C.S.I., Master of the Coombe Hospital, Dublin: "Drainage of the hydrocephalic head, by means of a small cannula introduced through the anterior fontanelle, will easily permit delivery and cannot be regarded as craniotomy in the ordinary acceptation of the term."

The following issue of *The Guardian,* July, 1928, p. 86, contained a question by Fr. Henry Davis, S.J., an eminent moral theologian, and a reply by Dr. Cassidy. Fr. Davis wanted a more complete explanation. He suggested that the procedure seemed much like craniotomy to non-medical men; and he added: "Is such drainage, of its very nature, calculated in all cases to kill the foetus? If it does, is it not a direct attack on the life of the foetus?"

To this query Dr. Cassidy replied:

Rev. H. Davis, S.J., asks what I mean by "drainage of the hydrocephalic head." This term connotes to the medical mind the withdrawal of so much of the excess fluid in the cranial cavity as will allow of the reduction of the foetal head to a relatively normal size, or will, at any rate, permit the delivery of the child by the normal passages. This withdrawal can usually be effected without injury to the brain, need not cause death, and is not, therefore, a direct attack on the life of the foetus.

Perhaps *The Guardian* later published some comment by Fr. Davis concerning Dr. Cassidy's reply; but I have no record of it. The earliest moral appraisal recorded in my notes is taken from *The Science of Ethics,* II (1939), by Msgr. Cronin. On page 697, Msgr. Cronin says of hydrocephalus:

To rid the child of the cerebro-spinal fluid in order that parturition may occur, but in such a way as *necessarily* to kill the child is no better morally than craniotomy. But to draw off the fluid gradually by means of a very fine needle gives the child its chance of continuing to the full its brief existence and is therefore lawful even though as a matter of fact death might occur. It is after all the very same operation that would be performed in favour of the child if the hydrocephalic were already born and gave hope of survival.

When I say that Msgr. Cronin's is the earliest moral appraisal I have, I am referring to the specific operation of drainage for hydrocephalus. In his *Principles of Ethics* (published in 1937) Fr. Thomas Verner Moore, M.D., mentions that there are certain cranial operations which do not necessarily kill the child and which are sometimes permissible; but he makes no specific reference to the problem of hydrocephalus. (See pp. 175-181.) The same idea is repeated in his article, "Moral Aspects of Therapeutic Abortion," in the *American Journal of Obstetrics and Gynecology,* Sept., 1940, pp. 422-428.

A later article in the *American Journal of Obstetrics and Gynecology,* March, 1942, pp. 521-524, should also be noted here. This article, "The Treatment of Hydrocephalus in Cephalic Presentation," is by Cornelius T. O'Connor, M.D., F.A.C.S., and Arthur J. Gorman, M.D., both of St. Elizabeth's Hospital, Brighton, Mass. They describe a case in which they had released the cerebro-spinal fluid by "intraventricular tap and drainage per vaginam with a spinal needle." The child was born alive and lived for two hours. Before using this procedure, the physicians had consulted the priest-superintendent of the hospital; and he had decided that it was in accord with sound ethics. The opinion was later confirmed by Fr. John C. Ford, S.J., in his annual survey of moral theology in *Theological Studies,* Dec., 1944, p. 514.

The Bulletin of the Margaret Hague Maternity Hospital, March, 1949, pp. 16-18, tells of the delivery of a hydrocephalic as follows:

A paracentesis trocar was inserted through the large anterior fontanelle, and about 600 ml. of fluid drained off. After another nine hours of labor (total 22 hours), the patient was delivered spontaneously of a living hydrocephalic infant; the presentation was left occiput anterior. The patient's postpartum course was uneventful, and she was discharged six days later. The baby is still alive eight weeks after delivery.

The discussion which followed the account of this case was led by Dr. Samuel A. Cosgrove, and it is so interesting that, if

I had the space, I would reproduce it here entirely. It was pointed out that the first doctors to use this procedure at the Margaret Hague Hospital were strict and conscientious Catholics who had, like Drs. O'Connor and Gorman, consulted Catholic moral authorities before having recourse to the drainage method. The present case was the fourth in which one or both ventricles of a hydrocephalic brain had been drained and the baby was born alive. In two cases the baby had lived only an hour or two; in one case it had lived 12 days; and in the present instance the child was still alive after eight weeks.

"The reason that I have pointed out the survival of no less than four babies," said the discussion leader, "is to establish, without any possibility of discussion, that the procedure does not necessarily and imminently kill the baby, and need not be used with any deliberate intent to do so."

To the foregoing data from printed sources, I would add that several obstetricians have told me that aspiration of the head can be accomplished without killing the baby and that, as a matter of fact, it is the very thing that would be done after the hydrocephalic was born. "Why not," they asked, "do it before delivery so that a successful delivery can be accomplished?"

CAUTIONS

In the preceding discussion, there has consistently been question of one basic procedure: drainage of the hydrocephalic head in such a way that delivery of a live child is made possible, and with an attempt to preserve its life, not to destroy it or to hasten its death. All the methods used—whether called aspiration or intraventricular tap; or whether a needle, trocar, or any other instrument is used—seem to come to that. Such a procedure is evidently morally sound; and it should not be forbidden in any of our hospitals.

Nevertheless, though the procedure, as outlined, squares with sound ethics, I should like to make certain precautionary observations before concluding this chapter.

102

I have a rather vague impression that some physicians refer to this life-saving procedure as a "craniotomy." Dorland's dictionary allows for this usage, because its first definition under "craniotomy" is, "any operation on the cranium." However, it seems to me that the ordinary meaning of this term—when it refers to the unborn baby—is rather the second definition given by Dorland: "The cutting in pieces of the fetal head to facilitate delivery." This is certainly what is described in Stander's *Textbook of Obstetrics,* 3rd ed., pp. 1116ff. I prefer to avoid this word when speaking of a life-saving operation on a fetus; and I think that physicians who wish to use the word "craniotomy" to designate such operations should make their meaning perfectly clear to us. Otherwise, there is bound to be misunderstanding.

A second observation is that obstetrical manuals are generally not very helpful in suggesting a method of treating hydrocephalus which is consonant with sound moral principles. Generally—as Drs. O'Connor, Gorman, and Cosgrove point out—these texts insist on the desirability of delivering a dead baby. However, the tenth edition of De Lee by Greenhill (1951) refers to the O'Connor-Gorman method as "the safest and simplest treatment." (p. 624) Cunningham also in *Textbook of Obstetrics* (2nd ed. 1954) on page 335 says:

If the head is presenting, it should be tapped via the cervical canal, using a spinal or long serum needle. The needle is inserted through one of the widely separated sutures. The cerebro-spinal fluid is allowed to drain away slowly until the head is sufficiently reduced in size to offer no difficulty in delivery. Labour is then allowed to proceed.

In breech delivery a fine trocar may be inserted just above the mastoid process after delivery of the body. The collapsed head can then be delivered. There is no ethical objection to employing this treatment as the operation does not kill the infant. The infant, however, should first be baptized.

As a final caution, let me refer to the fact that in reporting their method of intraventricular tap, Drs. O'Connor and Gorman had mentioned that one of its advantages is that it may "be used on Catholic patients." Dr. Cosgrove argued from this that "it may be used in Catholic hospitals and by Catholic physicians without offense to the moral code as promulgated by the Roman Catholic Church, provided certain vital intentions are conscientiously observed."

Dr. Cosgrove's conclusion is certainly legitimate; and I have no quarrel with it. But it would be advisable to avoid the expression used by Drs. O'Connor and Gorman. To say that a certain procedure "may be used on Catholic patients" implies that Catholics and non-Catholics are governed by different moral laws. This is simply not true when there is question of the principles and applications contained in the ethical section of the *Directives*. These are not laws made by the Catholic Church. They pertain to the natural law. They apply to everyone, regardless of his religion.

chapter | **14** |

The Morality of
Ectopic Operations

A S REGARDS ectopic operations, the practical moral principle generally followed today in the Catholic hospitals of
the United States and Canada is stated as follows:

> **In extrauterine pregnancy the affected part of the mother
> (e.g., an ovary or fallopian tube) may be removed, even
> though the life of the fetus is thus indirectly terminated, pro-
> vided the operation cannot be postponed without notably
> increasing the danger to the mother. Directive 20.** (See also
> the Canadian Code, article 19, and the U.S. Code, "Destruc-
> tion of Life," n. 6.)

It is sometimes said that this ruling represents a change in
the Church's teaching. The charge is not true if it means that
any official teaching of the Church has changed. On the other
hand, it is true that there has been a shift in theological
opinion; but even this shift has been concerned, not with a
moral principle, but rather with the medical data pertinent to
ectopic pregnancy. In a word, as the doctors were able to give
a clearer picture of the medical facts, the application of moral
principles, especially the possibility of applying the principle of
the double effect, also became clearer.

In the present chapter, I shall give some background material concerning the opinions of theologians and the official
teaching of the Holy See. Since the focal point of the problem
has usually been tubal pregnancy, I shall have this principally

in mind. The next chapter will deal specifically with abdominal pregnancy.

I. THEOLOGICAL OPINION

In view of what has been written in previous chapters, it is clear that there would be no disagreement among theologians on this point: any direct attack on fetal life, whether the pregnancy be uterine or extrauterine, is morally wrong. Thus, as regards tubal pregnancy, all would agree that the shelling out of an inviable, living fetus, killing the fetus by means of an electric current, and so forth, are always illicit. All would agree too that the ligation of the maternal arteries and removal of the tube is morally justifiable in order to check hemorrhage resulting from *rupture* of the tube. In this case, the loss of fetal life—if indeed the fetus is not already dead—would be merely the indirect effect of a procedure designed to save the mother's life.

The point of disagreement has been—and to some extent still is—concerned with the proper treatment of a tubal pregnancy before the rupture occurs. In general, the divergent views of theologians fall into these two classes:

a) According to some theologians, the ligation of the arteries and removal of the tube and fetus before rupture actually occurs constitute a direct attack on the life of the fetus and are therefore morally unjustifiable. This opinion is based on the view that the only source of danger before rupture is the fetus itself; hence, the operation is really an attempt to save the mother by means of the removal of the fetus. These theologians, therefore, consider that before rupture occurs the only permissible course is the use of expectancy treatment.

b) Other theologians contend that even before the rupture there is a constant disintegration of blood vessels, with consequent hemorrhage, and that the rupture of the tube simply adds more hemorrhage. In their view, therefore, the cutting off of the blood supply to the tube, even before rupture, is an operation directed to the checking of hemorrhage, and not to the killing of the fetus. Some among this group of theologians also explicitly demand that the doctor use expectancy treatment if possible; but they consider that, if this cannot be done without adding notably to the danger to the mother's life, then the arteries to the tube may be ligated and the entire pregnant tube may be excised just as the cancerous, pregnant uterus may be removed.

Why must expectancy treatment be used if possible and not too dangerous? Because it is not sufficient to establish that the operation is not a direct attack on the fetus; it is also necessary to have a sufficient reason for permitting the shortening of life for the fetus. To adopt a universal rule-of-thumb of performing this ligation operation as soon as a pregnant tube is discovered is hardly to take all reasonable means to save both lives—a condition which sound morality and ecclesiastical authority always demand. And I might add a good medical reason: if this rule-of-thumb is constantly followed, without any attempt at expectancy treatment, all medical progress in the treatment of ectopics is rendered impossible.

II. DECREES OF THE HOLY SEE

The decrees of the Holy See that are concerned specifically with ectopic pregnancy are as follows:

1. In 1886, the Archbishop of Cambrai referred to Rome a number of questions some of which concerned the killing or removal of an inviable ectopic fetus. The general reply to these questions, given by the Sacred Congregation of the Holy Office in August, 1889, was that "it cannot be safely taught in Catholic schools that any surgical operation which is a direct killing of either the child or the pregnant mother is allowed."

2. In 1898, it was asked if laparotomy is permissible in the case of ectopic pregnancy. The Holy See replied: "In case of urgent necessity, laparotomy for the removal of ectopic conceptions is licit, provided serious and opportune provision is

made, as far as possible, for the life of both the fetus and the mother."

3. Judged in its context, the decree of 1898 apparently referred to cases in which the ectopic fetus would be already viable; for other questions submitted at the same time merely concerned premature delivery. Hence, a more specific question was asked in 1900, namely, whether it is sometimes permissible to remove ectopic fetuses even when immature—i.e., before the expiration of the sixth month of pregnancy. The answer to this question, given in 1902, was "in the negative." The Holy Office pointed out that the decree of 1898 had made it clear that "in as far as possible, serious and opportune provision must be made for the life of both the fetus and the mother." It added that, in keeping with the same decree, "no hastening of delivery is allowed unless it be done at a time and in a manner which are favorable to the lives of the mother and the child, according to ordinary contingencies."

In explaining the opinions of theologians, I confined myself to their analyses of the ectopic problem itself. Actually, their differences of opinion concerned not merely the problem itself, but also the interpretation of the decrees of the Holy See. Roughly speaking, the differences of interpretation follow these three lines:

1. The decrees make no factual pronouncements on ectopic operations. They merely state that an ectopic fetus has the same right to life as an intrauterine fetus; hence, principles already clarified concerning the direct killing of and direct abortion of an intrauterine fetus must also be applied in the case of ectopics.

2. The decrees do make a factual pronouncement; for at least the third decree condemns the removal of the inviable fetus as a direct attack on the life of such a fetus. And this condemnation is still in force.

3. The decrees do contain the factual pronouncement just mentioned; but this condemnation is based on the medical facts

as then known. At that time it was thought that, before the rupture of the tube, the precise danger to the mother arose from the presence of the fetus; hence, the operation to save the mother was interpreted as a direct removal of the fetus. But progress in medical research has showed that the tube itself is pathologically affected (e.g., because of the disintegration of the blood vessels, with consequent hemorrhage); hence, an operation to remove this condition is not a direct attack on the fetus and is no longer condemned by the decree.

Theologians who hold that no operation is permissible before rupture of the tube would follow the second interpretation, I believe. Those who hold that the principle of the double effect is applicable even before actual rupture of the tube would follow either the first or third interpretation.

I have indicated these different interpretations of the Roman decrees partly to show why Catholic moralists can hold different opinions concerning ectopic operations and partly to suggest an answer to an ironical statement frequently made today: "The Church has changed her mind regarding ectopics; she will also change with regard to contraception." In the first place, it is not at all clear that, beyond the statement of certain general principles which are always valid, the Church has ever expressed her mind definitely on ectopic operations. In the second place, even if the Church had condemned ectopic operations because available medical facts portrayed such operations as a direct attack on the fetus, this condemnation would of its very nature be subject to change if further, factual research would show that the child is not directly attacked. Finally, just to cover all points, I might add that the decrees of the Roman Congregations, though a part of the Church's official teaching, are not infallible.

With regard to contraception, the case is entirely different. Pope Pius XI solemnly declared that, in condemning contraception, he was voicing an uninterrupted Christian tradition which concerned the natural law and the divinely revealed will of God. The Catholic teaching on contraception, therefore, is perfectly clear, and infallible. Error in such teaching is not only unlikely but impossible. Change is out of the question.

III. CONCLUDING OBSERVATIONS

The opinion allowing the application of the principle of the double effect even before actual rupture of the tube is by far the more common today. Doctors may safely follow this opinion unless further scientific research or a pronouncement of the Holy See should discredit it. I think I can safely say that such a pronouncement is not likely.

This opinion is based on medical data that a pregnant tube is in a state of disintegration and that the object of surgical intervention is to prevent the danger inherent in such disintegration. The objective, therefore, is *not* to terminate the inviable pregnancy—as some writers unfortunately explain it. The termination of the pregnancy is merely the unavoidable and unintended by-product of the operation.

chapter $\boxed{15}$

Abdominal Pregnancy

"SUPPOSE THE fallopian tube has ruptured and an ectopic fetus has attached itself to the mother's intestine. May this or any other abdominal pregnancy be terminated whenever it is found?" If the fetus has attained at least minimum viability so that its life can be preserved by modern methods, the rule for premature delivery as given in **directive 26** may be followed. This rule states:

For a very serious reason labor may be induced immediately after the fetus is viable. In a properly equipped hospital the fetus may sometimes be considered viable after 26 weeks (6 calendar months); otherwise, 28 weeks are required.

Essentially, the *serious reason* which would justify the removal of the fetus when it has attained minimum viability is reducible to this: the removal at this time would offer proportionately greater safety, or less danger, to mother and/or child than waiting till some further development in the pregnancy. In practice, the estimation of the fulfillment of this condition may be left to the judgment of competent obstetricians. According to medical authorities cited by Fr. Bouscaren, who treats this topic thoroughly in *Ethics of Ectopic Operations*,[1] it would hardly be considered good obstetrics to terminate an abdominal pregnancy at this point; rather, it would generally be much safer to wait till almost full term.

---

[1] Milwaukee: The Bruce Publishing Company, 1944, pp. 163-65.

111

As for the termination of the pregnancy before viability, the moralist's answer depends on what is meant by "terminating the pregnancy." Certainly the general principle is here applicable that no direct attack on the fetus is permissible. Consequently, no procedure which has as its sole immediate objective the removal of the inviable fetus may be allowed. This would be a *direct* termination of the pregnancy before viability—that is, a *direct* abortion. On the other hand, if the mother's intestine is already damaged and in urgent need of repair in order to save her life, the damage may be repaired, even though a fetus which adheres to the intestine should incidentally perish in the process. Also, if the mother were hemorrhaging, the ligation of maternal blood vessels required for stopping the hemorrhage would be permissible, even though this procedure would also cut off the blood supply of the fetus. In this case, the harm to the fetus would be merely a by-product of the ligation; and the termination of the pregnancy would, therefore, be merely *indirect.*

Those familiar with ethics realize that any procedure which terminates an inviable pregnancy can be justified only by the application of the principle of the double effect. According to this principle, an action which produces both good and bad effects is permitted if four conditions are fulfilled: *(a)* the action itself must not be morally evil; *(b)* the bad effect is not a means of obtaining the good; *(c)* the bad effect is sincerely not intended, but merely tolerated; and (d) the good effect is sufficiently important to balance or outweigh the bad effect.

Of the four conditions, all are important, but the first two are the most fundamental in medical problems because they concern the very nature of the operation or treatment to be appraised. And it is precisely regarding these two conditions that one notes a great difference between an inviable tubal pregnancy and an inviable abdominal pregnancy, with reference to the application of the principle of the double effect.

In a tubal pregnancy, even before the rupture of the tube

112

or before hemorrhage which creates an *imminent* danger of death for the mother, there is gradual disintegration of blood vessels that constitutes a pathological condition in the mother which is distinct from the mere fact that the fetus is present. Moreover, this condition exists in an organ which is not indispensable for the mother's life; hence, the sacrifice of it, when it is in a morbid condition, can save her life. These facts form the basis for the opinion, held by most theologians today, that ligation of the maternal blood vessels and removal of the tube is (a) not a morally evil action, because it is directed, not against the fetus, but against the pathological condition of the mother; and (b) it is not a case of attaining the good effect by means of the bad, because the mother's life is saved, not by the death of the fetus, but by the removal of the pathological condition.

These are the main points to be considered when a pregnant tube is removed because they show that the fetus is not *directly* killed. For the complete justification of the operation, the other conditions (good intention and proportionate reason) must be fulfilled; but we would not even consider those conditions unless it could be shown that the operation is not a direct attack on the fetus. If the operation consisted merely of opening the tube and shelling out the fetus, it could not be morally justified, because this would be a direct attack on the fetus (a violation of the first condition); and it would also mean that the mother is saved precisely by terminating the pregnancy before viability (a violation of the second condition).

In a nonviable abdominal pregnancy, it is very difficult to verify the two conditions. For one thing, the organ to which the fetus adheres may be so vital to the mother that the removal of this organ or part of it might be more unsafe for her than carrying the pregnancy; hence, there would really be no good effect of the operation. On the other hand, the removal of the fetus itself would be a direct attack on its life; and the saving of the mother by this means—if indeed it would not place her in greater jeopardy—would be to attain a good effect by means

113

of evil. Consequently, in abdominal pregnancy, the only legitimate alternatives seem to be to wait till the fetus dies or becomes viable or till some maternal condition develops which can be the direct object of a procedure designed to save her life and not to kill the fetus. As I mentioned previously, if the fetus should die as a result of such a procedure, the death would be an indirect effect, a mere by-product, of a life-saving operation. In this case, both conditions would be fulfilled.

What I have said here is expressed briefly and pointedly by Fr. Bouscaren: "We must wait until the child is viable (at least with the aid of the most modern incubator methods) or until the crisis of dangerous hemorrhage makes intervention necessary, in which case the removal of the fetus is incidental and indirect."[2]

It should be noted that in referring to Fr. Bouscaren's book, I have used the second edition. In this edition he calls attention to the fact that the opinion he expressed in the first edition[3] was less severe. This may explain why some doctors seem to think that Fr. Bouscaren would allow a direct intervention, even in the case of an inviable abdominal pregnancy, if there is urgent need of such intervention to save the life of the mother. This topic is much more clearly treated in the second edition; and the opinion expressed there (which I have quoted above) seems to be the only one that is morally defensible.

In conclusion, let me refer to an article entitled, "Full Term Abdominal Pregnancy," by R. J. Burleson, M.D. and J. C. Bragg, M.D.[4] This is a report on two cases of full-term abdominal pregnancy, in one of which the fetus was delivered alive and well. In the other case, the diagnosis was made too late. The fetus was found fully developed, but dead. The doctors concluded that, had the diagnosis been made in time, they could have safely delivered the fetus.

[2] *Op. cit.,* p. 165.

[3] Chicago: Loyola University Press, 1933.

[4] *Journal of the American Medical Association,* Dec., 1, 1951, pp. 1349-1350.

chapter $\boxed{16}$

Euthanasia

A T THE OUTSET, to clear up a source of confusion, let me mention the fact that some Catholic theologians speak of euthanasia as "the giving of drugs to a dying person to relieve him of pain." This is not absolutely forbidden, even though the drugs induce unconsciousness. In fact, with very definite restrictions, it is permitted by **directive 23**, which reads:

> **It is not euthanasia to give a dying person sedatives merely for the alleviation of pain, even to the extent of depriving the patient of the use of sense and reason, when this extreme measure is judged necessary. Such sedatives should not be given before the patient is properly prepared for death (in the case of a Catholic, this means the reception of the Last Sacraments); nor should they be given to patients who are able and willing to endure their sufferings for spiritual motives.**

As the term is more generally used today, euthanasia means more than killing pain; it means killing a person. It is advocated by some so-called humanitarians under the guise of "mercy." They speak of "mercy killing," or of "merciful release." And they urge this form of mercy in various degrees. Some plead for *voluntary* euthanasia, which means that the patient asks for and is given "an easy death." Some believe that the "privilege" should be extended to all incurables who are incapable of deciding for themselves, e.g., infants and mental defectives. Finally, some would make this easy death compulsory on all who are considered a burden on society.

From a moral point of view all these forms of mercy killing,

115

with or without the consent of the person, are absolutely wrong. They involve suicide, murder, or a combination of both. It is to these various ways of effecting mercy killing that **directive 21** refers:

Euthanasia ("mercy killing") in all its forms is forbidden.

There is a similar provision in article 13 of the Canadian Code and in number 6 of the General Section of the U.S. Code.

TEACHING OF THE HOLY SEE

As far as I know, the Holy See has never considered it necessary to issue an explicit condemnation of the euthanasia movement. Nevertheless, it is worth noting that this movement is imbued with the same principles, the same lack of appreciation of the meaning and value of human life, that characterized the "philosophy" of the totalitarian state and that resulted in the horrible mass murders of so-called useless persons. The Holy See has often condemned this totalitarianism, its principles, and its atrocities. Some of the papal statements already quoted concerning the inviolability of human life are applicable to this matter. Two others of special pertinence are the following:

In 1940, the Congregation of the Holy Office was asked to give an official reply to this question: "Whether it is licit, upon order from the public authority, to kill directly persons who, although they have committed no crime which merits death, are nevertheless, owing to psychic or physical defects, unable to be of any use to the nation, and are judged rather to be a burden to it and to be an obstacle to its vigor and strength."

The reply to the question runs as follows:

At the general session of the Supreme Sacred Congregation of the Holy Office on Wednesday, 27 Nov., 1940, the eminent Cardinals who are in charge of safeguarding matters of faith and morals, after having heard the opinions of the Reverend Consultors, decided to reply: In the negative, since this is against the natural law and the divine positive law.

116

His Holiness Pius XII approved and confirmed this reply and ordered it published, 1 Dec., 1940.

Given at Rome, from the Holy Office, 2 Dec., 1940.

Less than three years after this decree of the Holy Office, Pius XII saw fit to refer to the same subject in the following eloquent passage of his encyclical letter on The Mystical Body of Christ:

If the faithful strive to live in a spirit of lively faith, they will not only pay due honour and reverence to the more exalted members of this Mystical Body, especially those who according to Christ's mandate will have to render an account of our souls, but they will take to their hearts those members who are the object of our Saviour's special love: the weak, We mean, the wounded, and the sick who are in need of material or spiritual assistance; children whose innocence is so easily exposed to danger in these days, and whose young hearts can be moulded as wax; and finally the poor, in helping whom we recognize, as it were, through His supreme mercy, the very person of Jesus Christ.

For the Apostle with good reason admonishes us: "Much more those that seem to be the more feeble members of the Body are more necessary, and such as we think to be the less honourable members of the Body, about these we put more abundant honour." Conscious of the obligations of Our High Office We deem it necessary to reiterate this grave statement today, when to Our profound grief We see at times the deformed, the insane, and those suffering from hereditary disease deprived of their lives, as though they were a useless burden to society; and this procedure is hailed by some as a manifestation of human progress, and as something that is entirely in accordance with the common good. Yet who that is possessed of sound judgment does not recognize that this not only violates the natural and divine law written in the heart of every man, but that it outrages the noblest instincts of humanity? The blood of these unfortunate victims who are all the dearer to our Redeemer because they are deserving of greater pity "cries to God from the earth."

AGAINST THE DIVINE LAW

From these pronouncements it is clear that any movement that favors the direct killing of innocent persons is contrary to the divine law. That it is against the natural law is already

117

clear from the explanation of directive 12. But it is also contrary to the revealed law of God. For instance, in Holy Scripture we have these clear statements: "The innocent and just man thou shalt not put to death" (Exodus, 23:7); and "The innocent and just thou shalt not kill" (Daniel, 13:53). And these explicit statements of Holy Scripture are confirmed by a tradition that reaches back into Old Testament days and that extends without any break through the centuries of Christian civilization. This Judaeo-Christian tradition on the sacredness of human life is something more than a mere convention. It is a living expression of the divine law as entrusted to the human race.

UNCHRISTIAN VIEW OF SUFFERING

The foregoing are the main arguments against euthanasia; and they reduce themselves to the very simple statement: it is against the law of God. We can expand on them as we will; but they all come back to the unqualified prohibition: "The innocent and just thou shalt not kill."

But it is well to note in addition that the entire philosophy behind the euthanasia movement is anti-Christian. It likens man to a mere animal; it makes pain the greatest evil in the world. It ignores the fact that no one suffers save through the will of God; that through suffering a man can beautify his character, atone for his sins, take a special part in the sublime work of the Redemption, and win for himself an eternity of glory. This does not mean, of course, that Christians deify pain and sit idly by while men suffer. There is also something Christlike in alleviating pain, in helping the sufferer, and in trying to conquer disease. But there is nothing either Christian or Christlike in killing the sufferer to relieve his suffering.

CONCLUSION

The foregoing are what might be termed the *essential* arguments against euthanasia. Another line of argumentation,

118

which can be made very effective, is to show the evil consequences that would follow if euthanasia were permitted. I shall
not develop this myself; it can be found very well expressed in
some of the following references.

HELPFUL REFERENCE MATERIAL

1. "Euthanasia," by James T. Neary, Esq., in *The Linacre
Quarterly,* April, 1938, pp. 38-42. I commend this splendid
article to any member of the medical profession who must give
a talk on euthanasia. It is full of quotable passages. It stresses
the simple fact that life is a gift of God. It shows that the false
philosophy underlying the euthanasia movement involves the
concept that the measure of human life is usefulness to others.
In his concluding paragraph Mr. Neary says:

> Euthanasia is founded on a viewpoint that destruction of life is
> preferable to pain and suffering. If we inculcate this idea into the
> youthful mind, we engender a destructive fear of pain and suffering.
> Soldiers in time of war will hesitate to undergo hardship; suffering
> people in various occupations, whose lives are mere drudgery, will
> seek euthanasia or commit suicide. Women, frightened at the thought
> of bearing children, may seek euthanasia. The fear and dread of pain
> are often worse than the actuality; hence, life may be ended while
> hope of recovery is just around the corner.

2. *The Linacre Quarterly,* April 1947. The entire issue is
devoted to the subject of euthanasia. "Legal Aspects of Euthanasia," by Vincent C. Allred, LL.B., contains good citations
from Blackstone's *Commentaries,* and shows that, while there
is no legal precedent for euthanasia in this country, there is
undoubtedly a group with a new legal philosophy which favors
it. "Moral Aspects of Euthanasia," by Fr. Hilary R. Werts,
S.J., is a fine presentation of the moral arguments against
euthanasia. Particularly good, I think, is the concluding part
of Fr. Werts' article, in which he shows the inconsistency of the
philosophy behind euthanasia and the terrible consequences for
society, should euthanasia be permitted.

3. "Mercy Killing Turns Back the Clock," by Fr. Paul L.

119

Blakely, S.J., in America, Nov. 4, 1939, p. 90. The strong style of this article is a good antidote for the sentimentality that often characterizes the writings of euthanasians. Fr. Blakely paints a vivid contrast between the physician who labors night and day to conquer the "incurable" disease, and the physician who would turn back the clock of civilization by killing the patient. The euthanasians often point with supposed sympathy to the mother who, with tearfilled eyes, kills her incurable child. But "who," says Fr. Blakely, "will say that the mother who kills her sick child does as much to promote those decencies on which the permanence of civilization is conditioned, as the mother who by day and through watchful nights bends over her little one, seeking to help it, even though in her heart she has accepted the dread verdict that as yet medical science can offer no cure?"

4. *The Catholic Doctor,* by Fr. A. Bonnar, O.F.M., (ed. 1948), pp. 99-105. This is a good treatment of the attempt to legalize mercy killing in England, and it shows clearly that the real aim of the movement is much more than voluntary euthanasia.

5. *Catholic Teaching on the Morality of Euthanasia,* by Fr. Joseph V. Sullivan. (Catholic University Press, 1949.) This is Fr. Sullivan's doctoral dissertation, worked out under the direction of Fr. Francis J. Connell, C.SS.R. The printed volume contains only a part of the complete dissertation. However, even in its abbreviated form, it contains a good statement of the arguments against euthanasia, as well as informative historical material. (Fr. Sullivan's dissertation is now published, in the abbreviated form mentioned here, by the Newman Press, Westminster, Md. Its new title is *The Morality of Mercy Killing.*)

6. *The Linacre Quarterly,* Nov., 1950, pp. 3-9. In Dec., 1949, Dr. Hermann Sander calmly injected air into the veins of a cancer patient to put her out of her misery. This case was given considerable attention by the press; and it was the

occasion of many public statements by medical societies and physicians and of many articles on euthanasia. I made a survey of these statements and articles for *The Linacre Quarterly*. Although the survey is somewhat lengthy, I think it will be valuable to repeat it here because it adds many useful references to those already given. The survey follows:

MEDICAL SOCIETIES

The most wholesome aspect of the literature of 1950 which condemned euthanasia was the fact that much of it emanated from physicians themselves and from the secular press; the defense of good morals was not left entirely to priests. During that year, I noted many statements made by various medical groups, though I did not preserve a record of these. However, I do have in my notes a reference to a resolution adopted by the Medical Society of the State of New York to the effect that the society "go on record as being unalterably opposed to euthanasia and to any legislation that will legalize euthanasia." This society was composed of 23,000 doctors. The resolution was adopted unanimously by the 149 members of the house of delegates. Also, I have an Associated Press clipping saying that the World Medical Association, representing 41 national associations, voted to condemn euthanasia under any circumstances.

INDIVIDUAL PHYSICIANS

Individual physicians also spoke strongly against mercy killing. At Montreal, in an address before the Kiwanis Club, Dr. I. M. Rabinowitch, an internationally known Jewish medical authority and research director at Montreal General Hospital, unequivocally condemned euthanasia on religious and medical grounds. He pointed out that it is against both Jewish and Catholic doctrines. He insisted that "God is the Supreme Master of life and death and that no human being is allowed to usurp His dominion." Dr. Rabinowitch's address was reprinted in *The Catholic Mind* for June, 1951, pp. 351-359.

In Edinburgh, Dr. Alexander J. P. Graham delivered an address on euthanasia that showed a profound understanding of the practical, moral, and professional issues involved, and that gave a clear presentation of the moral principles pertaining not only to mercy killing, but also to the giving of drugs to relieve pain, even at the risk of unintentionally hastening death.

Dr. Graham presented the following outline of the types of cases for which euthanasia is likely to be recommended:

(1) A patient with carcinoma of the tongue involving the mandible and the fauces, had reached the stage of continuous pain, with inability to either swallow or articulate. Saliva mixed with blood and food debris dribbled continuously from his lips, whilst the foetor made attendance on him an unpleasant duty for relatives and nursing staff alike.

(2) A man with multiple bone metastases from a hypernephroma required constant narcosis.

(3) A soldier received a gun-shot wound of his spine leaving him with residual paralysis of lower limbs, incontinence of urine and faeces and severe root pain. His psychology was such that little response was forthcoming to efforts to interest him in rehabilitation or his future.

(4) A man with coronary sclerosis reached a state of invalidism due to frequent attacks of pain at rest or on effort.

The factors common to these cases were that they would die sooner or later in the not too distant future. Meanwhile they were experiencing severe pain and suffering, neither of which has any value in the eyes of the materialist. Though these are the types of cases for which euthanasia is usually suggested, some people advocate its use for cases similar to the following:

(5) Cases of senility who prove a financial or physical burden either on their children at home, or on the nursing staff or bed-situation in institutions for the aged and chronic sick.

(6) Infants and children with spina bifida beyond surgical aid, morons and aments.

It is not a far cry from assisting the demise of the first group to killing off the second, with consent, after persuasion, or without either. No great stretch of the imagination is required to visualize the possibility or the means.

Dr. Graham's address appeared in *The Catholic Medical Quarterly* for July, 1950, pp. 111-117. I have quoted him at length because his is an exceptionally good outline of the cases usually recommended for euthanasia. Having given this outline, he then offered a splendid presentation of the moral and professional issues. In the latter section, he discussed the means then at hand for relieving pain. In this connection, he referred to an address given at Edinburgh by Dr. J. C. White, of Boston, who said on that occasion, "So far as pain is concerned we can take care of it neuro-surgically." Dr. Graham remarked that the experience of others was similar to that of Dr. White; and he added:

The potent weapons of sympathectomy and alcohol-block of the sympathetic chains or posterior nerve roots, of neurectomy and of cordotomy at various levels, and possibly, on occasion, of leucotomy, lie in the hands of those qualified to use them. Those of us whose skill may lie in other fields of medicine or surgery should at least not be ignorant of their possibilities. From the purely medical point of view shortening or taking the life of a patient for the relief of pain is unnecessary. Moreover, it is a confession of professional failure or ignorance.

He then discussed the use of drugs to relieve pain; and he concluded with an appeal to Catholic doctors, who are fortunate enough to have sound principles to guide them, to enlighten others by their words and example.

1950 saw the beginning of a new magazine entitled *Pastoral Psychology,* the purpose of which seems to be to promote cooperative understanding between Protestant ministers and psychiatrists. In one of the early issues of this magazine there was an article defending euthanasia. The September number printed a rebuttal article by Dr. John F. Conlin. In his condemnation of euthanasia, Dr. Conlin made use of arguments from ethics, divine revelation and American law; he asserted its futility and harmfulness from a professional point of view; and he showed considerable skill in handling some of the fallacies that are occasionally introduced by proponents of euthanasia.

For instance, there is the objection that, if it is wrong to shorten life, then it must be wrong to lengthen it. Dr. Conlin pointed to the example of Christ as adequate justification, if justification be needed, for the physician's effort to save life. Then, there is the argument that, since some physicians practice euthanasia in secret, it would be better to bring it out into the open by legalizing it. To this Dr. Conlin replied that an intrinsically immoral act is not changed by legalizing it. Still another of the fallacies is that, if we have no right to end life, then we have no right to start it. Here again, said Dr. Conlin, if justification be needed, it can be found in the directive given our first parents to increase and multiply. Throughout his article, he insisted that the same God who gave this directive also ordered categorically: "The innocent and just person thou shalt not put to death."

Like Dr. Graham, Dr. Conlin called attention to the diverse methods of treating pain and of helping the sick to lead useful lives almost to the time of their death. He stressed the benefits obtained through hormone treatments, psychotherapy, occupational therapy, and neurosurgery. He concluded:

It becomes increasingly incumbent upon physicians to espouse unpopular causes. This is not for them a new role. Drastic remedies, radical surgery, amputations must often be prescribed "for the good of the patient." The good physician opposes euthanasia "for the good of the public." Morality is often unpleasant for us creatures. It is often unpopular. God's laws are clear and unequivocal. They must be obeyed. It's as simple as that!

I think I should add here that in the June, 1950, number of *Pastoral Psychology* there were three letters objecting to the article that had favored euthanasia. One of these letters was by a physician; the other two were from Protestant ministers. This was encouraging, because ministers have been so frequently quoted in favor of euthanasia.

124

SECULAR PRESS

The reaction to the Sander case brought condemnations of euthanasia even from the secular press. Worthy of special mention is an editorial published in the *Boston Traveler* for Jan. 9, 1950, which was reprinted in *The Catholic Mind* for March, 1950, pp. 178-179. The editorial insisted on the essential distinction between man and animal as something basic to the legal and religious traditions of Western civilization. It put primary emphasis on the ethical principle that no man has a right to kill the innocent, an argument which is stated very neatly in "the American way" when we say that all men are created equal. As secondary, and merely practical arguments, it condemns euthanasia on these two counts: the constant progress of medicine, and the impossibility of controlling mercy killing once it should be sanctioned by law.

DISCORDANT NOTE

Thus far I have surveyed excellent and morally sound discussions of euthanasia by physicians. I wish I could stop there. Yet, I must call attention to one decidedly discordant note. In *GP* for Sept., 1950, pp. 81-83, there was an article entitled "Ethics in Medicine," by Walter C. Alvarez, M.D., then editor of the magazine. Ostensibly, this article was a book review; but it soon became clear that Dr. Alvarez's primary purpose was to build a strong case for euthanasia. He had most of the time-worn arguments of the mercy killers: the mercy we show to the sick horse; the fact that St. Thomas More had the Utopians committing euthanasia; the pitiable condition of certain patients and of idiots. I shall say something about St. Thomas More later; the other arguments have already been covered very well by my preceding citations from physicians. One thing is clear: Dr. Alvarez was out of step with the most representative members of his profession.

125

PRIESTS

At about the time the Sander case was breaking into print, Fr. Robert F. Drinan, S.J., published an article entitled "Euthanasia: An Emergent Danger" in the *Homiletic and Pastoral Review,* for Dec., 1949. Fr. Drinan sketched the history of the euthanasia movement and its progress in America, and stressed especially that, in arguing against the movement, we should remember that its promoters no longer believe that physical suffering is according to the will of God, to be accepted with resignation. He suggested, therefore, that the main argument against these people is historical: namely, to show them that what they recommend is a return to barbarism, and that, in fact, even among barbarous people it was never institutionalized.

Incidentally, Fr. Drinan is one of several priest-writers who gave explicit consideration to the statement that St. Thomas More had his Utopians committing euthanasia. He admitted that the passage is in *Utopia;* but he rightly asserted that no one may legitimately argue from this that it was also More's opinion. *Utopia* is a fantasy. Moreover—and this is important —even if it were true that More had approved of euthanasia, it is clear that in this he would not be expressing a Catholic opinion; and his canonization would have been in spite of it and not because of it.

The same issue of the *Boston Traveler* that had the editorial against euthanasia also contained a discussion of the morality of euthanasia by Fr. John C. Ford, S.J. Fr. Ford's article is now available in pamphlet form under the title *Mercy Murder.* It can be obtained from the America Press, 70 East 45th St., New York 17, N.Y. The pamphlet contains a splendid presentation of the philosophical, theological, and practical objections to euthanasia. Incidentally, it offers the best answer I have seen to the euthanasians' claim to have St. Thomas More on their side. As Fr. Ford points out, More's Utopians not only permit mercy-suicide and mercy-murder; they also permit di-

126

vorce and they condemn bodily austerities. Yet More wore a hairshirt and practiced other bodily mortifications; and he went to his death rather than approve the divorce of Henry VIII. It seems obvious that *Utopia* does not express his own philosophy of life.

chapter 17

Preserving Life

I. THE ORDINARY MEANS OF PRESERVING LIFE

EUTHANASIA USUALLY implies the use of some positive means to end life: e.g., taking poison, a lethal dose of some drug, and so forth. But death can also be brought about in a negative way: i.e., by not taking or giving something which is necessary for sustaining life; and in some cases this failure to take or give what is necessary for preserving life is equivalently euthanasia. That is the general meaning of **directive 22**:

The failure to supply the ordinary means of preserving life is equivalent to euthanasia.

A complete explanation of this directive calls for an explanation of *ordinary* and *extraordinary* means of preserving life, as theologians use these terms, and also for an explanation of the duties of patients and doctors regarding the use of these means.

MEANING OF TERMS

Doctors and theologians might attach different meanings to the terms, "ordinary" and "extraordinary," as J. E. Drew, M.D., and Fr. John C. Ford, S.J., pointed out in their article, "Advising Radical Surgery: A Problem in Medical Morality."[1] Thus, as regards physicians, Dr. Drew and Fr. Ford write:

To the physician ordinary signifies standard, recognized, orthodox, or established medicines or procedures of that time period, at that

[1] *Journal of the American Medical Association,* Feb. 28, 1953, pp. 711-716.

level of medical practice, and within the limits of availability. Extraordinary signifies, from the physician's standpoint, a medicament or procedure that might be fanciful, bizarre, experimental, incompletely established, unorthodox, or not recognized.

Theologians use these terms in a different sense; and it is important to note this because the directive follows the theological meaning. As regards various hospital procedures, the theologian would say that *ordinary* means of preserving life are all medicines, treatments, and operations, which offer a reasonable hope of benefit for the patient and which can be obtained and used without excessive expense, pain, or other inconvenience. For example, suppose that a patient whose health is normally good has pneumonia. This patient is now facing a crisis; but from our experience we have every reason to believe that we can bring him through the crisis by means of certain drugs, such as penicillin, and the use of oxygen for a time. Once he passed the crisis he would be well on the way to complete recovery. Here we seem clearly to be dealing with *ordinary* means; for the use of the drugs and oxygen in these circumstances does not involve excessive inconvenience, and there is a very reasonable hope of success.

In contradistinction to ordinary are *extraordinary* means of preserving life. By these we mean all medicines, treatments, and operations, which cannot be obtained or used without excessive expense, pain, or other inconvenience, or which, if used, would not offer a reasonable hope of benefit. For example, consider a case like this. A young woman has a rare cardiac ailment. There is a chance of curing her with an extremely delicate operation; but it is only a chance. Without the operation, she can hardly live a year. With the operation, she may die on the table or shortly afterwards: but she also has a chance, though considerably less than an even chance, of surviving and of being at least comparatively cured. This operation seems to be a clear example of an *extraordinary* means of preserving life, especially because of the risk and uncertainty that it involves.

Another example. A patient, almost 90 years of age, has a cardiorenal disease and has been in a coma for two weeks, during which time he has received intravenous solution of glucose and some digitalis preparation. This coma is apparently terminal. In such a case, is the continued use of glucose and digitalis to be considered an ordinary or extraordinary means of preserving life? The answer may not be entirely clear and beyond debate; but I believe that moralists would generally say that, though the use of glucose and digitalis would be ordinary means if it were merely a matter of tiding a patient over a temporary crisis, yet in the present case the actual benefit they confer on the patient is so slight in comparison with the continued cost and difficulty of hospitalization and care that their use should be called an *extraordinary* means of preserving life.

THE DUTY

Every individual has the obligation to take the ordinary means of preserving his life. Deliberate neglect of such means is tantamount to suicide. Consequently, every patient has the duty to submit to any treatment which is clearly an ordinary means; and his doctor, as well as the nurses and hospital personnel, has the duty to use such means in treating the patient. To do less than this is equivalently euthanasia—as is stated in directive 22.

It should be noted, however, that the directive is here enunciating only a *minimum*: this is the least that must be done for any patient. As a matter of fact, there are some cases in which a patient might be obliged to use extraordinary means; and there are many cases in which the doctor is obliged to use them. In the next section, I shall try to indicate some norms for the use of extraordinary means in the care of patients. For the present, it seems sufficient merely to state the fact that the use of extraordinary means is sometimes obligatory.

HISTORICAL BACKGROUND

It is not always easy to distinguish between ordinary and extraordinary means of preserving life. I believe that the definitions I have given would meet with substantial approval by most moralists today; yet some might prefer to phrase them somewhat differently. For instance, one outstanding theologian suggests that ordinary means would include "the medicines, nursing, etc., usually adopted by persons of the same condition of life as the patient." This is perhaps a good working rule for most cases. I believe, however, that it should be considered as merely supplementary to the definitions I have given, because my definitions more explicitly include elements that are essential to the historical development of the terms, *ordinary* and *extraordinary* means of preserving life. The medical profession should know something of this history.

The moralists who coined the terms, *ordinary* and *extraordinary* means of preserving life, were deeply conscious (as Catholic moralists have always been) of a clear distinction between the duty of *avoiding* evil and the duty of *doing good*. One must, at all costs, avoid doing what is intrinsically evil; but there are reasonable and proportionate limits to one's duty of doing good. For example, the martyrs were not ordinarily obliged to seek out their persecutors in order to profess their faith before them; but when faced with the critical choice of either denying their faith or dying they were obliged to submit to death. The reason is that to deny one's faith in the one true God is intrinsically evil—something which may never be done, even to avoid torture and death. A modern example illustrating the same matter might be the problem of childbearing in marriage. Married people are not obliged to have all the children they possibly can, nor obliged to have children in the face of great inconveniences; but they are clearly obliged to avoid contraception because it is intrinsically evil.

With this distinction between doing good and avoiding evil in mind, the old moralists approached the problem of preserv-

131

ing life. They were not disturbed by the problem of "mercy killing"; they knew that suicide and murder are always wrong and that no inconveniences can justify them. But to preserve one's life is to do good; and the duty of doing good is usually circumscribed by certain limits. The moralists set out to make a prudent estimate of the limits of this duty. In other words, they wanted to answer the simple question that any good man might ask: "How much does God demand that I do in order to preserve this life which belongs to God and of which I am only a steward?" In answering this question, they discussed such practical, concrete things as expense, pain, repugnance, and other inconveniences.

INCONVENIENCE

For example, regarding expense, they considered it obvious that a man would have to go to some expense in caring for his health. Yet he need not spend money or incur a debt which would impose a very great hardship on himself or his family, because this kind of hardship would be more than a "reasonable" or "moderate" care of health and therefore more than God would ordinarily demand.

And so of other things. The moralists spoke of great pain, e.g., the enduring of a serious operation in days when there were no effective anesthetics. It took heroism to undergo such an ordeal; and the moralists prudently estimated that an individual would not ordinarily be obliged to submit to it. They spoke of other inconveniences, too: e.g., of moving to another climate or another country to preserve one's life. For people whose lives were, so to speak, rooted in the land, and whose native town or village was as dear as life itself, and for whom, moreover, travel was always difficult and often dangerous—for such people, moving to another country or climate was a truly great hardship, and more than God would demand as a "reasonable" means of preserving one's health and life.

The foregoing are merely examples of the way the older

moralists considered the means of preserving life in terms of inconvenience. If the inconvenience involved in preserving life was excessive by reason of expense, pain, or other hardship to onself or others, then this particular means of preserving life was called *extraordinary*. On the other hand, when no excessive inconvenience was involved, the means of preserving life would generally be considered *ordinary*.

USEFULNESS

There is one more point to be discussed before I can give a complete idea of the historical notions of *ordinary* and *extraordinary*. I can illustrate this point by an example taken from another section of moral theology: the duty of charity towards one's neighbor.

Suppose that I see my neighbor drowning, but that I am a very poor swimmer and would have very little chance of saving him. Am I obliged to make the attempt? Catholic moralists would say that I might be heroic to try, but that I would have no strict obligation to do so. In giving such an answer, they are simply applying a sound principle of both philosophy and common sense, namely, that no one is obliged to do what is practically useless.

Moralists have applied this same principle when discussing the duty of preserving one's own life, especially by taking medicines, undergoing operations, and so forth. As a matter of fact, we know that some of these things help, and some do not; some offer great hope of success; others offer very slight hope. The old moralists realized this too; and they introduced this element of "hope of success" into their concepts of ordinary and extraordinary means of preserving life. A means was considered *extraordinary* if it involved excessive inconvenience *or* if it offered no reasonable hope of benefit. A means was considered *ordinary* if it did not involve excessive inconvenience *and* it offered a reasonable hope of benefit.

The foregoing are the main points that mark the development

133

of the moralists' discussion of ordinary and extraordinary means of preserving life. We can apply them to the vast number of artificial life-sustainers now at the disposal of the medical profession by judging two elements, *convenience* and *utility*. A medicine, treatment, etc., is to be considered an ordinary means if it can be obtained and used with *relative convenience* and if it offers *reasonable hope of benefit*. When either of these conditions is lacking, the means is extraordinary.

It should also be noted that the moralists were primarily concerned with the duty of the individual (i.e., the patient), not his doctor. They thus chose the easier course, because the doctor's problem is much more complicated. The patient is obliged to use ordinary means; as for extraordinary means, he may use them if he wishes, but, apart from very special circumstances, he is not obliged to do so.

I have heard it said that the doctor's duty is exactly the same as the patient's. This is not correct. The doctor (as well as nurses and hospital authorities and personnel) must do not only what the patient is obliged to do but also what the patient reasonably wants and what the recognized standards of the medical profession require. I shall discuss these points in the next section.

It is important to note that, though the notions of ordinary and extraordinary remain the same, their applications can vary with changing circumstances. For example, major operations used to be considered extraordinary means of preserving life on two counts: first, because the pain was practically unbearable for most people; and secondly, because the outcome was often very uncertain, e.g., because of the danger of infection. Today we have means of controlling both the pain and the danger of infection; hence, many operations that would have been extraordinary in former times have now become ordinary means of preserving life.

II. EXTRAORDINARY MEANS OF PROLONGING LIFE

In the preceding section it was pointed out that, in terms of modern medical procedures, *extraordinary* means of preserving life are all medicines, treatments, and operations, which cannot be obtained or used without excessive expense, pain, or other inconvenience for the patient or for others, or which, if used, would not offer a reasonable hope of benefit to the patient. One example given was that of a very dangerous and uncertain operation; another was the use of such things as intravenous feeding to prolong life in a terminal coma. Still another example, culled from medical literature, is the case "when life can be somewhat prolonged by a gastroenterostomy or an entero-anastomosis," as mentioned by Walter C. Alvarez, M.D.[2]

In concrete cases it is not always easy to determine when a given procedure is an *extraordinary* means. It is not computed according to a mathematical formula, but according to the reasonable judgment of prudent and conscientious men. Granted such a judgment, the patient himself is not generally obliged to use or to submit to the procedure. He may, with a good conscience refuse it except in special cases when a prolongation of his life is necessary: (a) for the common good, as might happen in the case of a great soldier or statesman; and (b) for his own eternal welfare, as might be the case when he has not yet had the opportunity of receiving the Last Sacraments.

Here I want to consider the *duty* of the doctor to use *extraordinary* means of preserving life. Under the term "doctor," I include not only the attending physician but also all who assist him in the care of the patient, i.e., nurses and hospital personnel. To avoid unnecessary complications we shall limit the discussion to patients who are in some sense "paying" patients, i.e., those whose expenses are being paid by themselves, their relatives, an insurance company, etc. In other words, we are

---

[2] *Journal of the American Medical Association,* Sept. 13, 1952, p. 91.

excluding the purely charity case in which the medical care is given *gratis*.

Lest there be a misunderstanding, let me add that my sole reason for excluding the charity patient is to avoid the complicating question of how much free service hospitals and doctors are obliged to give to the sick. I do not wish to imply that basic rights of patients would differ according to their means of paying for services. For example, in the chapter on experimentation, I insist on the necessity of the enlightened consent of the patient. This holds for all patients, regardless of their ability to pay.

THE PATIENT'S WISH

How is the doctor to judge whether he is obliged to use an *extraordinary* means? The first rule for judging is indicated by Dr. Alvarez when he speaks of prolonging life somewhat by a gastroenterostomy or an enteroanastomosis: *"the wishes of the patient* should be ascertained." The words I have italicized contain the first rule concerning the doctor's duty: he must do what the patient wishes. It is the patient who has the right to use or to refuse the extraordinary means; hence, it is primarily the patient who must be consulted. Obviously there are many cases in which it is impossible to consult the patient, e.g., when he is delirious or in a coma, or when he is a small child. In these cases the right to make the decision is vested in those who are closest to the patient, i.e., husband, wife, parents, guardians. Thus, Dr. Alvarez rightly says that the wishes of the family must be consulted when there is question of efforts at resuscitation by means of oxygen and "endless injections of stimulants" in the case of an old person who is close to death. I might add here that the relatives do not make this decision precisely in their own name, but rather as representing the patient; hence, they should try to determine what he would reasonably want done under the circumstances. (Perhaps some further distinction could be made regarding relatives and guardians who merely administer the property of the sick man and those who pay his medical bills out of their own money; but I believe such a distinction is not pertinent to our present discussion.)

There are cases, no doubt, when consultation with the patient or the relatives would be impossible, or inadvisable, or useless: e.g., when they would not understand the issues or are too much distraught to make decisions, and so forth. In such cases, it seems to me, the doctor should follow the plan previously suggested for the relatives: that is, try to make a prudent estimate of what the patient would reasonably want if he could be asked. This would mean that the doctor would do what he sincerely judged to be for the best interests of his patient. If other means are lacking for determining this, the golden rule should be helpful. What would the doctor himself want if he were in the patient's condition?

STRICT PROFESSIONAL STANDARD

Thus far we have considered only the doctor-patient relationship; and what has been said may be reduced to this: in his use of extraordinary means, the doctor should follow the expressed wishes of the patient or his representatives; and when their wishes cannot be explicitly ascertained, he should do what he thinks the patient would want or what he sincerely judges to be for the patient's best interests. Even these relatively simple rules are sometimes difficult to apply; but the problem of using or not using *extraordinary* means may be even further complicated by the question of "professional standards."

When I speak of professional standards, I mean this: is there a line of conduct dictated by his profession itself which requires the doctor to take means of prolonging life that might not be required merely by the physician-patient relationship? To make this problem more concrete, let me say that in discussions with conscientious physicians I have observed two different professional standards in this matter.

137

One group of these conscientous physicians believes that the doctor's duty is to preserve life as long as he can, by any means at his disposal, and no matter how hopeless the case seems to be. We can call this the *strict,* or *extreme,* professional standard. The doctors who uphold this standard admit the right of the patient or his representatives to refuse *extraordinary* means; but they think that, insofar as the judgment is left to the doctor himself, he must simply keep trying to prolong life right to the very end.

The following of this strict standard has several advantages. In the first place, it gives euthanasia the widest berth possible. Secondly, it completely avoids defeatism. These doctors not only keep trying to conquer a disease, they also keep trying to save the individual patient. And there is no doubt about it: they can sometimes show us cases in which a former patient is now alive and well two, three, or many years after he was supposed to be "hopeless." Finally, strict though it is, this standard is easiest on the doctor's own conscience because he is never forced to make the painful decision to cease using intravenous feeding, oxygen, and so forth, in the case of a dying patient.

MODERATE STANDARD

As I said, there are many conscientious doctors who follow the *strict* standard to which reference has just been made. But there are others, equally conscientious, who believe that a more *moderate* standard should be followed. These doctors try to effect a cure as long as there is any reasonable hope of doing so; they try to preserve life as long as the patient himself can reap any tangible benefits from the prolongation. But they also think there is a point when such efforts become futile gestures; and they believe that at this point the sole duty of the doctor is to see that the patient gets good nursing care and that his pain is alleviated.

The advantages of the strict standard are the disadvantages

of the moderate standard. The doctors who follow this latter standard certainly have no sympathy for euthanasia; yet their failure to take certain means of prolonging life might at times create the impression of favoring euthanasia. They are not defeatists; yet, through their willingness to consider some cases hopeless according to present medical knowledge, they might occasionally lose a battle that the stricter doctors would win. Moreover, their occasional decisions to discontinue stimulants or artificial feeding are seldom made with perfect mental peace. Such a decision easily generates worry.

But it must be admitted that the moderate standard is not without its advantages. For one thing, it seems to be very much in accord with the traditional policy of Catholic theologians of interpreting obligations according to a reasonable limit—as we have seen, for example, in their explanation of the individual's duty of caring for his own health.

The moderate standard also seems to square with a good Christian attitude. I once asked the mother superior of a home for incurable cancer patients whether they used such things as intravenous feeding to prolong life. She replied that they did not. They gave all patients devoted nursing care; they tried to alleviate pain; and they helped the patients to make the best possible spiritual preparation for death. Many very good people with whom I have spoken about this matter think these sisters have the right idea—"the good Christian attitude toward life and death," as they call it. This is really an exemplification of the moderate standard.

Finally, it seems evident that the moderate standard is less likely to impose excessive burdens on the patient's relatives. Relatives often endure terrific strain and undergo great expense while life is being prolonged by artificial means; and in some cases—e.g., the terminal coma—very little good seems to be accomplished. The moderate standard spares them some of this strain and expense.

139

CONCLUSION

I have dwelt at some length on these two views of conscientious physicians because I wanted to make it clear that as yet there is no clear-cut professional standard regarding what I might respectfully call "the fine points" of care of the dying. I may add that among moral theologians a somewhat similar condition prevails: up to a certain point duties are clear and there is agreement on what must be done; beyond that point the rules of obligation become obscure and there is room for differences of opinion.

Some time ago, I published in the Jesuit quarterly, *Theological Studies,* a rather lengthy article entitled "The Duty of Using Artificial Means of Preserving Life."[3] The purpose of this article was to stimulate discussion among theologians concerning what seemed to be a cardinal problem in modern medical practice. Later, in the same magazine, I published a shorter article entitled "The Duty to Preserve Life,"[4] which included the points that had been brought out in our discussions. This second article concluded with a statement which substantially expresses the minds of many competent theologians. Perhaps it will help to reprint it here. It runs as follows:

1. It is not contrary to the common good for a doctor to admit that a patient is incurable and to cease trying to effect a cure. But it would be contrary to the common good to cease trying to find a remedy for the disease itself.

2. As long as there is even a slight hope of curing a patient or checking the progress of his illness, the doctor should use every probable remedy at his command. The common good demands this rule of conduct for the doctor; and it should be followed as long as the patient makes no objection. The patient, however, is entitled to refuse any treatment that would be extraordinary.

3. When a doctor and his consultants have sincerely judged that a patient is incurable, the decision concerning further treatment should be in terms of the patient's own interests and reasonable wishes,

---

[3] *Theological Studies,* June, 1950, pp. 203-220.
[4] *Ibid.,* Dec., 1951, pp. 550-556.

expressed or implied. Proper treatment certainly includes the use of all natural means of preserving life (food, drink, etc.), good nursing care, appropriate measures to relieve physical and mental pain, and the opportunity of preparing for death. Since the professional standards of conscientious physicians vary somewhat regarding the use of further means, such as artificial life-sustainers, the doctor should feel free in conscience to use or not use these things, according to the circumstances of each case. In general, it may be said that he has no moral obligation to use them unless they offer the hope of some real benefit to his patient without imposing a disproportionate inconvenience on others, or unless, by reason of special conditions, failure to use such means would reflect unfavorably on his profession.

All of us who sponsored this statement realize that it may need improvement and further clarification. Even as it stands, however, it should help doctors to solve these difficult cases with a realization of a certain degree of liberty of judgment and with a consequent peace of conscience.

$\boxed{18}$

Elective Induction of Labor

"IS THE INDUCTION of labor, at or near term, for the convenience of the doctor or the mother morally justifiable?" This question has been presented to The Catholic Hospital Association so often in recent years that it cannot be ignored. Basically, the moralists' answer to the question depends on the obstetrical evaluation of the procedure; hence, since receiving the questions, I have tried to obtain the needed obstetrical information by consultation and by keeping in touch with the medical literature on this topic.

OBSTETRICAL CONSULTANTS

Some years ago, I sent to seven very competent obstetricians located in various parts of the country this question: "Is the doctor justified in inducing labor a few days or a few weeks early so that he may be able to take his vacation according to plan; or so that the mother may be out of the hospital for the Christmas holidays; or so that the doctor can take care of a number of deliveries at approximately the same time?" The parts of this question included various aspects of the problem that had been referred to me.

The most complete answer came from an obstetrician who stated that, although he himself rarely induced labor, he had seen it done by good and careful men with remarkable results. He wrote:

If the method of induction employed is admittedly hazardous, then obviously it is wrong. I believe, however, that with reasonable skill and good judgment a great number, perhaps a majority, of multiparas could be induced without danger to mother or baby. By "without danger" I mean without demonstrable increase in morbidity or mortality. But this can be done only if the candidates for induction are carefully chosen and if proper means of induction are used. The criteria I would set down for the selection of the patient are the following:

1. Induction should be employed only in multiparas; 2. the history of previous labors and deliveries should be essentially normal, i.e., no previous prolonged labor, traumatic delivery, etc.; 3. the head should be engaged; 4. the cervix should be soft and patulous—i.e., relaxed and preferably partially open; 5. the pelvis should be adequate; 6. the patient should be close to term, one week or possibly two. Under those conditions the patient should be "ripe" and the baby, for all practical purposes, mature.

With such criteria and safeguards, it would hardly be possible to arrange it so that all deliveries would be in the daylight hours, or so that one could clear the decks for a two-week vacation. To observe reasonable care almost necessitates that such induction be the exception rather than the rule. If it were done very frequently, or if it were attempted on all patients coming due during a given period of time, then it would almost certainly be abused and lead to difficulty.

Thus, in summary, I think induction of labor for the convenience of the doctor might be condoned from a medical standpoint if proper care is observed in the choice of the patient and of the means of induction. It is a practice admittedly open to abuse and, for this reason, probably should be discouraged.

This answer stresses the need of individualization. Certain signs must be present; and this means that routine induction, without reference to these signs, is not good obstetrics. Other doctors consulted stressed this same point; and there is no need of quoting them here.

The doctor whom I have quoted at length indicated that induction for the convenience of the obstetrician might be medically condoned. Another of my consultants thought that induction for the personal convenience of the doctor is never justifiable; he believed that, aside from strictly medical indications, the only reason for induction might be the prevention of precipitate labor. Still another mentioned that justifying reasons might be the availability of transportation of the patient, proper attendance of the obstetrician by appointment, facility for domestic arrangement in a home with other small children, and perhaps even economic reasons.

MEDICAL LITERATURE

My study of medical literature has obviously been limited by both time and other factors. I found the following references and opinions especially interesting and informative; and I think they may be of use to others, especially to obstetrical supervisors.

Baird writes:

Like Caesarean section, the operation is very frequently abused. There is no method of inducing labor which is absolutely safe to mother and child, and induction should therefore be avoided except when it is definitely indicated. All too frequently it is employed as an operation of convenience, either for the mother or for her doctor. In the great majority of cases no harm results, but the risk exists, and in a large series of cases is likely to show itself in increased morbidity figures.[1]

Another medical reference is a question in the *Journal of the American Medical Association*.[2] The editor was asked whether the "increasingly common practice to induce labor for no other indication than the convenience of the attendant or the parturient" could be considered good obstetric practice. The main part of the reply, which seems to say substantially what I was told by obstetricians, is as follows:

The answer is unquestionably that this is not good practice in general. One must, however, consider in this problem the following factors. 1. The group at Evanston Hospital, Evanston, Ill., found that it was perfectly safe to induce labor by rupture of the membranes if the patient was near term, the cervix was soft and effaced, and if there were no contraindications such as malposition. 2. There is an increasing number of patients with very short labors with their first pregnancy

---

[1] Baird, Dugald, *Combined Textbook of Obstetrics and Gynaecology* (Baltimore: Williams and Wilkins, 1950), p. 897.
[2] Dec. 22, 1951, pp. 1719-1720.

and there are many multiparas who barely get to the hospital in time for delivery. 3. With the advantage of the sulfonamides, the antibiotics and better prenatal and intranatal care, there is now such a low morbidity and mortality that many procedures are probably done now that never would have been dreamed of 20 years ago. . . .

Perhaps in a few more years we will consider this normal practice and until then accept an attitude of tongue-in-cheek toward it, rather than one of lifted eyebrows. Certainly the burden of proof of its safety is on the shoulders of those who practice early induction.

This reply was given in 1951. A careful following of the *Year Book of Obstetrics and Gynecology*,[3] in subsequent years shows that the more recent literature on elective induction is voluminous and that there is much controversy over the question of induction for convenience. From these annual reports I shall select only two items.

The 1953-1954 *Year Book* contains a lengthy survey of an article by J. Robert Willson, M.D., about induced labors at Temple University Hospital. Later, Dr. Willson himself refers to this Temple University study and makes this very pertinent observation:

. . . The convenience of elective induction of labor has led to its widespread use, both by skillful obstetricians in well-equipped and well-staffed institutions, and by others less able and willing to select patients suitable for the procedure. The reported excellent results of the former, however, are not typical of the increased morbidity and mortality occurring in those patients in whom attempts are made to induce labor in the face of contraindications to the procedure.[4]

In the *Year Book* for 1954-1955, Dr. J. P. Greenhill, the editor, makes this comment:

No one will argue about necessary induction of labor, as, for example, toxemia of pregnancy which does not improve with conservative therapy, some cases of diabetes with a large baby and selected cases of erythroblastosis. However, there is considerable discussion about elective induction for the convenience of either the doctor or the patient.

---

[3] Cf. the *Year Books* for 1952, pp. 183-187; 1953-1954, pp. 161-163; 1954-1955, pp. 148-153.
[4] Titus-Willson, *The Management of Obstetrical Difficulties* (St. Louis: C. V. Mosby Co., 1955), p. 477.

If a patient lives at a distance from a hospital or has had rapid labors, there is no question in my mind that induction is justifiable. The controversy is whether many patients near term should be induced because of someone's convenience. I disapprove of this procedure.

Incidentally, Dr. Greenhill's opinion about elective induction for those who live a distance from the hospital or have rapid labors agrees with the observation of one of my first obstetrical consultants. On this particular topic, Willson's edition of Titus says:

> Elective induction may be justifiable in multiparae with previous short labors or for those who live a considerable distance from the hospital and whose means of transportation is unreliable. Such an indication rarely is present during the first pregnancy unless the patient lives many miles from the hospital in which she intends to have her baby.[5]

METHODS

The literature also contains much about the methods of induction, and no little controversy over the best method: e.g., whether by simple rupture of the membranes or by the use of oxytocics. It would be impossible for me to summarize this literature; but I have the impression that it agrees fairly well with the opinions originally given by my obstetrical advisers. One of these advisers (whom I quoted at length) favored simple rupture of the membranes, with perhaps some castor oil by mouth. He thought that pitocin and other oxytocics add some small element of risk, even when skillfully employed, and that this risk should not be incurred without necessity. He admitted there might be some debate about the advisability of using pituitrin and pitocin. Several other consultants thought that small doses of pitocin could be used with perfect safety. One summarized the matter as follows:

> Oxytocics are not generally necessary. Pituitary extract is potentially a *most* dangerous drug. It must be used, if at all, only in minute dosage to stimulate the naturally present irritability of the uterus. Its

---

[5] *Ibid.*, p. 477.

use otherwise condemns the procedure [of induction]. The obstetrician who uses analgesia and anesthesia *wisely* in normal, spontaneous labor applies the same modalities with the same safety in induced labor.

CONCLUSIONS: MEDICAL

Even an obstetrician might have considerable difficulty appraising these and similar medical opinions concerning induction. It is with decided hesitation, therefore, that I suggest the following as medical conclusions:

1. To be at all justifiable, the elective induction of labor supposes the existence of certain indications that the mother is physiologically ready and that the baby is sufficiently mature. These signs are mentioned in the first letter I quoted and in the reply given in the *Journal of the American Medical Association*.

2. The use of drugs is somewhat debatable. But everyone would agree that, if used at all, they must be used skillfully and in very small dosage.

3. Induction before the proper signs are present can be justified only for definite medical reasons which would warrant the running of one risk in order to avoid a greater risk for baby and/or mother.

4. Granted the presence of the signs, it is not clear that induction is really "premature" (in the more profound physiological meaning of the word) or unsafe. Evidence is mounting that it can be safely performed when patients are carefully selected. This may be an indication for progressively greater liberty in the practice of induction. Good obstetricians recognize this possibility of progress; and they do not wish to suppress it. Hence, they manifest a more or less general unwillingness to approve any ruling which rigidly limits induction to strictly medical reasons. On the other hand, however, they recognize a great danger of abuse and they believe that sound obstetrics requires a careful plan of control.

CONCLUSIONS: MORAL

The moralist can make these conclusions his own. The use of drugs in any induction must be in accord with sound obstetric norms of safety. Induction before the mother is physiologically ready and the baby mature is morally justifiable only for proportionately serious medical reasons. Granted the readiness and maturity, the procedure *can* be morally justified, even for non-medical reasons; but since the tendency to induction is now coupled with a tendency toward abuse, hospital authorities and staffs have the duty to take necessary and effective means to curtail abuse.

What means should be taken to curtail abuse? By way of opinion, let me suggest that it would be much better to leave the choice of such means to the voluntary, reasonable action of the staff than to have administrators impose regulations on the staff. I know of several places in which voluntary control by the staff is producing excellent results. The means of control used in these places is very simple. Elective inductions are not forbidden; but every physician who induces labor is asked to sign a special book in which he also states the reason for the procedure. This simple ruling, adopted by the staff itself, is apparently controlling any tendency to abuse.

I think that the procedure suggested in the previous paragraph is very likely sufficient to control any tendency toward abuse in hospitals that are staffed by very competent men and where medical standards are high. But I am impressed by Willson's observation that the growing tendency towards elective induction is found not only among skillful obstetricians, but also among others who are "less able and willing to select patients suitable for the procedure." Where this latter condition exists, more stringent staff regulation of elective induction may be required; and if it is impossible to get the proper staff action, administrators should present their problem to one of the medical societies.

148

19

Catholic Teaching on Contraception and Sterilization

THERE IS PERHAPS no aspect of medical morality in which the line between "Catholic" and "non-Catholic" thought is more clearly drawn than the question of artificial birth-prevention: that is, contraception and direct sterilization. I do not mean, of course, that all Catholics live according to the Church's teaching; for this is obviously not true. Nor do I mean that all Catholics understand what the Church teaches. It is not unheard of that even good Catholic physicians occasionally ask whether certain patients may get "permission" to have a direct sterilization or to practice contraception. They would certainly not ask such questions if they really understood the teaching of the Church.

Nor do I mean that all non-Catholics disagree with what the Church teaches. I have seen statements by non-Catholic individuals and groups that agree perfectly with our own teaching. But these are unquestionably in the minority. As for non-Catholic physicians in particular, I think it is rather typical that even very competent and conscientious doctors, whose general attitude toward the child-bearing function is both wholesome and reverent, think that there are *some* cases in which artificial birth-prevention is the only reasonable solution to an acute problem.

Because of the decided difference between Catholic and

149

non-Catholic views on artificial birth-control, and because the topic is concerned with everyday life, it is important that physicians have a clear understanding of what the Church teaches, of the reasons underlying this teaching, and of its practical implications. The purpose of the present chapter is to explain these three points; yet, before I do so, I should like to deal with what I might term an "approach" problem.

It is sometimes said that there is no such thing as "Catholic ethics"—that the truths of ethics concern the natural law and can be learned by reason alone, without the aid of divine revelation or the teaching of the Church. All this is true; but it is not the whole truth. And because it is not the whole truth, it can be misleading and the cause of unnecessary misunderstandings. The whole truth is to be found in the complete teaching of the Church regarding the power of reason to know the natural law. It is of no little importance, it seems to me, to explain this teaching, even though it may take considerable space, before proceeding to the three points mentioned above. The chapter, therefore, will have four parts: I. Man's Power to Know the Natural Law. II. Official Catholic Teaching on Artificial Birth Prevention. III. The Reasons Underlying this Teaching. IV. Some Practical Applications in the Sphere of Medicine.

I. MAN'S POWER TO KNOW THE NATURAL LAW

In the encyclical *Humani generis,* one of the most important theological documents of our time, Pope Pius XII acknowledged the power of human reason when he said that "absolutely speaking, human reason can, by its natural power and light, arrive at a true and certain knowledge of the one personal God whose providence watches over and governs the world, and also of the natural law which the Creator has written in our hearts." But the Pope hastened to add that:

not a few obstacles prevent reason from using its natural ability effectively and profitably. For the truths that have to do with God and the relations between God and men transcend completely the

150

sensible order, and where there is question of their practical application and realization, call for self-surrender and self-abnegation. In the acquisition of such truths, the human intellect is hampered, not only by the impulses of the senses and the imagination, but also by evil passions stemming from original sin. As a result, men readily persuade themselves in such matters that what they do not wish to be true is false or at least doubtful.

It is for this reason that divine revelation must be called morally necessary, so that those religious and moral truths which are not of their nature beyond the reach of reason may, also in the present condition of the human race, be known by all with ease, with unwavering certitude, and without any admixture of error.

In theological language, *divine revelation* refers to the communication of truth to man by God. In nature itself God makes some communications: the visible things of this world speak to us of the invisible things of God—they tell us of His existence, His power, and so forth. This is called *natural* revelation. Over and above this, God has spoken to us through the Patriarchs and Prophets of the Old Law and through His Son and the Apostles in the New Law. It was to this latter, which is called *supernatural* revelation, that Pope Pius XII was referring when he used the expression "divine revelation." And in speaking of this supernatural revelation, he implied a distinction that is very familiar to Catholic theologians. Supernatural revelation contains some truths that we call *mysteries:* e.g., The Blessed Trinity, Original Sin, The Incarnation, and so forth. For us to know these truths supernatural revelation is *absolutely* necessary; the unaided human reason could never discover them. On the other hand, supernatural revelation contains some truths which, though very profound in their implications, are already indicated in natural revelation and are not absolutely beyond the power of reason: e.g., the existence of God; that God is the first cause of all things; that He governs the world by His providence; that we must worship God; that we must be just to our fellowmen, and so forth. Such truths pertain to natural religion; and by careful study man can learn much about them, even without the special aid of supernatural revelation.

Nevertheless, in life as it is actually lived, many obstacles hamper men in attaining an adequate knowledge of the natural truths just by the use of their reason. For one thing, the truths themselves, as the Pope observed, are supra-sensible: long study and close reasoning are often required for gaining a clear knowledge of them. Moreover, as regards the natural law, the principles and conclusions are often "hard to take," because they impose obligations that "call for self-surrender and self-abnegation." Then, too, passions and prejudices make it difficult to see, and particularly to accept, these conclusions. To these difficulties, the Pope might have added others explained by St. Thomas Aquinas in his *Summa contra gentiles:* e.g., that many men lack the leisure for a serious study of these fundamental natural truths; that others lack interest; and that still others lack the necessary mental equipment.

Some or all of the difficulties just mentioned are more or less the common lot of mankind and have been such since the fall of Adam. It is for this reason that the Vatican Council taught that, although supernatural revelation is not an absolute requisite for knowing the natural truths of religion, yet it is a *moral,* or *practical,* necessity for knowing such truths with ease, with certitude, and without any admixture of error. The Vatican Council did not expressly mention the natural law as a part of the truths of natural religion; but theologians have always understood that it was in some way included. The *Humani generis* expressly included it.

The official custodian of divine revelation is the Church. This has been the constant teaching of Catholic theology; it was so understood by the Vatican Council; and it was clearly indicated by Pius XII at the beginning of the *Humani generis.* Two years later, in a radio message on "The Christian Conscience as an Object of Education," the Pope made this point even clearer as regards moral precepts:

But where can both the educator and the one to be educated find the Christian moral law with ease and certitude? In the law of the

Creator, engraved in the heart of every man (cf. Rom. 2: 14-16), and in revelation, that is, in all the truths and precepts that the divine Master taught. Both of these—the natural law written in the heart, and the truths and precepts of supernatural revelation—Jesus, our Redeemer gave to His Church as the moral treasure of humanity in order that she might preach them to all creatures, explain them and hand them on intact and safeguarded from all contamination and error from one generation to another.

In the preceding paragraphs, we have clear official statements of the Catholic teaching that (1) supernatural revelation is a practical necessity for an adequate knowledge of the natural law; and (2) that this revelation has been entrusted to the Church to be preserved and explained. It follows, therefore, that the teaching of the Church is a practical necessity for an adequate knowledge of the natural law; and we should not be surprised or shocked when those who lack the benefit of this teaching are in error as to the existence or extent of some obligations. It follows also that the complete truth is not expressed by the statement that there is no such thing as "Catholic ethics." This is certainly true in the sense that the duties studied in ethics are duties of *human beings,* regardless of the religion they profess; and, for this reason, we cannot admit two objective standards in matters of medical ethics: one for Catholics, the other for non-Catholics. The statement is true, also, in the sense that men can learn much about the natural law without the guidance of the Church. But it is definitely not true if it means that the generality of men can get a clear and adequate knowledge of the natural law, especially as regards its finer points, without the guidance of the Church. In our age, this guidance seems to be particularly necessary in the matter of artificial birth prevention; and it has been given repeatedly and solemnly, especially by two Popes, Pius XI and Pius XII.

II. OFFICIAL CATHOLIC TEACHING

The official Latin text of the encyclical on Christian Marriage, issued by Pope Pius XI on Dec. 31, 1930, is divided into three parts. The first part is positive, explaining Christian marriage in terms of its beauty and blessings. The second part is negative, and is concerned with false theories and abuses. The third part is constructive, outlining the steps to be taken to preserve the beauty of Christian wedlock and to eradicate or forestall the abuses.

First among the abuses of marriage discussed by the Pope is contraception—that is, the frustrating of the marriage act. Several times in the course of this section, he refers to this practice as something intrinsically against nature; and he makes it clear that no reason, howsoever grave, even the direst financial condition or the illness of the mother—conditions to which he refers with the most profound sympathy—can justify such an act. Moreover, in this same section is found the following paragraph, which is perhaps the most solemnly-worded statement in the entire encyclical:

Since, therefore, openly departing from the uninterrupted Christian tradition some recently have judged it possible solemnly to declare another doctrine regarding this question, the Catholic Church, to whom God has entrusted the defense of the integrity and purity of morals, standing erect in the midst of the moral ruin which surrounds her, in order that she may preserve the chastity of the nuptial union from being defiled by this foul stain, raises her voice in token of her divine ambassadorship and through Our mouth proclaims anew: any use whatsoever of matrimony exercised in such a way that the act is deliberately frustrated in its natural power to generate life is an offense against the law of God and of nature; and those who indulge in such are branded with the guilt of a grave sin.

These solemn words, as well as the context of the encyclical, leave no room for doubt about the absolute position of the Catholic Church as regards the moral status of contraception. It is not in the class of acts (e.g., certain mutilations) which are occasionally justified for good reasons; rather, it is *absolutely* and *always* wrong. There can be no question of a justifying reason, nor of a "permission," for even one act of contraception. The only possible excuse is a subjective one, such as, for example, ignorance of this divine prohibition.

154

The encyclical did not deal directly with the broad problem of medical sterilization; but it explicitly condemned eugenic sterilization, whether involuntary or voluntary. The Pope insisted on the principle that the state has no power to mutilate an innocent man against his will; and he added that the individual's right to self-mutilation is limited by the natural purposes of his members. This latter assertion clearly excludes voluntary eugenic sterilization, because the individual may not give to a doctor or the state a right which he himself does not possess.

Shortly after the publication of the encyclical on Christian Marriage, the Sacred Congregation of the Holy Office was asked: "What is to be thought of the so-called 'Eugenic' theory, whether 'positive' or 'negative,' and of the means which it proposes for the improvement of human progeny, in disregard of the laws, natural, divine, or ecclesiastical, pertaining to marriage and the rights of individuals?" The reply given by the Holy Office, with the approval of Pope Pius XI, was: "That theory is to be absolutely disapproved, held as false, and condemned, as is declared in the Encyclical on Christian Marriage, *Casti connubii,* of 31 Dec., 1930." This reply was given on March 21, 1931. Almost ten years later, the same Sacred Congregation was asked: "Whether the direct sterilization of man or woman, whether perpetual or temporary is licit." The reply, dated Feb. 24, 1940, and officially approved by Pope Pius XII, stated: "In the negative; it is forbidden by the law of nature, and, as regards eugenic sterilization, it has already been condemned by the Decree of this Sacred Congregation of 21 Mar., 1931."

Several points are worth noting about this last-mentioned decree (1940). First, it is explicitly limited to *direct* sterilization: that is, to any procedure by which sterility is *purposely* induced. (When sterility is merely the unintentional by-product of some therapeutic procedure—e.g., removal of cancerous ovaries or tubes—the sterilization is *indirect.*) Secondly, it

155

clearly includes all kinds of direct sterilization of the innocent and is not limited to eugenic. Thirdly, it includes procedures which are designed to effect a merely temporary sterilization. Lastly, the decree states without qualification that all these forms of direct sterilization are against the natural law.

My final citation of the teaching of the Church will be taken from the address given by Pope Pius XII on the moral problems of married life, Oct. 29, 1951. The following paragraphs, taken from the third part of that address, contain a splendid summary of all the documents previously cited:

> Our predecessor, Pius XI, of happy memory, in his encyclical *Casti connubii*, December 31, 1930, solemnly proclaimed anew the fundamental law governing the marital act and conjugal relations: that any attempt on the part of the husband and wife to deprive this act of its inherent force and to impede the procreation of a new life, either in the performance of the act itself or in the course of the development of its natural consequences, is immoral; and that no alleged "indication" or need can convert an intrinsically immoral act into a moral and lawful one.

> This precept is as valid today as it was yesterday; and it will be the same tomorrow and always, because it does not imply a precept of human law but is the expression of a law which is natural and divine. Let Our words be your unfailing guide in all cases where your profession and your apostolate demand of you a clear and unequivocal decision.

> It would be more than a mere want of readiness in the service of life if the attempt made by man were to concern not only an individual act but should affect the entire organism itself, with the intention of depriving it, by means of sterilization, of the faculty of procreating a new life. Here, too, you have a clearly-established ruling in the Church's teaching which governs your behavior both internally and externally. Direct sterilization—that is, the sterilization which aims, either as a means or as an end in itself, to render child-bearing impossible—is a grave violation of the moral law, and therefore unlawful. Even public authority has no right, whatever "indication" it may use as an excuse, to permit it, and much less to prescribe it or use it to the detriment of innocent human beings. This principle had already been enunciated in the above mentioned encyclical of Pius XI on marriage. Therefore, ten years ago, when sterilization came to be more widely

156

used, the Holy See found it necessary to make an explicit and solemn declaration that direct sterilization, whether permanent or temporary, of the man or of the woman, is unlawful, and this by virtue of the natural law from which the Church herself, as you well know, has no power to dispense.

III. REASONS UNDERLYING THE PAPAL TEACHING

This heading would perhaps be more accurate in the singular, because both popes, in explaining their teaching that contraceptive practices and direct sterilization are against the natural law, stressed *one* reason: namely, that these things are contrary to the natural purpose of the generative act and the generative faculty. As regards sterilization, Pope Pius XI at least insinuated this when, after showing that the state has no right to mutilate an innocent person, he added that private individuals themselves "have no other power over the members of their bodies than that which pertains to *their natural purposes.*" (Italics mine.) This argument from natural finality is much more explicit in his condemnation of contraception as "intrinsically against nature" and never justifiable for any reason, howsoever grave. "Since, therefore," he said, "the conjugal act is destined primarily by nature for the begetting of children, those who, in exercising it, deliberately frustrate its natural power and purpose, sin against nature and commit a deed which is shameful and intrinsically vicious."

This same argument—from finality—is given somewhat more completely by Pope Pius XII near the beginning of his address on the moral problems of married life (Oct. 29, 1951).

The order to be observed here has been established by God's sovereign intelligence and is directed to His creative purpose; it concerns the external activity of human beings and the internal adherence of their free will; it determines what they are bound to do and what it is their duty to avoid. Nature puts at man's disposal the whole chain of causes which will result in the appearance of a new human life; it is for him to release this vital force and it is for nature to develop its course and bring it to completion. When once man has done his part and set in motion the marvellous process which will produce a new life, it is

157

his bounden duty to let it take its course. He must not arrest it or frustrate its natural development.

In the last analysis, the argument from finality is *the* argument against artificial birth prevention. Nevertheless, it must be admitted, as Monsignor John A. Ryan once pointed out, that the argument is to a great extent *intuitive:* one either grasps it or one does not. Moreover, being metaphysical, the argument has no appeal to the emotions; whereas the so-called arguments in favor of artificial birth prevention are cast in a highly emotional frame-work: the sick mother, the dire poverty of a tenement family, and so forth. For these reasons Catholics who write against artificial birth prevention often develop indirect arguments that are in reality secondary but which may have more popular appeal. For example, these writers show the harmful effects of artificial birth prevention on the individual character and on society; they explain how the justification of contraceptive practices, for any reason whatsoever, leads logically and inevitably to the undermining of sex ethics; and so forth.

Since my main purpose is to explain the papal teaching, I will not dwell on those other arguments. I should like, however, to quote a few paragraphs from the statement made by Fr. William J. Kenealy, S.J. before the Joint Committee on Public Health of the Commonwealth of Massachusetts, April 8, 1948. These paragraphs strike me as especially impressive:

If a person can violate the natural integrity of the marital act with moral impunity, then I challenge anyone to show me the essential immorality of any sexual aberration. Allow me to explain this point.

All men of every age have realized the sacredness of the reproductive function and its paramount importance to society; they have also realized that the vehemence of sexual pleasure leads to grave abuses to human and civil society. The common consent of mankind, civilized and uncivilized, agrees that it is of supreme importance that *some* line be drawn between the lawful use and the unlawful abuse of the sex faculty, not merely as to extra-marital relations but also as to the use of the sexual powers within marriage. *Where* should that line be drawn?

If we study the nature of the reproductive faculties, the line obviously should be determined by *the natural integrity of the marital act*. But, if the natural integrity of the marital act does *not* determine the line, what does? What reason would we have for declaring *any* unnatural act between spouses immoral? If medical or economic or other considerations justify artificial contraception, why would not the same reasons justify sodomitic and other unnatural intercourse between husband and wife? I have never read or heard a logical argument to show an essential difference which would justify the one and outlaw the other.[1]

To return to the papal teaching, we should add here that the popes consider their interpretation of the natural law to be confirmed by divine relevation. Thus, Pope Pius XI, after giving the reason why contraception is intrinsically against nature, added:

Small wonder, therefore, if Holy Writ bears witness that the Divine Majesty regards with the greatest detestation this horrible crime and at times has punished it with death. As St. Augustine notes, "Intercourse even with one's legitimate wife is unlawful and wicked where the conception of the offspring is prevented. Onan, the son of Juda, did this, and the Lord killed him for it."

The story of Onan, to which this passage refers, is given thus in the Douay Version of the Old Testament (Genesis, 38: 8-10):

Juda therefore said to Onan his son: Go in to thy brother's wife and marry her that thou mayest raise seed to thy brother. He knowing that the children should not be his, when he went in to his brother's wife, spilled his seed upon the ground, lest children be born in his brother's name. And therefore the Lord slew him, because he did a detestable thing.

The reference here is to what is called the Levirate Law—a Jewish law according to which, if a man died without offspring, his brother or next-of-kin was supposed to marry the widow and raise up children for his deceased brother. Some non-Catholics have interpreted Onan's slaying as being a punish-

---

[1] For the entire text of Fr. Kenealy's excellent statement, see "Contraception—A Violation of God's Law," *The Catholic Mind,* Sept., 1948, pp. 552-564.

ment for his unwillingness to fulfill this law, his selfish disregard of his deceased brother's interests. This interpretation is by no means universal even among non-Catholics; both Catholic scholars and Catholic tradition reject it and say that Onan was slain precisely for frustrating the marriage act. Pope Pius XI cited St. Augustine, not for the saint's personal view, but because his teaching may be taken as typical of early Christian tradition. Twelve centuries after Augustine, St. Francis de Sales, a doctor of the Church who was noted for his charming graciousness, wrote these strong words on the same subject:

> Of a truth, the shameful and execrable act committed by Onan in his marriage was detestable in the sight of God as the holy text says in the thirty-eighth chapter of Genesis; and although certain heretics of our age . . . have tried to prove that it was the perverse intention of this wicked man which displeased God, the Scripture nevertheless speaks quite otherwise, and asserts emphatically that the *thing* itself which he did was *detestable* and abominable in the sight of God.[2]

IV. SOME APPLICATIONS IN THE SPHERE OF MEDICINE

There was a time when diaphragms, spermicidal jellies, and so forth, were advertised under the euphemistic heading of feminine hygiene. This is sometimes done even today; but the prevailing tendency seems to be to call a spade a spade and advertise them as contraceptives—"the ideal contraceptive," as many of the advertisements put it. Whatever be the advertising, it is obvious that these things are purely and simply contraceptives; hence, the use of them is contrary to the natural law; and so too is prescribing or advising their use.

What is said of feminine contraceptives is true *a fortiori* of the use of a condom, as well as of the Onanistic practice of withdrawal with ejaculation outside the vagina. In both these cases, not only are the natural effects of *coitus* impeded, but the *coitus* itself is rendered unnatural, because the minimum essential of natural *coitus* is ejaculation within the vagina.

---

[2] *Introduction to the Devout Life,* translation by Allan Ross, (Westminster, Md.: The Newman Press, 1953), p. 210.

In recent years, there has been much talk about the so-called infertility pills. As Fr. John J. Lynch, S.J., has explained, the use of such pills to suppress fertility is clearly a contraceptive measure—a temporary direct sterilization; and, since they are such, or at least intended as such, it is morally wrong to use them or to prescribe them.[3]

The preceding brief paragraphs about contraceptive practices are sufficient for our purpose. Of greater concern to the physician are the various surgical procedures (and their equivalent, e.g., irradiation) that effect sterility. It is my impression that physicians usually refer to all these procedures under the one general term, "sterilization"; but, from the moral point of view, it is important to avoid the general term and speak more specifically of *direct* sterilization, in which sterility is purposely induced (e.g., when healthy tubes are ligated to prevent a pregnancy that would be dangerous because of heart disease), and *indirect* sterilization, in which the resultant sterility is an unintentional by-product of a genuine therapeutic procedure (e.g., when a cancerous uterus is removed). Since a direct sterilization is really a contraceptive measure, it is never permitted; an indirect sterilization, like mutilations of non-reproductive organs, is permitted when sound medical reasons call for the therapeutic procedure.

In the subsequent paragraphs, I shall run through the more common sterilizing procedures and point out which are direct, and which are indirect. Before doing this, however, I should like to make some general observations:

1) It is obvious that the excision of a generative organ for a diseased condition which threatens the life or physical welfare of a patient *independently of pregnancy* is not a direct

---

[3] *The Linacre Quarterly,* Aug. and Nov., 1953, pp. 83-88, 118-122. Fr. Lynch's discussion is concerned with phosphorylated hesperidin. For a discussion of other drugs, such as synthetic progesterone, see William J. Gibbons, S.J., "Antifertility Drugs and Morality," *America,* Dec. 14, 1957, pp. 346-348.

sterilization. Sterility is merely an unavoidable by-product of such an operation. No moralist would consider it illicit. Moreover, even if the operation also included the excision of healthy tissue, there would be no objection to the removal when it is in conformity with sound medical practice. This observation applies to such things as the removal of a cancerous uterus or of cancerous ovaries, with concomitant removal of the uterus, and so forth.

2) There are some cases in which it is not easy to judge whether the sterilization is direct or indirect. This is especially true when an existing morbid condition of a generative organ is contingent on pregnancy for its further development. Differences of opinion among moralists as to the licitness of such operations are to be expected; but it should be noted that the differences mainly concern the evaluation of the facts and not a moral principle. This observation is especially pertinent to hysterectomy with repeat cesarean, as will be mentioned later.

3) The mere fact that sterilization is indirect does not necessarily mean that an operation is permissible. There must be a medically sound reason for the operation; otherwise it is unnecessary surgery and, as such, it is morally unjustifiable. In my survey of procedures, I am stressing the distinction between direct and indirect sterilization; I am not trying to give a final judgment concerning the necessity of the surgery.

4) In cases that are thoroughly discussed in other chapters, I shall merely indicate this and thus avoid much useless repetition.

Having made these preliminary observations, we can now consider specifically the various sterilizing procedures. Roughly speaking, these are: ligation or resection of fallopian tubes; oophorectomy; hysterectomy; ligation or resection of the *vasa deferentia* and orchiectomy. There can be combinations of these procedures (e.g., the Porro operation); but, for judging these, it is sufficient to note my first general observation. Also, the equivalent effects of surgery can be produced by other means (e.g., irradiation). What is said here of surgical operations applies also to these other procedures.

Ligation or resection of fallopian tubes—Some years ago I was asked, under rather embarrassing circumstances, to give a moral appraisal of the Falk operation, which, as I understand it, consists essentially in the cornual resection of infected tubes —the resection being done to prevent recurring infection from below, and the tube being left *in situ* to conserve the blood supply from the ovary. I say that I received this problem under rather embarrassing circumstances because, when the question arose in one of our hospitals, two physicians distinguished for both conscientiousness and competence disagreed strongly about it; and I was supposed to settle the disagreement. Upon further investigation, I have found much disagreement among other physicians, too, but with a rather evident preponderance of opinion that the operation is not medically indicated. Whatever be the final judgment as to medical necessity or advisability of the operation, it seems to me that the procedure is not a direct sterilization: first, because its purpose is to prevent recurring infection, not pregnancy; and, secondly, because in many cases the tubes have apparently already lost their patency.[4]

With the possible exception of the Falk operation, it seems that tubal ligation or resection is always a direct sterilization— at least, in actual medical practice. This statement can be illustrated by a brief consideration of an article entitled "Indications for the Sterilization of Women," by James F. Donnelly, M.D., and Frank R. Lock, M.D., F.A.C.S.[5] The authors begin by explaining and praising the North Carolina eugenics law; then under the heading of "Voluntary Sterilization" they con-

---

[4] Cf. also article by Fr. Thomas J. O'Donnell, S.J., "The Falk Procedure," *The Linacre Quarterly*, Aug., 1957, pp. 90-91.

[5] The article first appeared in the *North Carolina Medical Journal*, Jan., 1953. It was reprinted in the *Bulletin of the American College of Surgeons*, May-June, 1953, pp. 97-102.

sider two groups of cases in which tubal ligation is done. In the first group, which comprises cases in which the authors believe that sterilization is indicated, are the following: hypertensive cardiovascular disease, heart disease, tuberculosis, hereditary diseases, psychiatric disturbances, repeated cesarean sections, and multiparity. In the second group, comprising cases in which sterilization is not indicated, are: Rh incompatibility, heart murmurs, difficult delivery, *hyperemesis gravidarum,* repeated fetal loss, associated operative procedures (e.g., sterilization with appendectomy), lack of desire for children, disability of husband, economic and social factors.

It should be noted that the authors' division between indications and non-indications is not iron-bound. They do not consider that tubal ligation is always indicated in the cases of the first group or that it is never indicated in the cases of the second group. This point is not of pertinence here. The special value of the article for my purpose is that it gives a rather complete listing of the cases in which tubal ligation is sometimes practiced. In every case the precise purpose of the operation is to prevent future pregnancies; and the operation itself has no immediate effect as a therapeutic measure. The operations, therefore, are direct sterilizations.

Oophorectomy—In recent medical literature, there have been many references to unnecessary removal of the ovaries. This practice, like other unnecessary surgery, is certainly immoral. Moreover, in some of these cases, the real reason for the operation may be a desire to sterilize; and, if that be the case, the oophorectomy is a direct sterilization.

A specifically modern problem concerns oophorectomy as a means of palliation and for the prevention of metastasis in cases of carcinoma of the breast. This problem is discussed in chapter 24.

Hysterectomy—Unnecessary hysterectomy seems to be among the most common forms of unnecessary surgery. As such, it is morally objectionable; and, if the operation is performed in order to induce sterility—as it seems to be in some cases—it has the added stigma of contraception. Some special questions about hysterectomy are discussed in chapter 25.

Resection or ligation of the vasa deferentia—Fr. Charles J. McFadden, O.S.A., mentions that, according to reliable medical authorities, an enlarged prostate can sometimes be treated successfully by the ligature or irradiation of the *vasa deferentia.* I have never had this case presented to me; but I would agree with Fr. McFadden that the ligature would not be a direct sterilization, since its *immediate* purpose is to treat a pathological condition; and I would also agree with his judgment that, if the prostatectomy itself would be either impossible or gravely dangerous, there would be a sufficient reason for the ligature.[6]

Much more familiar to me is the problem of vasectomy *with* prostatectomy, as a means of preventing epididymitis and orchitis. This question is treated lengthily in chapter 23. It suffices to say here that the vasectomy seems clearly not to be a direct sterilization; on the other hand, in view of the fact that we now have the sulfa drugs and antibiotics, the justifiable indications for the vasectomy are much less frequent than they used to be.

Aside from special cases like those just indicated—in which ligation or resection of the *vasa* is used to suppress pathological conditions—the destruction of the *vasa* is always a direct sterilization.

Orchiectomy—Excellent medical authorities say that some form of castration is called for in the treatment of carcinoma of the prostate—the reason being that reduction of the supply of androgens alleviates pain and retards the growth of the cancer. As is explained in chapter 24, castration in this case is not a direct sterilization and it can be permitted. I think this is the only problem that merits mention in this section. It

---

[6] Cf. *Medical Ethics* (Philadelphia: F. A. Davis Co., 1956), p. 344.

would be rare indeed that doctors would recommend orchiectomy merely as a sterilizing procedure.

REFERENCE MATERIAL

A valuable booklet is *The Encyclical "Humani Generis,"* by A. C. Cotter, S.J. It contains the original Latin text, with a readable English translation on opposite pages, also an excellent commentary. In my quotations from this encyclical, I used Fr. Cotter's translation, with only a few changes of punctuation. The booklet is published by the Weston College Press, Weston 93, Mass.

In his *Summa Theologiae* (I, q. 1, a. 1), St. Thomas Aquinas says that supernatural revelation is necessary, even as regards the truths about God that can be known by reason, because without this revelation only a small number of men would gain this knowledge, and even they would take a long time and would not avoid many errors. In Book I, Chapter IV, of his *Summa contra gentiles,* he explains these points in a profound yet simple and common-sense manner. Anyone who reads this short chapter thoughtfully should realize that Catholics are very reasonable in looking for the guidance of the Church, even in matters that concern the natural law.

An excellent discussion of ignorance of the natural law, regarding contraception in particular and with specific reference to conditions in the United States, is contained in *The Possibility of Invincible Ignorance of the Natural Law,* by Fr. Stanley Bertke. This is a doctoral dissertation, published in 1941 by the Catholic University of America Press, Washington, D.C.

My quotations from the encyclical on Christian Marriage are taken from the translation published by the Paulist Press. The quotation in the third part of my article from the address of Pope Pius XII on the moral problems of married life is taken from the translation of this address made by Canon George D.

Smith and published in *The Clergy Review,* December, 1951, and January, 1952. For the other quotations from this address, as well as the quotation from the radio message on the education of the Christian conscience, I have used the translations given in *Catholic Documents* (VI and VIII); but I have not followed these literally. The translations of the decrees of the Sacred Congregation of the Holy Office on the eugenic theory and on direct sterilization are taken from *The Canon Law Digest,* by Fr. T. L. Bouscaren, S.J. (Milwaukee: Bruce Publishing Company), Vol. 1 (1934), pp. 677-678; Vol. 2 (1943), p. 96.

chapter 20

The Morality of Rhythm

Continence, either periodic or continuous, is the only form of birth control not in itself morally objectionable. Directive 30. (Cf. U.S. Code, "Reproductive Organs and Functions," n. 5; and the Canadian Code, article 33.)

A DISCUSSION of the morality of birth control must necessarily include a consideration of what is sinful and what is not; hence, it seems well to preface the discussion of this directive with a reference to a few familiar ideas about sin. Sin, as we know, can be committed in two ways: by doing something evil, or by not doing something good. But, as we also know, the mere omitting of something good is not sinful unless the good is something one is obliged to do. Thus, the Catholic who omits Mass on an ordinary weekday does not sin because there is no obligation to go to Mass on those days. Were he to attend Mass on weekdays, he would be doing something good for his own soul and something very pleasing to God and edifying to his neighbor—but it is a good which, as the military saying goes, is "beyond the call of duty." On the other hand, attendance at Mass on Sundays, unless one has a good excuse, is a matter of obligation; hence, the deliberate missing of the Sunday Mass without such an excuse is sinful.

Each of the foregoing very simple and very familiar ideas has its application in a discussion of the morality of birth control. But, before applying them, it will be well to indicate briefly what is meant by birth control. By birth control we mean

168

here some method of avoiding conception. In general, there are two methods: one called "artificial," which consists in the practice of some form of contraception; the other called "natural," which consists in abstaining from marital intercourse. This abstinence might be continuous or it might be restricted to the periods in which the marital act is apt to be fertile. Periodic abstinence is often referred to as "the rhythm"; and we shall keep that term here.

Chapter 19 explained the Catholic teaching on the morality of artificial birth prevention. The present chapter will be limited to a discussion of the moral aspects of natural birth control, especially by periodic continence. In chapter 21, I shall outline some points that seem to be of special pertinence for doctors in dealing with their patients.

THE RHYTHM: PRINCIPAL MORAL CONSIDERATIONS

The Church teaches that contraception is a sin because it means doing what is evil. It is not the same with rhythm. Those who practice the rhythm do nothing evil. They simply omit doing something good—that is, they abstain from intercourse at the time when it might be fertile. Therefore, the morality of using rhythm must be judged in the same way as other omissions: if the abstinence from intercourse is a neglect of duty, it is sinful; if it does not imply a neglect of duty, it is not sinful. A simple means of determining whether any duty is neglected is had by asking these three questions: (a) Are both parties *willing* to practice the rhythm? (b) Are both *able* to practice it? (c) Do they have a *sufficient reason* for avoiding or postponing childbirth? If all these questions can be answered with a "yes," then no duty is neglected and the use of rhythm is not sinful. If any one of these questions must be answered "no," then some duty would be neglected; and, according to the importance of that duty, the use of rhythm would be sinful. A brief explanation of the questions will show the duties that must be considered.

169

a) *Are both parties willing?* By reason of the marriage contract, each party assumes a serious obligation of granting the other's reasonable requests for sexual intercourse. That is why St. Paul refers to conjugal intercourse as the marriage "debt." For one party to insist on the practice of rhythm against the reasonable objection of the other would be a violation, and a very serious one, of this fundamental marital duty. Hence, the first requirement for the licit use of rhythm—that both be *willing* to practice it.

b) *Are both able to practice it?* This question refers to the "secondary" purposes of marriage: the fostering of mutual love and harmony between husband and wife and the safeguarding of their chastity. These purposes are very important. Moreover, in the ordinary providence of God, the conjugal act is certainly one of the principal means of achieving these ends; and married people are obliged to use this means insofar as it is necessary. There is no doubt that for many couples the attempt to use rhythm might seriously jeopardize these purposes. The methodical restriction of intercourse to certain periods can create tensions in married life; and it can be the occasion of vehement temptations against chastity.

Among the dangers associated with the practice of the rhythm, the main one is very likely concerned with chastity. The restriction of intercourse to the sterile periods calls for no little self-control. The attempt to make this restriction is apt to lead to sins of self-abuse, to mutual fondling to the point of culpable orgasm outside of intercourse, and even to sins of adultery. These dangers are greater for men than for women; but it would be unwise to think that women are exempt from them. A not insignificant number of women are strongly passionate; and, even among those who are not usually passionate, many experience strong sexual desire during the fertile period.

As for the other dangers, though they may be less important and especially less tangible, than that of incontinence, they are

170

just as real. For example, when children are avoided entirely, the harmony which ought to exist between man and wife is imperiled, and the maternal instinct is likely to be thwarted. This instinct is strong in most women, even though they do not recognize it. When they have no children, they are likely to begin mothering their husbands (or cats and dogs), and they are exposed to a great loneliness about the time of the menopause—just the time when they may be most in need of comfort. When the family is unduly limited to one or two children, the children may suffer; ordinarily speaking, their characters develop better in the large family. Lastly, in all practices of birth limitation, there is the resultant social evil: namely, alarming reduction of the birth rate and the breaking down of esteem for large families.

No doubt, a mature couple with a good reason for using rhythm and a willingness to cooperate with the grace of God can make the adjustment necessary for removing the personal dangers—i.e., the dangers to their chastity, mutual harmony, and so forth. But the adjustment calls for self-control and an understanding spirit of charity. That is what I mean when I say that both parties must be *able*.

c) *Do they have a sufficient reason* for avoiding or postponing childbirth? This question refers to the "primary" ends of marriage: the procreation and education of children. Parenthood is the chief glory of marriage; and children are its chief blessing. They are a blessing to the parents, to the state, to the Church. Thus, in his address on the moral problems of married life, Oct. 29, 1951, Pope Pius XII said: "The individual and society, the people and the nation, the Church herself, all depend for their existence, in the order God has established, upon fertile marriage." It is little wonder then that the same Pope declared officially that on married people "who make use of this right by the specific act of their state [i.e., by marital intercourse], nature and the Creator impose the function of providing for the conservation of the human race."

171

In a word, Pope Pius XII has made it clear that married people who choose to have intercourse are obliged to have children if they can. He did not attempt to define this obligation in terms of the number of children; but he declared that it is possible to be excused from the duty "for a long time and even for the whole duration of married life, if there are serious reasons, such as those often provided in the so-called 'indications' of the medical, eugenical, economic, and social order." When reasons such as these exist, the duty of childbearing is suspended and the use of rhythm is permitted.

The Pope gave only general headings, not specific examples, of the reasons that would excuse from the duty of childbearing. Some specific examples that would fit under one or more of these headings might be the following: danger to the mother in childbirth; illness of husband, wife, or of a child already born, that would make it exceptionally difficult to care for another child; the fact that conception usually results in miscarriage or stillbirth; the real probability that future children would be mentally defective or have some other serious hereditary defect; the fact that parents are financially unable to provide for more children according to the standards of decent living frequently outlined by the Church—standards which include frugal comfort in living conditions, the possibility of properly educating the children, and the ability to save reasonably for the future; the lack of proper housing facilities; employment that is not conducive to childbearing, e.g., military service.

The careful reader will note that these reasons vary considerably in seriousness. Some (e.g., those concerning illness) might be of such a nature as to exempt permanently from the duty of childbearing; others (e.g., inadequate housing facilities) might be merely temporary, so that they would justify the postponement of the next pregnancy or a spacing of births but would not constitute a permanent excuse from childbearing.

I trust that the preceding paragraphs sufficiently explain the three questions that must be answered in deciding whether the use of rhythm is permitted. There are cases, no doubt, in which a sincere and mature couple can readily answer the questions and judge for themselves whether they may practice rhythm. But in most cases they need the help of a prudent counselor. It is often said that Catholics should consult their confessor. This should not be taken too literally, because the confessional has its limitations. In the confessional a priest talks to only one party and frequently does not know the person. For advice about using the rhythm, it would be much better for husband and wife to go together to a priest whom they know and who understands them and the conditions under which they live. In this way they can obtain help not only in judging what they are permitted to do but also in making the proper adjustment to the difficulties they might face in carrying out their decision.

SOME SPECIAL OBSERVATIONS

As regards the reasons for practicing rhythm, I should like to make a few further observations. First, I wish to re-emphasize the point that, in considering the economic reason, we must think not merely in terms of frugal support but also of the possibility of moderate saving for the future. As the Administrative Board of the NCWC declared on Feb. 7, 1940, "a saving wage constitutes an essential part of the definition of a living wage." Those who so readily accuse our Catholic people of seeking specious excuses for practicing the rhythm might well ponder how many of them actually get a family living wage according to Catholic standards.

Secondly, the social and economic reasons are, for the most part, defects in society itself. Resort to the rhythm may be the only possible solution for an individual couple; but a social order which imposes such a solution should be changed. If the papal teaching on the reconstruction of the social order were put into practice, these reasons would seldom exist.

Thirdly, when we speak of excusing causes we are speaking

173

in terms of obligation. Generous Catholic couples will often neglect these reasons and, trusting in divine providence, will continue to build a family.

Fourthly, there is the question: are the excusing causes suggested by the Pope the only limitations on the duty to procreate, or is this duty, like many other obligations to the neighbor and to society, itself limited?

The answer to this is not perfectly clear. However, in a discussion of this topic in June, 1952, the majority of a large group of theologians favored the opinion that, generally speaking, married people who have more than four or five children are not only doing their duty but are acting "beyond the call of duty." According to this opinion—to put it concretely—the use of rhythm to restrict the size of the family to four or five children would not be sinful for those who are *willing* and *able* to use it. One advantage of this opinion is that it gives to parents of large families a tribute that they seem richly to deserve: namely, that their appreciation of the chief blessing of marriage is such that they willingly act beyond the call of duty. Another advantage is that it gives to people who wish to do their duty but who lack the spiritual idealism to want to do more, a sort of practical working-norm for the number of children they should have if they are able. These advantages square with the traditional policy of the Church of (a) teaching Catholics what they are obliged to do, and (b) urging them to do even more than this for the glory of God and their own sanctification.[1]

CONTINUOUS ABSTINENCE

The Blessed Virgin and St. Joseph, though truly married, lived lives of perfect virginity. And some married saints have followed their example. But, in the ordinary providence of

---

[1] This question is more completely discussed in my article, "Rhythm in Marriage: Duty and Idealism," *America*, May 3, 1952, pp. 128-130.

God, marriage and virginity are distinct vocations; and married people usually do the will of God, and thus sanctify themselves, by moderately using their marriage rights, not by foregoing them. Nevertheless, there are some situations in which, though perfect virginity may not be called for, continuous abstinence from the complete sexual act (i.e., intercourse) may be indicated. I refer to the case in which childbirth would be dangerous and the use of rhythm would not be effective. In this case the only permissible means of avoiding the risk would be continuous abstinence from intercourse. The Church admits that such abstinence is heroism; but she solemnly affirms that the heroism is possible with the grace of God. We are sometimes inclined to assume a defeatist attitude regarding this matter; and it would be well for all of us to recall frequently these forceful words of Pope Pius XII when he spoke on the moral problems of married life:

> It is an injustice to the men and women of our time to regard them as incapable of prolonged heroism. Nowadays for many reasons—perhaps under the yoke of hard necessity, sometimes even in the service of an unjust cause—heroism is exercised to a degree and an extent that in times past would have been deemed impossible. Why, then, must this heroism, if the circumstances really call for it, halt at the frontiers of passion and natural inclination? Obviously, anyone who does not want to control himself will not be able to do so; and anyone who thinks he can control himself relying only on his own strength, and without sincerely and perseveringly asking God's help is doomed to disillusionment.

It should be noted that the Pope did not say that married people are always obliged to abstain from intercourse in order to avoid a serious risk in childbirth. Certainly there are some cases in which they might lead a normal married life and trust in divine providence. But a decision of this kind is very difficult; and it should not be made without prayer and sound spiritual guidance.

chapter 21

The Doctor and Rhythm

THE TWO preceding chapters explained the distinction made in directive 30: namely, that artificial birth control may never be practiced, but that natural birth control (i.e., by either periodic or continuous continence) is permitted under certain circumstances. These topics are closely connected with the question of what the physician may do as regards giving information, advice, and help to couples who wish to avoid or space children. This question is answered in the U.S. Code, "Reproductive Organs and Functions," nn. 4-5; in the Canadian Code, articles 33-34; and in **directive 33**. This directive reads:

> **All operations, treatments, and devices designed to render conception impossible are morally objectionable. Advising or otherwise encouraging contraceptive practices is not permitted.**
>
> **(Note: Continence is not contraception. A physician is entitled to advise and explain the practice of periodic continence to those who have need of such knowledge.)**

Further explanation of the statement about advising or encouraging contraceptive practices seems unnecessary. My remarks, therefore, will mainly concern the doctor's role with patients who ask for and/or need information about rhythm. I shall add something on continuous continence. The remarks are intended mostly as pastoral counsels; and they reflect my own experience as adviser to physicians and to married people themselves.

THE CHRISTIAN IDEAL

Discussions of the morality of birth control tend to create a negative mentality. They get us thinking only in terms of what is sinful and what is not. It is not good to have our mental outlook limited in that way. Our approach to the problems of Christian living should be more positive, more in terms of the advisable thing to do, the better thing to do. It is especially important, it seems to me, that doctors not only know what is sinful and not sinful about family limitation, but also that they have this positive point of view.

To create and preserve this positive mentality, one should realize that the Catholic *ideal* is the large family. This does not mean that the Church urges Catholics to have as many children as they possibly can, irrespective of circumstances; but it does mean that, granted the proper conditions for begetting and rearing children, it is better to have many children than few. This teaching is based on the sound, natural, psychological fact that, other things being equal, character formation is better achieved in the large family than in the small family; also on the natural fact that children are a boon to the community and the nation; and especially on the supernatural fact that children are born not merely for earth but for heaven.

It is not in keeping with this ideal to stress the Ogino-Knaus discoveries only under the aspect of avoiding children. As physicians well know, these discoveries can also be used to promote fertility; and this is obviously one reason why God enabled us to learn about the cycle of sterile and fertile periods. The truly Christian physician will use his knowledge of these discoveries and of other medical facts to create favorable attitudes toward childbearing. In doing this, he is helping to foster the traditional idealism of Christianity, which is being insidiously undermined in our times.

Nor is it in keeping with this sound idealism to overstress the secondary ends of marriage. It is true, I think, that before

177

the encyclical on Christian Marriage not enough attention was given to the fact that one of the purposes of marriage is the mutual perfecting of husband and wife. After the encyclical, much attention was focused on this purpose; and many beautiful and salutary things were written about it. But, as can happen even with good things, some writers began to emphasize this purpose to the point of denying its subordination to the begetting and rearing of children. The teaching of the Church is very clear on this point. The procreation and education of children constitute the *primary* end of marriage. The other purposes of marriage—mutual love and harmony between husband and wife and the safeguarding of their chastity—are certainly important and essential; but they are subordinated to the primary end.

Such is the ideal. I have stressed it here, not because it solves all the practical problems of family life, but because a realization of it is the best approach to a wholesome solution of these problems.

THE COUPLE IN NEED

One of the problems concerns the case in which, according to sound medical standards, further childbearing would be dangerous to health. The doctor who makes this judgment is not only entitled to tell his patient what he thinks; he has a real duty to do so. However, the judgment that a patient should not have more children should not be "narrow"; it should take in the whole picture—and often the whole picture means more than a mere medical decision that subsequent childbirth would be dangerous. One has to take into account the couple's desire for children, their ability to practice continence, and particularly their trust in the providence of God.

In this connection, I am reminded of the following incident. I was leading a discussion on marriage with a group of college women; and I put them this little problem: "You are a young wife; and you have just had your first baby. The doctor tells you that another pregnancy would very likely result in your death. What do you do?" One of the young women quickly replied: "Father, the doctor told my mother that; but she has had nine children since then."

I do not cite this example to make the physician look ridiculous. This story concerned a couple who greatly desired a family, who had an intense faith and a profound trust in God. They were willing to take the risk; and God blessed their willingness. The physician in this case may have made his decision on the soundest kind of medical basis and with the most delicate conscientiousness. But there are times, it seems to me, when physicians are too ready to conclude that a subsequent childbirth would be dangerous. And there are other times when the very real physical danger is only one side of the picture. It can happen that, in trying to avoid one evil (the bodily danger connected with childbirth), a couple will fall into another and a greater evil (constant sins of incontinence and the loss of interior peace and exterior harmony).

Because the matter is many-sided, physicians ought to enlist the help, or have their patients enlist the help, of a capable spiritual counselor, when they judge it necessary to avoid childbirth.

Granted that all the factors, spiritual and temporal, are properly considered, there are certainly many cases in which the avoidance of childbirth is justifiable and advisable. The only permissible means is continence, continuous or periodic. In such cases, doctors can do a great service to sound morality by patiently helping deserving couples to use the rhythm correctly. And I may add that it would be well for them to inform priests that they are interested in this; for priests are often called upon to suggest doctors who will give the advice and encouragement needed for the successful following of rhythm.

In connection with what I have written in the preceding paragraphs, I should like to mention an excellent editorial that appeared in the *Catholic Medical Quarterly,* April, 1952. The editorial referred to the third part of the address of Pope Pius XII on the moral problems of married life (Oct. 29, 1951), and saw in the Pope's words two challenges to the Catholic physician. The first challenge concerns rhythm. If further research is to be done on "cyclic variations in fertility," it must be done by physicians who realize that there is a profound moral difference between rhythm and contraception; it will hardly be done by those who see in these things only "differences of technique." And, if deserving married people are to be helped in the practice of rhythm, this help must be given by physicians who realize that profound moral values are at stake, as well as peace of mind. "To a varying extent," the editorial explained, "the reliability of the infertile period depends upon factors which are peculiar to the individual patient and a doctor's advice is therefore always involved. To us at least it seems highly undesirable that patients should be left to solve so complex a problem as this by the unaided use of charts and calendars that make no allowance for individual circumstances and physiological peculiarities that only a medical practitioner can assess with accuracy."[1]

MERELY INFORMATION

The preceding problem concerned a case of real need for information about rhythm. A different kind of problem is presented in the following question that doctors have often asked me: "Suppose that a young woman, apparently healthy, comes

---

[1] Unquestionably, patients need the help of the doctor in order to make proper use of charts, calendars, and written explanations of rhythm. But, granted the personal interest and help of the doctor, these materials can be very useful. In particular, I should like to recommend these publications by Henry Fallon: *Rhythm-Cal,* and *Temp-o-Graf.* They can be obtained from the R-C Publishing Company, Sunny Slope Station, Kansas City 10, Missouri. And they can be used, not only to help those who have a good reason to control conception, but also to promote fertility. In fact, the latter use should be stressed.

to me either shortly before her marriage or shortly afterwards, and asks for instruction in the practice of rhythm? Am I allowed to give such instruction?" From the point of view of what is *allowed,* my answer would be a simple "Yes." Instruction on the rhythm is instruction on nature's own way of functioning; and there is no moral wrong in either giving or acquiring the knowledge. Whether or not they intend to use it, married people have a right to this knowledge; and the proper place to obtain it is from the medical profession. As Pius XII said to the midwives—and he was really speaking to the entire medical profession: "It is your office, not that of the priest, to instruct married people either when they come for private consultation or through serious publications on the biological and technical aspects of the theory."

A full answer to this question, however, is not given merely by saying what is *allowable.* It seems to me that a zealous doctor might take advantage of a request like this to do a great deal of good, if he would tactfully inquire of the young woman whether she intends to use rhythm at the very beginning of her marriage. Not a few young couples plan to use rhythm because they have an exaggerated fear of childbirth or an exaggerated notion of the financial requirements involved in having children. A doctor whose tactful questions would bring out points like this could then, with equal tact, proceed to dissipate the exaggerated fears or notions and thus help the couple to start marriage with the proper idea of childbearing and its blessings.

CONTINUOUS CONTINENCE

The foregoing problems concern the practice of rhythm. But there are cases that go beyond this, cases in which the only permissible way of avoiding risk is continuous abstinence from marital intercourse. I have already cited the statement of Pius XII that such continence is possible through cooperation with the grace of God and that we do an injustice to the men

181

and women of our times to think them incapable of such heroism. For many people, this teaching about the possibility of continuous continence is a hard saying; and against it they raise the cry that abstention from intercourse causes mental breakdowns. The defense of the psychological sanity of the Catholic teaching on this subject is the second challenge to which the editorial in the *Catholic Medical Quarterly* referred. The editorial accepted the challenge and had a strong statement against a defeatist attitude. Here is a partial quotation from this splendid statement:

To claim it is impossible to give up what one desires without a mental breakdown is not only not compatible with the conclusions of reliable psychiatrists, but is in fact directly contrary to them. It is in addition contrary to any valid understanding of the dignity and responsibility of adult human beings and to the evidence of history. Within recall even of the most limited memories we have had an example of the separation of husbands and wives on a scale that has few parallels, and no one suggested at the time that one of the results of conscription would be that half the nation would be psychotics or adulterers. It may be objected that there the separation was a physical one enforced from outside and not the result of a personal decision. But such an objection begs the question in that it apparently assumes that what men and women may legitimately be expected to do for a national cause they may not be expected to do out of regard for moral principles, and it appears also to be founded on the wholly invalid assumption that men are capable of giving up only what they are physically incapable of having. The fact is that hundreds of thousands of married couples lived apart, and at times no doubt they found it extremely difficult to do so, but the majority succeeded without either mental or moral collapse. The majority returned to continue a married life in no way impaired by its temporary suspension and the minority whose marriages broke down and in due course ended in divorce were heirs to a policy that has all along been a denial of man's ability to repair a damaged relationship and restore it to a state of harmony.

chapter 22

Procedures Causing Sterility

DIRECTIVES 29-31 give the principles that generally govern procedures involving the reproductive functions and organs. Number 29—The unnatural use of the sex faculty (e.g., masturbation) is never permitted, even for a laudable purpose— has already been briefly explained in chapter 1; and it will be further explained in connection with directives 38-39. Number 30 was completely explained in chapters 19-21. In my discussion of contraception, I stressed the fact that, as regards surgical and equivalent procedures that effect sterility, we must pay particular attention to the purpose of the procedure: that is, whether sterility is intentionally or merely incidentally induced. In the many examples given in that chapter, I emphasized this distinction; but I also indicated that, even when sterility is not purposely induced, there must be a proportionate reason for the procedure.

The number of operations and treatments that probably or certainly induce sterility is almost countless. Because of their frequency, it is important to have at hand a principle which gives in some detail the conditions required for justifying them. These conditions are stated clearly in **directive 31** :

> **Procedures that induce sterility, whether permanent or temporary, are permitted when:**
>
> **a) they are immediately directed to the cure, diminution, or prevention of a serious pathological condition;**
>
> **b) a simpler treatment is not reasonably available; and**

c) the sterility itself is an unintended and, in the circumstances, an unavoidable effect.

(See also the Canadian Code, article 25; and the U.S. Code, "Reproductive Organs and Functions," Principle 1.)

SOME GENERAL OBSERVATIONS

Regarding this directive, let me note that it is formulated with a view to ordinary medical practice: that is, practice in which the *good of the patient* is the primary consideration. It does not refer to mutilating procedures for *the good of others,* e.g., medical experimentation and organic transplantation. Of course, it should be clear even now that these latter procedures are certainly illicit if they involve contraception (e.g., eugenic sterilization); but whether they can be justified when they are not contraceptive will be discussed later, in chapters 28-29.

I think I have already sufficiently stressed the fact that the direct causing of sterility is always forbidden. For this reason, my subsequent remarks in this chapter and in the three following chapters will be mainly concerned with the justification of indirect sterilization. We can put this in another way, and still very briefly, by saying that an indirect sterilization is justified when there is a *sound medical indication* for it. This proportionate reason, or sound medical indication, is had when the first two conditions of directive 31 are fulfilled: namely, *(a)* the procedure is used to cure, diminish, or prevent a serious pathological condition; and *(b)* a simpler treatment is not reasonably available.

In subsequent chapters, I shall consider a number of present-day problems that pertain specifically to directives 31-36. In the remainder of the present chapter, I shall briefly discuss two other modern problems, as well as two that are mainly of ancient vintage. The older problems will be outlined first.

EUPHONIC CASTRATION

The subject of castration is seldom discussed without someone's asking why the Church once approved of the castration of boys to preserve their sweet voices for choir purposes. This question, of course, supposes that the Church *did* approve of this practice. As far as I have been able to gather from much study of this question, the *Church* never did approve the practice. It is true that some theologians thought it could be justified. But they were a decided minority. The greater number of theologians considered it unjustifiable; and Cardinal Lambertini, later Pope Benedict XIV, strongly repudiated it.[1] Certainly it is clear that this practice of euphonic castration—as it is sometimes termed—would not square with the conditions outlined in directive 31; and no theologian today would attempt to justify it.

I thought it would be well to include a brief mention of this historical case because it is a rather celebrated example of confusing the opinions of a small number of theologians with the teaching of the Church itself. For further clarification of the case, I should like to mention a point brought out by Fr. Michael Riquet in a scholarly article on castration. He stressed the fact that doctors of the Middle Ages and the Renaissance were prone to castrate on many therapeutic pretexts, e.g., to cure hernia; and that in many instances the *castrati* used in various ecclesiastical choirs were victims of either this type of surgery or of some kind of accident. In the words of Fr. Riquet:

> In 1676, an investigation undertaken by the [French] Royal Society of Medicine revealed that in the diocese of Saint-Papoul more than 500 children had been castrated for hernia. It was the same in Italy where there was no dearth of herniated people. Amongst them it was not difficult to find six or seven eunuchs for the Sistine Chapel. Was not this merely to offer to the victims of a surgery still barbarous, a position which made some compensation of their loss?
>
> Hence to permit eunuchs to sing in the churches does not necessarily mean the approbation of criminal mutilation, but rather, perhaps the utilisation for choral singing of the results of operations then frequently performed on therapeutic grounds. Moreover, more than

---

[1] Cf. *De synodo dioecesana,* book 2, ch. 5.

185

one eunuch who became famous in later life attributed his castration to an accident in his youth or to a surgical operation necessitated by hernia or other illness.

That is why we believe that the Church is free from want of logic or candour when she condemns all castrations unjustified by the need of saving a life threatened by disease of an organ, and at the same time permits the employment in her choirs, of eunuchs whose mutilation does not necessarily render them guilty.[2]

CASTRATION TO PRESERVE CHASTITY

Also of ancient vintage is the question of castration as a means of suppressing vehement temptations. To put it simply, the problem, as phrased by the ancient writers, was this: would a man be justified in having himself castrated in order to suppress very vehement temptations against chastity? The tendency of the older authors was simply to deny that this mutilation would be either necessary or even useful for this spiritual purpose. Some modern theologians have showed themselves willing at least to consider the possibility that an abnormally strong sexual urge may be caused by abnormal gonadal function. Granted this supposition, they would say that the castration might be justified if there were no simpler way of quieting the urge. In a word, these authors would say the castration would be morally justified *if* it were an effective means of suppressing a violent sexual urge dependent on abnormal gonadal function and *if* there were no less drastic way of accomplishing the same result. Should both these *ifs* be verified, the conditions of directive 31 might be fulfilled. The final solution to the problem, therefore, would depend on sound medical judgment of the need and effectiveness of the castration. I feel

---

[2] Fr. Riquet's article, "Castration: A Historical, Moral and Medico-Legal Study," first appeared in *Cahiers Laënnec,* July-Sept., 1937, pp. 113ff. A translation was published in the *Catholic Medical Guardian,* Jan., 1938, pp. 6-23. The words I have quoted are from p. 16 of the *Guardian.* Another translation of Fr. Riquet's article is given in *New Problems in Medical Ethics,* Vol. 3 (Westminster, Md.; The Newman Press, 1956).

sure that few, if any, doctors would be willing to vouch for either the need or the effectiveness of the operation.

Under a slightly different aspect, the problem just outlined is not entirely impractical and certainly not ancient. In defense of a state law that permits castration of certain sexual criminals, C. C. Hawke, M.D., has argued that castrated criminals have become peaceful citizens, psychologically stabilized, and even happily married.[3] Theologians would not necessarily deny the beneficial effects that Dr. Hawke attributes to punitive castration; but they would want more evidence than he or anyone else has been able to adduce. The question of marriage, however, is very different. One of the most drastic effects of male castration is that it creates the impediment of impotence. A castrated man is incapable of marriage by reason of the natural law itself; and from this law neither the Church nor the state can dispense.[4]

UTERINE BLEEDING AND OVARIAN FUNCTION

It is at least fifteen years since I was first faced with problems about the suppression of ovarian function in the treatment of functional uterine bleeding. One case concerned a married woman who had had an operation for interposition of the uterus and, as a result of the operation, was experiencing prolonged and very painful menstrual periods. The bleeding was excessive; and her condition incapacitated her for a long period each month. Her physician wished to know whether he could be morally justified in suppressing the ovarian function by irradiation in order to put a stop to the excessive bleeding and pain.

---

[3] Cf. *Journal of the Kansas Medical Society,* Oct., 1950, pp. 470-473.
[4] For a complete discussion of the impediment of impotence, see the explanation of canon 1068 given in Bouscaren-Ellis *Canon Law: A Text and Commentary* (Milwaukee: The Bruce Publishing Company, 1957). For a more specialized discussion, see Fr. John C. Ford, S.J., "Double Vasectomy and Impotence," *Theological Studies,* Dec., 1955, pp. 533-557.

In another case, the patient was approaching the menopause; but her periods were still regular every month; and during each period there was excessive bleeding lasting from five to fifteen days. The doctor wished to stop the bleeding by X-ray treatment of the ovaries, which would almost certainly result in sterility. Incidentally, I recall a similar case in which the doctor wished to stop the bleeding by oophorectomy.

Excessive bleeding for a long period each month, with its inconvenience and incapacitating effects, is undoubtedly serious pathology; hence, it is easy to see that the suppression of ovarian function, by irradiation or oophorectomy, might fulfill the first condition of directive 31. It is clear also that the third condition would also be fulfilled, because (apart from a contraceptive intent of the doctor—which was certainly not present in the cases presented to me) the resultant sterility would be an unintended and unavoidable effect. The solution of both these problems, therefore, would rest on the fulfillment of the second condition: that no simpler treatment was reasonably available. As I recall the cases, the doctors assured me that all other usual treatments had been tried and found futile; hence, I considered the drastic procedures permissible. Perhaps this solution is also "historical" rather than practical. Obviously, I cannot keep up on all gynecologic literature; but I do read the *Year Book* faithfully and I keep in touch with eminent doctors. In general, the tendency of both the literature and my consultants is to say that the complete suppression of ovarian function would not now be necessary in the cases I have described. If that is true, the procedures would not be justified. I confess, however, that the picture is not perfectly clear to me. If I were again presented with the same problems, I would not feel qualified to decide whether the second condition of n. 31 was verified. I would have to leave that to competent medical judgment.

DYSMENORRHEA AND STILBESTROL

Since stilbestrol induces a temporary sterility by suppressing ovarian function, its use must be governed by the conditions of directive 31. I would not hesitate to say that the first condition is fulfilled, because it seems to me that severe pain may be rightly termed a pathological condition; and the stilbestrol is given precisely to relieve this condition. The third condition seems also to be fulfilled: the purpose of the stilbestrol treatment is to suppress ovarian function as the basic cause of pain; sterility itself is merely an unintended and unavoidable by-product. Here again, therefore, the solution of the problem rests on the fulfillment of the second condition: namely, whether equally effective means of relieving the pain are available. An article by Fr. Lynch contains an excellent survey of the other possible measures.[5] He does not draw any absolute conclusion regarding the use of stilbestrol because, as he rightly says, the doctors themselves must decide whether this is the preferential treatment. The most the moralist can say is that, when the use of stilbestrol is medically indicated as the best treatment of dysmenorrhea, it is morally justified.

It might be well to add here that what has been said about the use of stilbestrol for dysmenorrhea in particular is also true concerning the use of stilbestrol in the treatment of endometriosis, of which dysmenorrhea is often but one symptom.

---

[5] Cf. *The Linacre Quarterly,* Feb., 1955, pp. 27-31.

chapter 23

Vasectomy with Prostatectomy

THERE WAS A TIME when routine vasectomy with prostatectomy was more or less generally accepted by doctors because it was the only effective means of preventing infection of the epididymes and testicles. The procedure was also acceptable on moral grounds: the infection was at least a relatively serious pathological condition; the vasectomy was the only effective means of preventing it; and the vasectomy produced this result, not precisely by destroying fertility, but by eliminating the pathway along which the infection might spread. Thus, the conditions outlined in directive 31 were at least probably, if not certainly, fulfilled.

With the advent of the sulfa drugs and the antibiotics, many began to question this procedure. Their claim was that these new drugs could prevent the infection, without vasectomy; also, even if the infection occurred, the drugs could keep it under control in most cases. There were many objections, therefore, to the routine use of vasectomy. Inevitably, these objections were referred to The Catholic Hospital Association. Essentially, the point at issue was this: in view of the discovery of the new drugs, is there now a proportionate reason for the vasectomy, especially routine vasectomy? To answer this question, many factors had to be considered: the actual harm done by the vasectomy; the good it accomplished; and the possibility of gaining the same benefit by a simpler means, e.g., the new drugs. Clearly, all these points have to do with medical facts.

Doctors, not moralists, should supply medical facts. With the aid of several priests and nurses, I managed to question about twenty-five doctors, mostly urologists, in various parts of the country, about the pertinent medical facts. This survey of medical opinion was made in 1948 and early 1949. I believe that my original report of it is still of great interest and value; hence, I am retaining it here, and I shall merely supplement it with a brief statement about the morality of vasectomy today (i.e., in 1957).

EXISTING PRACTICE

In making our survey, the best approach to this problem seemed to be to inquire into the actual practice of routine vasectomy. Of the doctors we questioned, none practiced routine vasectomy in the sense of using it with all prostatectomies. However, three of them did a vasectomy with all suprapubic and perineal prostatectomies and with transurethral resections when the patient had cystitis. One did it on all patients over sixty, with the consent of their wives; and one did it on all except bachelors and married men with young wives.

What about the practice of others? The unquestionable answer seemed to be that, with the increased use of the antibiotics, the trend was very strong not only against routine, but also against frequent, vasectomy. Nevertheless it seemed that some apparently capable physicians still believed in and practiced routine vasectomy. Asked what they thought of this practice by others, most of our doctors were content with stating that they did not think the vasectomy necessary. Three strongly condemned the routine practice; but four others thought that one should preserve a rather tolerant attitude.

Why did some physicians continue the practice of routine vasectomy? Suggested explanations followed these lines: they were accustomed to the old technique; they were still suspicious of the effectiveness of drugs; they were especially fearful of the danger and the effects of epididymitis and wished to take the greatest possible precautions against it.

All whom we consulted, even those most strongly opposed to routine vasectomy, thought that vasectomy was necessary or advisable in *some* cases. Typical descriptions of the cases in which it would be called for are the following: "In those occasional cases in which recurrent epididymitis has preceded the surgery. . . . In seriously ill patients or in patients in the older group (65 yrs. and over) in whom an epididymo-orchitis might seriously jeopardize convalescence. . . . In cases in which a high temperature may cause a fatality. . . . In elderly men with infection of the genito-urinary tract which does not respond satisfactorily to medication. . . . In old men who are admittedly past the reproductive period and whose condition is poor enough to make the epididymitis a great increase of risk. . . . When there is a history of epididymitis. . . . When a patient has tuberculosis of the prostate." All these answers are based on the physical condition of the patient. One answer I received, however, mentioned the financial condition of the patient; the physician thought that the vasectomy would be justified when the patient was too poor to stand the extra expense of hospitalization and especially of drugs.

The foregoing list of typical cases that call for vasectomy represents a combination of various answers by various doctors. Whether *all* doctors would agree on *all* cases I could not say; yet it seemed that there would be substantial agreement on most of them, because they had much in common: e.g., special susceptibility to infection; special necessity for taking all possible precautions to avoid infection; and so forth.

The answers given seemed to indicate rather clearly definable cases; yet, when we asked whether the cases requiring vasectomy could be clearly determined before the prostatectomy, only seven of the fourteen physicians who answered the question were willing to reply with an unqualified "yes." The other seven either asserted that they could not be so determined or qualified their reply by saying, "in most instances, yes."

INCIDENCE OF EPIDIDYMITIS

What is the incidence, statistically, of epididymitis with prostatectomy? An article by Doctors Lynn and Nesbit (*Journal of Urology*, Jan., 1948), cited two reports of 20 and 21.4 per cent for open prostatectomies. These reports seem to have been made before the use of the sulphonamides, and certainly before the use of antibiotics, became common. Lynn and Nesbit themselves reported on 600 cases of transurethral resection. All these patients received sulphadiazine from the time of the insertion of the catheter until its withdrawal. Vasectomy was done on 300; no vasectomy was performed on the other 300. (Patients with clinical evidence of epididymitis at the time of the operation were not included in this report.) Epididymitis developed in 8 of the vasectomized patients; in 12 of the others. Among the non-vasectomized there were two cases of suppurative orchitis necessitating unilateral orchiectomy. Among the vasectomized were two cases of abscess of the operative site that required drainage and one case of scrotal hematoma.

The Lynn-Nesbit report concludes: "Epididymitis is not a frequent complication following transurethral prostatic resection. In 600 consecutive resections there was a 3.3 per cent incidence. Vas section at the time of the transurethral prostatectomy does not significantly reduce the occurrence of postoperative epididymitis." (One reader of this report observed that the force of the last conclusion depends on one's interpretation of "significantly." It is true, he said, that the total incidence in these cases was rather small; but some might consider the ratio in favor of vasectomy as being of some significance.)

Our doctors were asked to give their own estimates of the incidence of epididymitis, and especially its relative incidence with the various types of prostatectomy. It is difficult to express a common denominator of these estimates. In general, they seem to agree with the figures cited by Lynn and Nesbit; nevertheless, it was not a little surprising that many thought the danger should be greater with transurethral than with open prostatectomy.

SERIOUSNESS

How serious a condition is epididymitis? The answers we received to this question may be reduced to this: in some patients (e.g., those for whom a high temperature might be very dangerous), it is certainly a serious condition; in general, it is more troublesome than dangerous. By "serious" or "dangerous," the physicians seemed to mean that it involved some risk of life. By "troublesome," they seemed to mean that it involved pain, extra expense, extra hospitalization. The extent of this hospitalization was variously estimated from a few days to several weeks. I believe, though I am not sure, that this wide divergence of estimates concerning extra hospitalization may be accounted for partly by the possible degrees of seriousness of the infection and partly by the fact that some of the physicians were thinking in terms of using antibiotic drugs and some were not.

VASECTOMY AND STERILITY

How much harm is actually done by the vasectomy? Readers may be surprised at this question. They may immediately reply to themselves: vasectomy induces sterility; and that is serious harm. Nevertheless, in seeking answers to the question from physicians, we received our most interesting and, I might add, most inexplicably contradictory replies.

We were led to investigate this point by the fact that at the very beginning of our survey one doctor insisted that, even without vasectomy, the prostatectomy itself would destroy fertility by damaging the ejaculatory ducts and eliminating the continuity of the vasa. This, of course, is a highly significant observation; for, if the patient would be sterile even without the vasectomy, the proportionate reason for permitting the slight additional mutilation need not be very serious.

We asked six urologists what damage to the ejaculatory ducts is done by the various types of prostatectomy. Four said that no damage to the ducts should normally result from any kind of prostatectomy. One said there should be no damage with transurethral, but there should be with suprapubic and probably also with perineal. One answered that there is definitely damage with all complete prostatectomies.

Of the four who said the ducts are not damaged, two added that, in spite of this fact, emission would not result if the internal sphincter of the bladder were broken in the operation. One of these said it is always broken; the other was of the opinion that it is almost always broken in a suprapubic and perineal, but not usually in transurethral, prostatectomy.

Having received this sufficiently confusing collection of answers, we rephrased our question before consulting other urologists. First, we asked: does the prostatectomy itself break the continuity with the vasa? One urologist answered with an unqualified "no"; another admitted, "I'm not sure"; and two others replied that the continuity *may* be preserved. Three gave these somewhat longer responses: "I feel that certain transurethral operations may save the ejaculatory ducts. I think that suprapubic and perineal operations break the continuity with the vasa." "In suprapubic and perineal prostatectomy this continuity is often broken. It often is not broken in the transurethral method." "The continuity of the ejaculatory ducts may or may not be destroyed, depending on whether it becomes incorporated in the tissue to be removed. This is usually not the case."

We asked secondly: is the internal sphincter of the bladder always or usually broken; and, if so, does this interfere with seminal emission? Three doctors were of the opinion that it is usually broken, but that this has no influence on seminal emission. Two others, who agreed that it is not usually broken, considered that, when broken, it does interfere with emission because the semen, instead of passing outwards with ejaculation, goes retrograde into the bladder.

To add to the complications of these answers, one doctor suggested that the ducts are often blocked by scarred tissue after the operation; another said the verumontanum is usually injured in the prostatectomy, and that this is the reason why the ejaculate passes into the bladder; and still another asserted that, even without the vasectomy or the various injuries just mentioned, the prostatectomy tends to make a man sterile by depriving him of the prostatic fluid, which is necessary for activating the spermatozoa.

It would require someone more skilled than I at working puzzles to fit those various answers into a clearly delineated picture. Insofar as I could draw any definite information from them, I would put it briefly as follows: the doctors denied that prostatectomy always makes a man sterile; but they admitted that, even without the vasectomy, the patient is often "for some reason or other" sterile after the prostatectomy. In other words, it seemed that in many cases the vasectomy has no actual effect on fertility.

SUBSTITUTES

Is there a good substitute for vasectomy in preventing epididymitis? Only one of the twenty-five physicians we consulted mentioned the feasibility of a temporary vas ligation in place of the vasectomy. He stated that he has used this technique successfully over a long period of years and in hundreds of cases. I was not a little surprised that no other physician mentioned it. Most of them immediately cited the antibiotics as the simplest means of reducing the incidence of the complication and the seriousness of its implications. There was no agreement, however, concerning the comparative effectiveness of the drugs and vasectomy. A few seemed to think that the vasectomy adds little to the effectiveness of the drugs; a few others were of the opinion that the vasectomy would be the only really certain way of preventing epididymitis. These answers were rough estimates; they were not based on statistics.

I believe that, in the foregoing paragraphs, I have presented all the pertinent information (and perhaps some that is not pertinent) that my associates and I obtained from our questioning of physicians. The total picture is quite complicated. One reason for this may be that our own lack of expert knowledge prevented us from properly phrasing questions or from correctly evaluating answers. But another reason, I think, is that we were inquiring into a matter which was in the stage of transition; and even the physicians themselves experienced mental and psychological difficulties in appraising the relative values of the old and the new.

CONCLUSIONS

The foregoing survey, made in 1948-1949, showed a rather complicated picture. The literature of the subsequent seven years helped to clarify the picture; but it did not remove all the complications. In view of the results of the survey and of the subsequent literature, I suggest the following practical conclusions:

1. There is no moral objection to vasectomy with prostatectomy when it is limited to selected cases.

2. There might be some differences of opinion among doctors themselves as to the proper indications for vasectomy; but I believe the indications I have given on p. 192 constitute a good summary.

3. It seems rather clear that there is no real medical justification today for routine vasectomy with prostatectomy. In

some cases it is not needed and should be classified as unnecessary surgery.

4. I realize that there are still some doctors who favor routine vasectomy and who would, therefore, consider my conclusions too strict. I do not wish to insist on the conclusions to the extent of urging administrative actions against these doctors. I think that, since this is primarily a question of good medicine, the ultimate judgment of what is to be allowed should be made by the staffs of individual hospitals.

chapter 24

Castration for Cancer

Castration, surgical or otherwise, is permitted when required for the removal or diminution of a serious pathological condition, even in other organs. Hence: oophorectomy or irradiation of the ovaries may be allowed in treating carcinoma of the breast and metastasis therefrom; and orchidectomy is permitted in the treatment of carcinoma of the prostate. In all cases the procedure least harmful to the reproductive organs should be used, if equally effective with other procedures. **Directive 32.** (The same provision is made in the U.S. Code, "Reproductive Organs and Functions," n. 8; and in the Canadian Code, article 30.)

THIS DIRECTIVE is really but a concrete application of n. 31 with special reference to two serious pathological conditions: carcinoma of the prostate and carcinoma of the breast. A brief consideration of each of these problems may prove helpful.

CARCINOMA OF THE PROSTATE

An early ethical appraisal of castration for prostatic carcinoma was made by Fr. John J. Clifford, S.J.[1] On the clinical side, Fr. Clifford stressed these points: the disease was rarely diagnosed in time for complete cure; without treatment it would become incapacitating and excruciatingly painful; in the incurable cases, considerable palliation could be had

---

[1] *Theological Studies,* Dec. 1944, pp. 439-452.

through estrogen therapy and/or orchiectomy. The rationale of these procedures is based on the theory that androgens favor the growth of the cancer and metastasis; hence, the necessity of neutralizing or suppressing the androgens.

In the subsequent twelve years, there has been little change in the clinical picture. Except in the special cases of regular routine rectal examinations of men approaching middle age, early diagnosis of prostatic cancer is still rare. The disease is admittedly fatal and fiercely painful unless properly treated. But with endocrine control of the neoplasm, the patients gain weight, are dramatically relieved of metastatic pain, and are enabled to carry on their normal activities for a considerable period of time. The principal methods of endocrine control are still estrogen therapy and/or orchiectomy. Most authors consider that both forms of therapy are required; some add that adrenalectomy is also useful.

I could document this clinical picture by almost innumerable references; but I think the following summary of an excellent discussion by Frank Hinman, M.D., and Frederick S. Howard, M.D., should suffice:

Cancer of the prostate is common but is usually not seen until it has spread locally to such an extent that surgical removal is impossible. Radical prostatectomy is indicated in early cases. However the number of early, operative cases can only be increased by doing more routine rectal examinations in men past 50.

The etiology of prostatic carcinoma is unknown. Although occult, unsuspected cancer is frequently found on study of routine autopsy specimens, proof is lacking that these small lesions will necessarily become clinical cancer of the prostate.

As a sexual organ, the prostate is under endocrine control requiring a favorable androgen-estrogen ratio for its growth and maintenance. The great majority of prostatic cancers similarly are under control by the sex hormone and are inhibited by deprivation of androgen. Although administration of androgen stimulates clinical carcinoma of the prostate, there is no evidence that it causes prostatic cancer to appear.

Effective anti-androgenic control can be achieved either by bilateral orchiectomy or by continuous administration of estrogen, but the best results seem to be produced by application of both measures. It is probably better to start such treatment early rather than to wait for symptoms or evident metastases.

Perineal needle biopsy of late cancer of the prostate is valuable to prove the diagnosis before treatment.

Most patients with inoperable cancer of the prostate will receive effective palliation and control of their lesions for long periods by continuous treatment of their condition as a chronic although incurable disease. In case of relapse, effective but usually brief palliation can be achieved by either "medical adrenalectomy" with cortisone, or perhaps, surgical adrenalectomy.[2]

MORAL APPRAISAL

The authors speak not only of estrogen therapy and orchiectomy but also of adrenalectomy. This last procedure is being mentioned more and more in present-day literature as an effective palliative measure in the treatment of carcinoma of the prostate and of the breast. I shall say something of adrenalectomy in my concluding remarks; for the present, we can limit our moral considerations to castration.

Whether we consider estrogen therapy or orchiectomy or both, it is obvious that the treatment is directed to the diminution of a serious pathological condition. Moreover, according to all the medical literature there is no simpler way of producing the same result. Finally, since the objective is to suppress androgen output, it is clear that the loss of fertility (in case the patient is still fertile) is merely indirect. Hence, all the conditions required by directive 31 for the justification of procedures inducing sterility are fulfilled.

When Fr. Clifford wrote his pioneering article on this problem, he specified that if estrogen therapy alone would produce the desired result of palliation there would be no sufficient reason for the evisceration of the gonads. As a theoretical statement, this is certainly true. In practice, however, there is no

---

[2] This summary concludes an article entitled "Management of Prostatic Carcinoma," *GP*, April 1955, pp. 105-113.

great problem for the moralist, because the best authorities, if not all, state that both estrogen therapy and orchiectomy are usually required. The one source of dispute among medical authorities seems to concern the appropriate time for resorting to orchiectomy. This is a problem for the doctors themselves to decide; and the moralist can abide by their judgment.

THE HEALTHY ORGAN

I have never known a moral theologian who disagreed with the foregoing analysis; nor have I seen any objection to it in print. Nevertheless, as late as 1953, the Italian Society of Urologists asked Pope Pius XII to give an official decision about the removal of the sex glands in the treatment of cancer of the prostate. Perhaps the reason for this request was merely to have a definite topic for the papal address to the Society; perhaps the reason was the growing tendency of the laity to want their moral problems solved by the Holy See; and perhaps the reason was simply a difficulty in understanding why organs in themselves healthy could be removed. Even this problem of the healthy organ had been sufficiently explained by the moralists; yet it may be that the Society of Urologists was unaware of this. Pope Pius XII put the doctors' minds to rest by giving the common theological teaching in the following words:

The decisive point here is not that the organ which is removed or rendered inoperative be itself diseased, but that its preservation or its functioning entails directly or indirectly a serious threat to the whole body. It is quite possible that, by its normal function, a healthy organ may exercise on a diseased one so harmful an effect as to aggravate the disease and its repercussions on the whole body. It can also happen that the removal of a healthy organ and the suppression of its normal function may remove from a disease—cancer, for example—the area for development or, in any case, essentially alter its conditions of existence. If no other remedy is available, surgical intervention is permissible in both cases.[3]

[3] The address to urologists was given Oct. 8, 1953. The main points are briefly summarized in *The Linacre Quarterly*, Nov., 1953, pp. 106-107.

CARCINOMA OF THE BREAST

When I first wrote on this subject, there was a wide difference of medical opinion concerning the utility and advisability of suppressing ovarian function as a palliative treatment of cancer of the breast. A close following of the more recent literature has convinced me that a substantial majority of doctors now favor the suppression of ovarian function as a palliative treatment in these cases. There would be some dispute as to the cases that would benefit by the treatment, also some disagreement as to the best time and method (e.g., roentgen or surgical) for performing the castration; but certainly disagreements about the value of the treatment are much less than they used to be. Also, as in the case with cancer of the prostate, there is a growing tendency to advocate adrenalectomy.

The moral evaluation of castration for breast carcinoma is essentially the same as what I have previously given regarding prostatic cancer. Here, too, we have the added problem of adrenalectomy (and sometimes hypophysectomy), which I shall consider presently. Also, with reference to this particular problem, there is a special difficulty about pregnancy that will be considered later. But, prescinding from these special problems, doctors and hospitals can safely follow the rule given in directive 32—a rule which amounts to this: castration as a palliative measure is permitted at the discretion of the attending physician and his consultants.

FURTHER OBSERVATIONS

My discussion of carcinoma of the prostate was primarily concerned with surgical castration because this is most commonly mentioned in the medical literature. Nevertheless, I have seen some reference to x-ray castration; and I have been told by some distinguished urologists that this procedure produces the same good results as surgical castration. This is rather a question of technique than of principle; and I leave the judgment to physicians.

More and more articles are advocating adrenalectomy in the treatment of both cancer of the prostate and cancer of the breast. Also, some rather recent literature mentions hypophysectomy in certain cases of cancer of the breast. It seems to me that these operations are still largely in the experimental stage; however, I may be wrong on that point. At any rate, even though largely experimental, they would be permitted if the patients wish to try them. We are dealing here with such serious pathology that any experiment that offers some genuine hope of added benefit for the patient seems to be justifiable, provided, of course, that the patient understands the risks and is willing to take them.

My explanation of the licitness of castration for cancer of the breast was based on a theory similar to that which justifies castration for cancer of the prostate. The theory is that the ovarian hormone favors the growth of neoplastic tissue. The removal or destruction of the ovaries, therefore, is not a contraceptive procedure. It is designed to suppress the endocrine function of the ovaries; the fact that the woman is thereby rendered sterile is simply an unavoidable by-product of the procedure. I might mention, however, that a doctor once challenged the provision of directive 32 because, he said, there is no added danger to the woman with breast cancer unless she becomes pregnant. He contended, therefore, that we were really allowing a contraceptive procedure.

Much might be said about this doctor's contention. In the first place, it is not agreed that pregnancy adds to the danger of metastasis. Secondly, even if pregnancy is harmful—as many authorities do hold—that does not detract from the very generally admitted fact that the ovarian hormones are also harmful, whether the woman should become pregnant or not. Thirdly, if pregnancy were the only source of danger, few doctors would recommend oophorectomy; those interested in contraception would, no doubt, favor the much less drastic procedure of fallectomy.

This brings me to a point of confusing terminology which I have already mentioned in the chapter on contraception and direct sterilization. Doctors are too much inclined to speak of sterilization without any qualifying adjective; and I know of many cases in which this has caused misunderstanding, especially with reference to the treatment of cancer of the breast. I have seen many reports in which consultants advised "sterilization" and have thus alarmed hospital supervisors and administrators; yet, when the report was examined closely, it was evident that the consultants meant castration, not mere sterilization. The following question and answer taken from the *Journal of the American Medical Association*,[4] may illustrate what I mean:

TO THE EDITOR:—A 32-year-old woman had a radical breast amputation two weeks after she noticed a lump in her breast. Thirty-two axillary lymph glands were examined, and one showed spread of the carcinoma. Histologically this was an adenocarcinoma. Is sterilization indicated, and if so should it be done surgically or by x-ray therapy?

Answer:—Sterilization is certainly indicated in this case and should be surgical. Oophorectomy has definite advantages over sterilization by x-ray. The surgical method is certain and permanent and removes ovarian function abruptly.

It seems clear enough that both the questioner and the consultant were talking about castration. Yet, if the consultant had not added the explanation about oophorectomy and the stopping of ovarian function, one might easily have concluded that both doctors were talking about direct sterilization.

---

[4] July 3, 1954, p. 950.

205

chapter | **25**

Hysterectomy

THE CONDITIONS REQUIRED for the licit removal of a pregnant uterus are explained above (chapter 1, number VI). **Directives 34-36** concern hysterectomy in the absence of pregnancy. These directives read as follows:

34. Hysterectomy is permitted when it is sincerely judged to be the only effective remedy for prolapse of the uterus, or when it is a necessary means of removing some other serious pathology.

35. Hysterectomy is not permitted as a routine procedure after any definite number of cesarean sections. In these cases the pathology of each patient must be considered individually; and care must be had that hysterectomy is not performed as a merely contraceptive measure.

36. Even after the childbearing function has ceased, hysterectomy is still a mutilation, and it must not be performed unless sound medical reasons call for it.

The same material is covered by the Canadian Code, articles 26-28. The question of hysterectomy after the childbearing function has ceased is not explicitly mentioned in the U.S. Code; the other provisions about hysterectomy are contained in the U.S. Code, "Reproductive Organs and Functions," nn. 2-3.

Of the three directives, the first two are but practical applications of directive 31, because they refer to cases in which hysterectomy causes sterility. Directive 36 applies to cases in which the patient is already sterile, either because ovulation has ceased naturally or because some operation, treatment, or disease has destroyed the ovaries, suppressed ovarian function, closed or removed the tubes, and so forth. Before commenting on the individual directives, I should like to make a few general remarks.

For several years we have been made more and more conscious of the fact that unnecessary hysterectomies have been and are frequent. I accept this fact; even though I think it is sometimes exaggerated. Acceptance of the fact, however, should not lead to the other extreme of not performing hysterectomies when they are properly indicated. There is no need, unless the patient herself wishes it, to subject a woman to almost appalling hardship—financial, physical, and psychological—in order to preserve a uterus.

I have heard it said, by both Catholic and non-Catholic doctors, that hysterectomy is more common in Catholic hospitals than in others. I have at times asked for a proof of this, but I have never received it. The one case in which I personally think it might be verified is the case of hysterectomy with cesarean section. As I shall point out in explaining n. 35, there is controversy among Catholic moralists about the removal of the badly damaged uterus. By reason of the principle of probabilism we can allow this procedure, granted the conditions to be outlined. In non-Catholic hospitals this may be less common because the doctors solve their problem simply by cutting the tubes. To Catholic moralists generally, cutting tubes is merely a contraceptive procedure;[1] whereas the same moralists are divided on the moral appraisal of hysterectomy. I sincerely doubt that, with the exception of this difficult case, anyone could show a greater incidence of hysterectomy in Catholic than in non-Catholic hospitals.

For almost twenty years I have followed the trends of medical opinion concerning hysterectomy. I have done this through

---

[1] See above, chapter 19.

reading medical literature, through discussions with doctors, and through problems presented to me for solution. I would say very frankly that the principal result of this experience has been to impress on me that almost every so-called indication for hysterectomy seems to be controversial. As Drs. Burch and Lavely say in their very readable and enlightening monograph on hysterectomy: "In the surgery of the pelvis there are few if any absolutes."[2] The one absolute that moralists would insist on is that hysterectomy is never permitted as a contraceptive procedure. Granted this, it seems that one can only say that there are *some* conditions that *sometimes* require hysterectomy. More definite judgment has to be determined by the individual case, as it presents itself—and that means a consideration of the total picture: the disease itself, the physical and psychological effects of the disease, the effects of hysterectomy or of other possible procedures on the patient.

In all the cases that I shall outline here, I should like this observation kept in mind: namely, that I am not speaking in terms of absolutes and that I am simply giving illustrations of cases in which, granted the particular conditions, hysterectomy is morally permissible because *in these cases,* as well as in cases that might follow a similar pattern, the requisites for licit hysterectomy are, in my opinion, fulfilled.

DIRECTIVE 34: PROLAPSE AND OTHER PATHOLOGY

There is much difference of opinion among doctors as to the value or need of hysterectomy in cases of uterine prolapse. And there would be, I think, a somewhat similar difference of opinion among theologians. I think the main point around which the differences of opinion would center may be found in the expression used in the directive: namely, that hysterectomy is permitted "when it is sincerely judged to be *the only effective remedy* for prolapse of the uterus" (italics added). It

---

[2] John C. Burch, M.D., F.A.C.S., and Horace T. Lavely, M.D., *Hysterectomy* (Springfield, Ill.: Charles C. Thomas, 1954), p. 22.

seems to me that the true meaning of this directive—and perhaps a key to some of the differences of opinion—can be had only by keeping in mind that the directive is for all Catholic hospitals, whether large or small, whether located in a medical center or in a small town far away from the large medical centers. In the large medical centers there will generally be specialists who can remedy even a severe prolapse without resorting to hysterectomy or to any other procedure which would interfere with the normal physiology of the uterus. In such places, hysterectomy would rarely be the proper treatment of uterine prolapse. But in smaller and more remote places, where the services of highly trained specialists are not available, hysterectomy might more frequently be necessary.

For a good discussion of many other pathological conditions in which hysterectomy is sometimes indicated, I recommend the monograph by Drs. Burch and Lavely. As for myself, I shall merely give here some of the cases previously published in *Medico-Moral Problems*. These cases, I admit, are somewhat old; and the conditions outlined in them might no longer be verified. Nevertheless, antiquated or not, the cases serve as good illustrations of how the moral principle enunciated in directive 31 is applicable to problems of hysterectomy; and it is for that reason that I am retaining the cases as originally published.

THE CASES

Case 1: This concerned a young woman whose menstrual period regularly lasted from ten to fifteen days, during which time she suffered great pain, and the bleeding was so excessive as to prevent her from doing her work. As I recall the matter, there was a possibility, but not a certainty, of curing her by means of a long and expensive treatment. On the other hand, a hysterectomy would definitely remove the trouble. The precise moral problem to be solved was this: could the girl licitly choose the hysterectomy in preference to the prolonged, expensive, and problematical treatment?

Case 2: A young married woman who had three children had tuberculosis and was also afflicted by excessive menstrual bleeding over periods covering ten or twelve days. Several physicians consulted about the case were all of the opinion that the excessive bleeding was seriously harmful to one in her condition, and they wished to know whether it would be morally permissible to stop the uterine bleeding by hysterectomy.

Case 3: A woman had several children by normal, vaginal delivery. As a result of these pregnancies, the cervix had become eroded, lacerated, infected; subinvolution of the uterus had taken place; the uterus had become heavy and boggy and had developed weakened support and efficiency. Because of this uterine condition, the woman suffered anemia, physical disability, pain, and other distress. Her doctor estimated that for much less distress other operations such as appendectomy or cholecystectomy would be medically indicated; and it was his opinion that in the present case hysterectomy was medically indicated for restoring the health of the patient. Would the hysterectomy, he asked, be morally justifiable?

Case 4. The woman in this case was 40 years old, the mother of a very large family. In some of her early pregnancies and in her three most recent deliveries, she had experienced severe hemorrhages. She lived in a rural community, but, because of the history of hemorrhage, she had been brought to a large city hospital for all recent deliveries. In this hospital, all possible precautions had been taken against the postpartum hemorrhage; nevertheless, in the last few pregnancies her life had been in grave danger and she had been saved only by transfusions. When she became pregnant again, her doctor thought that the best precaution against postpartum hemorrhage would be a cesarean section with hysterectomy. He wanted to know whether the hysterectomy would be permitted.

SOLUTIONS

In all the foregoing cases, hysterectomy would effect sterility; hence, it can be justified only if the three conditions of directive 31 are fulfilled. In my previously-published solutions to the problems, I expressed the opinion that, granted the circumstances of the individual cases, these conditions were fulfilled and the hysterectomy would be permissible. As regards the third condition—that the sterility be not intended—there seems to be no room for reasonable doubt. At any rate, it seems clear to me that there was no question of contraceptive intent on the part of either the patients or the physicians; hence, I believe that no more need be said here about the fulfillment of the third condition. My remarks, therefore, will be confined to the first two conditions: namely, whether the proposed hysterectomies would be "immediately directed to the cure, diminution, or prevention of a serious pathological condition," and whether "a simpler treatment is not reasonably available."

In the first case, the bleeding was prolonged and heavy; the young woman was incapacitated for a long period each month. It seems to me that this is serious pathology, even though no malignancy or danger to life is involved. One suggested cure was hysterectomy, which, of course, would render the young woman permanently sterile. The alternative cure was a treatment which would leave the reproductive system intact, but would extend over a long period of time, would be very expensive, and would leave the cure somewhat doubtful.

Granted that this outline of the case is substantially correct, I believe that the girl would be justified in asking for the hysterectomy and that the doctor would be justified in performing the operation. For the treatment, which is the only alternative remedy, involves much greater inconvenience and offers less hope of success. Under these circumstances the drastic mutilation (hysterectomy) may be said to be the only reasonably available and efficacious remedy.

The second case introduces a new pathological factor: namely, that the bleeding was especially harmful because of the tubercular condition. This, as I understand it, was the judgment of all the doctors consulted on the case; and they were definitely not interested in seeking an excuse for sterilizing the patient. Moreover, they seem to have agreed that hysterectomy was the best remedy. Under these circumstances the hysterectomy would be permissible, despite the fact that the woman was young and obviously quite fertile.

As for the third case, my own opinion—which, I believe, is based on sound common sense—is that the continuous distress and quasi-incapacitation of the patient constitute a condition of ill health which is very serious, especially since it prevents a married woman from properly caring for her family. Moreover, it was the physician's considered judgment that there was no other reasonably available remedy. There seemed to be no moral obstacle, therefore, to the removal of the uterus.

In the final case, there was question of preventing a serious danger rather than removing an existent pathology. In this case, too, other remedies had been tried in past deliveries and had succeeded; but the doctor realized that there was only a thin line between dramatic success and complete failure. He was afraid to run the risk of postpartum hemorrhage again; and he believed the most secure means of avoiding the risk was cesarean hysterectomy. Granted the correctness of his judgment—and it is not for a theologian to question such judgments—there seems to be no reason for objecting to the hysterectomy on moral grounds.

The foregoing cases, as I have previously indicated, are all old. Perhaps more recent medical techniques would obviate the necessity of hysterectomy. If so, the moral solutions would have to be changed accordingly. Even so, the cases illustrate how directives 31 and 34 should be applied to problems involving hysterectomy as a remedy for, or a prevention of, pathological conditions.

DIRECTIVE 35: REPEAT CESAREAN

Directive 35 makes three points indisputably clear. First, *routine* hysterectomy after any certain number of cesareans (e.g., two or three) is not permitted. Whatever may be said of the past, such routine hysterectomy is not good obstetrics today and, for this reason if for no other, it is not good morality, either. Secondly, hysterectomy is *never* permitted for the precise purpose of sterilizing, i.e., as a contraceptive measure. Thirdly, hysterectomy is certainly permitted when the damage done by previous cesareans or by another cause is such that the cesarean hysterectomy is required in order to protect the mother from a danger that is now present, e.g., hemorrhage, infection, etc.

One problem is not clearly solved by the directive. This concerns the uterus which has been severely damaged by previous cesareans, but not to the extent that it creates danger here and now. For example, suppose that, when he does a cesarean section, the doctor finds that the uterine wall has become "paper thin" or that the scar is getting very weak. He then presents this problem; "I can sew up this uterus, but I cannot repair it so that it will function safely in gestation. Because of the weakness of the wall or scar, or because of other damage, it is very likely that it will cause serious danger in another pregnancy. May it be removed now instead of waiting till the actual danger develops in another pregnancy?"

Theologians do not agree in their answer to this question. Some think that, since the actual danger would arise only in the pregnancy, the removal of the uterus now would be a contraceptive measure. Others think that, since the damaged condition that would cause the danger is already present, the uterus may be removed now because it is already a seriously pathological and relatively useless organ. At the conclusion of this chapter, I shall give a comprehensive list of moralists who have expressed their views on this difficult topic. At this point, it seems sufficient to state that the question is still an open one;

213

consequently, when competent physicians judge that, by reason of repeated cesareans (or some similar cause) a uterus is so badly damaged that it will very likely not function safely in another pregnancy, they may, with the consent of the patient, remove the uterus as a seriously pathological organ.

DIRECTIVE 36: NON-STERILIZING HYSTERECTOMY

This directive refers not only to hysterectomy after the completion of the natural menopause, but also to hysterectomy after both ovaries have been removed or their function destroyed (e.g., by irradiation) or after both fallopian tubes have been removed, irreparably occluded, and so forth. And—perhaps even more practically—the directive refers to cases in which a still healthy uterus is removed on the occasion of another operation such as the removal of malignant ovaries.

I shall confine myself to the last case. It is obvious that the hysterectomy is not a sterilizing procedure because the necessary oophorectomy itself renders the woman sterile (if, indeed, the malignancy has not already done so). The precise point to be determined, therefore (and this would hold for the other cases outlined in the preceding paragraph), is whether the removal of the undiseased uterus would conform with the demands of sound medicine. If it does so conform, there is no moral objection to the removal of the uterus; if, on the other hand, the hysterectomy is not medically indicated, it would be unnecessary surgery, hence morally reprehensible.

An abstract in the *Year Book of Obstetrics and Gynecology*,[3] says: "Malignant ovarian tumors should receive radical surgery with bilateral salpingo-oophorectomy and total hysterectomy." A later abstract,[4] after surveying a number of cases of primary ovarian malignancy, concludes: "Analysis of treatment showed that total hysterectomy, bilateral salpingo-oopho-

---

[3] 1953-1954 Series, pp. 484-485.
[4] 1954-1955 Series, pp. 468-469

rectomy, and postoperative x-radiation therapy offer the best hope for survival." Finally, according to Taylor,[5] there is general agreement that hysterectomy should accompany the removal of malignant ovaries.

Perhaps this topic is controversial. Yet, in view of the foregoing references, there seems to be no reason for opposing the hysterectomy on the ground of unnecessary surgery.

APPENDIX

This appendix will present the comprehensive list of theologians' opinions on the question: "Is it permissible to remove a uterus which, in the opinion of competent and conscientious physicians, has been so badly damaged by previous cesarean sections that it would very likely create serious danger in another pregnancy?" The supposition is that the pathological condition of the uterus is not such that, even independently of future pregnancies, the woman's health would be seriously affected.

Many of these references are to theological journals to which doctors would not have ready access; but I include these for the convenience of theologians and professors of ethics who might want to make a thorough study of the arguments.

Bender, Louis, O.P.: *Angelicum,* July-Sept., 1953, pp. 273-280. He considers the operation a direct sterilization, therefore illicit.

Cambo, Miguel, S.J.: *Sal Terrae,* July, 1954, pp. 364-366. He reviews some recent literature and concludes that both affirmative and negative opinions are probable.

Connell, Francis J., C.SS.R.: *American Ecclesiastical Review,* Dec., 1949, p. 507, and May, 1950, p. 221. In his analysis of the case, it is the future pregnancy, not the damaged condition of the uterus, that will cause the trouble; hence, removal of the uterus would really be a contraceptive measure.

[5] Cited by Crossen and Crossen, *Diseases of Women,* (St. Louis: The C. V. Mosby Co., 9th ed., 1944), p. 733.

Connery, John R., S.J.: *Theological Studies,* Dec., 1955, pp. 575-576. He is clearly in favor of the opinion that allows the hysterectomy.

Ford, John C., S.J.: *Theological Studies,* Dec., 1942, pp. 592-593; Dec., 1944, pp. 516-517; March, 1954, pp. 68-71. In the first two of these references, Fr. Ford expressed the opinion that the hysterectomy seemed to be a direct sterilization. However, having carefully and profoundly considered all the pros and cons over a number of years, he concluded that the arguments permitting the hysterectomy are solidly probable, and he stated this in the third of the references. I think particular attention should be called to this, because the article in the March, 1954, *Theological Studies,* was written in collaboration with me, and some authors seem to think that the opinion about the damaged uterus is merely mine. This is not true. Every opinion given in that article was sponsored by both writers.

Healy, Edwin F., S.J.: *Medical Ethics* (Chicago: Loyola University Press, 1956), pp. 174-175. He considers the hysterectomy a direct sterilization and denies all probability to the opposing view.

Kelly, Gerald, S.J.: *Theological Studies,* March, 1947, pp. 103-104; March, 1951, pp. 69-73; March, 1954, pp. 68-71. I have always defended the intrinsic and practical probability of the opinion allowing the hysterectomy. The various arguments are given in some detail in these references.

Lohkamp, Nicholas, O.F.M.: *The Morality of Hysterectomy Operations* (Washington: Catholic University of America Press, 1956), pp. 130-142. His own opinion is that the operation is not permitted; he admits, however, that it is, as yet, an unsolved problem.

Lynch, John J., S.J.: *Theological Studies,* June, 1957, pp. 230-232. He favors the opinion allowing the hysterectomy; in a word, he is convinced that there is not only extrinsic authority for the opinion but also that the arguments for it are solidly probable.

McReavy, L.L.: *The Clergy Review,* Aug., 1956, pp. 485-489. He is not as yet convinced by the intrinsic arguments but he admits extrinsic probability for the opinion allowing the hysterectomy.

O'Brien, Patrick, C.M.: In his revision of Fr. Finney's *Moral Problems in Hospital Practice* (St. Louis: Herder, 1956), p. 224, Fr. O'Brien gives only the opinion that the hysterectomy is illicit. No mention is made of the contrary opinion.

O'Donnell, Thomas J., S.J.: *Morals in Medicine* (Westminster, Md.: Newman Press, 1956), pp. 108-110. He explains both opinions and favors the affirmative view.

Paquin, Jules, S.J.: *Morale et Médecine* (Montréal: Comité des Hôpitaux du Québec, 2nd, ed., 1957), pp. 265-267. He admits the practical probability of the opinion allowing the hysterectomy.

Zalba, M., S.J.: in Regatillo-Zalba, *Theologiae moralis summa,* 2 (Madrid: Biblioteca de Autores Christianos, 1953), p. 265. Fr. Zalba considers the negative opinion more probable; but from the wording of his text he apparently thinks the affirmative view is solidly probable.

In summary, it seems clear that, of the foregoing authors, the following admit the practical probability of the opinion allowing the removal of the uterus which cannot be safely repaired—that is, regardless of their own speculative views, they would allow this opinion to be followed in practice, unless further discussion or a pronouncement of the Holy See would render the opinion improbable: Frs. Cambo, Connery, Ford, Kelly, Lynch, McReavy, O'Donnell, Paquin, and Zalba. Of the other five authors cited, it is not perfectly clear that all would deny even the practical probability of the opinion allowing the hysterectomy.

chapter $\boxed{26}$

Moral Aspects of Sterility Tests

IN AN AGE in which so much time, expense, and medical skill are spent in perfecting and explaining techniques of contraception, it is comforting to know that a large amount of effort and research is also being expended to cure infertility. The cure, of course, includes not only the therapy, but also the diagnostic procedures necessary to determine the cause of the infertility. One "cure" often recommended today is artificial insemination. The next chapter will be devoted to that topic. In the present chapter, I shall consider the moral aspects of some diagnostic procedures.

I. EXAMINATION OF THE WOMAN

Examination of a woman for possible causes of infertility include such things as general physical and psychic check-up, tests for uterine malposition, vaginal smears, the Rubins Test for tubal patency, uterosalpingography to determine the point of obstruction of the tubes, endometrial biopsy to detect functional generative deficiencies, culdoscopy and/or culdotomy to determine ovulation pecularities, and so forth.

It is accepted as good medical practice to perform the various tests only in such a way that no harm will be done to the patient and at such a time that there will be no interference with a possible pregnancy. A moralist would also emphasize these two points in determining the licitness of the tests. But, since there seems to be absolutely no conflict between accepted medical practice and morality in these matters, it is unnecessary to say anything special on the matter. One further test often used on the woman—the Huhner Test, to determine sperm motility in the vagina and cervix—will be specifically considered in the next section, because the precise moral problem concerns the removal of semen after intercourse.[1]

II. EXAMINATION OF THE MAN

The main problem relative to testing male infertility concerns the methods of obtaining semen for analysis. Unfortunately, we do not have the same harmony here between accepted medical practice and sound morality that exists with regard to diagnosis of the woman. All too often, physicians take it for granted that masturbation or some form of unnatural coitus is a permissible method of obtaining semen. Pope Pius XII scored this error in his address to participants in the Second World Congress of Fertility and Sterility, May 19, 1956. His condemnation explicitly referred only to masturbation, but it applies equally to any other unnatural sex act. Moreover, he was not stating anything new; he was simply giving the long-standing teaching of Catholic moralists, a teaching which is concisely formulated in **directives 29 and 38.** which read as follows:

29. The unnatural use of the sex faculty (e.g., masturbation) is never permitted, even for a laudable purpose.

38. Sterility tests involving the procurement of the male specimen by masturbation or unnatural intercourse are morally objectionable.

It is sometimes thought that the Catholic moralist has no

---

[1] An excellent survey of the fertility tests used on women is given by Walter J. Reich, M.D., "Sterility—Diagnosis and Management," *GP*, June, 1950, pp. 49-56. See also the symposium, "A Plan for Parenthood," in *The Linacre Quarterly*, May, 1954, pp. 37-63. Both these discussions outline and explain the diagnosis and treatment of infertility in men and women.

sympathy with the doctor who wishes to examine the male semen and that he simply rejects as illicit all methods of obtaining semen. This is a decided misrepresentation of the facts. There are some methods of obtaining semen to which no sound moral objection can be made and other methods which are theologically controversial. The doctor may use any of these methods (that is, those which are certainly or probably licit); and most doctors of good will would admit that, within this range of permissible methods, they can easily obtain satisfactory testing results.

In the following paragraphs I shall discuss the methods of obtaining semen under three classifications: (1) certainly illicit; (2) probably licit; and (3) certainly licit. Under each of these heads, I shall list and briefly discuss *all* the methods that are usually discussed in theological literature. Before doing so I should like to emphasize the fact that I am not passing judgment on the *scientific* value of the various methods. In preparing this survey, I was inclined to omit some of the methods because many physicians have told me that they are useless for the purpose of obtaining an apt specimen for examination. However, my experience in dealing with the medical profession is that physicians very often disagree on points like these; hence, I thought it advisable to omit nothing.

To preclude a serious misunderstanding, I should note that, when I first worked out this survey of testing methods, I was thinking only of the examination of *married* men. But the problem of infertility arises at least occasionally even before a man is married; consequently, doctors wish to know what testing methods may be used on the unmarried. To answer this question without adding unnecessarily to the length of this chapter, I am putting an asterisk before each method that may be used in examining unmarried men.

With these preliminary observations in mind, we can now give the three classifications to which I referred above.

220

1. Sterility tests are *certainly illicit* when they involve the procuring of semen in any of the following ways.

a) masturbation;

b) the use of an unperforated condom or of a vaginal sheath which is the equivalent of a condom;

c) withdrawal before orgasm, with ejaculation outside the vagina.

In each of these cases there is an unnatural sex act: that is, the psycho-physical processes that lead to the sexual orgasm are used in such a way that the orgasm itself takes place outside of coitus. It is true that there is an appearance of coitus in the second and third cases; but it is only an appearance. Ejaculation into the vagina is the determining factor of true coitus. The practices, therefore, are morally objectionable because they violate the principle: *It is never lawful, even for a laudable purpose, to use the generative faculty in an unnatural way.*

2. Sterility tests are *probably licit* when they involve the procuring of semen in any of the following ways:

a) intercourse with a condom so perforated that it allows some semen to be deposited in the vagina of the wife and also retains some semen for examination;

b) removal of semen, immediately or very soon after normal coitus, from the genital tract of the wife;

*c) direct removal of semen, by aspiration, from testicles or epididymes;

*d) expression of seminal fluid by massage, from seminal vesicles.

An action is said to be "probably licit" when it is neither certainly right nor certainly wrong. That is the present status of each of the testing methods mentioned under this heading. Theologians are still debating them; and up to the present time reasons have been offered for and against each of these methods. It may be that in the future—even the very near future—some of the debatable points will be settled. Until these moral issues are further clarified, however, physicians may follow this practical rule: *When a testing method is not clearly wrong, that is, when there is some soundly probable reason for approving it, it may be used.*

A brief explanation of the theological controversies over these various methods may be helpful. As far as I know, the first theologian to mention the use of the perforated condom in his written works was the late Fr. Arthur Vermeersch, S.J., of the Gregorian University, Rome.[2] Fr. Vermeersch considered this method of obtaining semen to be immoral. His reason was that it involves the direct will to deposit some of the ejaculate outside of the vagina—something which makes it a "partial onanism." Agreeing with Fr. Vermeersch is Fr. Francis J. Connell, C.SS.R. of the Catholic University of America.[3]

Favoring the licitness of the use of the perforated condom is Fr. J. McCarthy, of Maynooth College, Ireland, one of the clearest and most capable of present-day theological writers.[4] Fr. McCarthy believes that it is a mistake to analyze only the part of the act which involves the retaining of semen within the condom. He says that if the *entire* act is analyzed, it is seen to be *substantially natural* because a fair percentage of the semen is ejaculated into the vagina; and he believes that the mutilating of the act by retaining a small portion of the ejaculate in the condom may be justified for a proportionate reason. Fr. John J. Clifford, S.J., of the Seminary of St. Mary

---

[2] *De castitate* (Rome: Gregorian University, 1921), p. 403.

[3] "The Catholic Doctor," *American Ecclesiastical Review,* Dec., 1944, pp. 439-448.—In citing articles in this chapter, I am giving the complete reference, and not merely the page on which the pertinent opinions are stated.

[4] "A Lawful Method of Procuring Seminal Specimens for Sterility Tests," *Irish Ecclesiastical Record,* June, 1948, pp. 533-536. The article is now incorporated into a book, *Problems in Theology—I. The Sacraments* (Westminster, Md.: The Newman Press, 1956), pp. 430-433.

of the Lake, Mundelein, Illinois, also thought the perforated condom may be used for obtaining a seminal specimen.[5]

The foregoing are some of the prominent theologians who have written for and against the licitness of using the perforated condom. From my own experience in discussing this matter with theologians, I believe that the opinions of those who have not written on the subject would follow about the same ratio. It is important to note, however, that even those who think that Fr. McCarthy's analysis of this case is theoretically more correct than Fr. Vermeersch's would prefer that physicians avoid this method if they can get satisfactory specimens in some other licit or probably licit manner. The obvious reason for this preference is that the perforated-condom procedure can readily be misunderstood and can thus lead to morally harmful results.

Although Fr. Vermeersch was opposed to the use of the perforated condom, he was very openly cooperative with physicians in trying to find a morally unobjectionable manner of obtaining a seminal specimen. It was he who first suggested that removal of semen from testicles or epididymes by aspiration or from vesicles by massage might be permitted. His reason for approving these methods was that the semen is thus obtained without stimulating the orgasmic processes; hence, there is no abuse of the sex faculty. Against Fr. Vermeersch, Fr. Benedict Merkelbach, O.P., of the Angelicum, the Dominican university in Rome, argued that man's sole right to use his semen is confined to the exercise of the conjugal act.[6] Prominent theologians have lined up on each side of this debate; and today, though the original contestants are both deceased, the debate still goes on. The complete discussions may be read in some of the sources cited in this chapter and in chap-

---

[5] "Sterility Tests and Their Morality," *American Ecclesiastical Review*, Nov., 1942, pp. 358-367.

[6] *Quaestiones de castitate et luxuria* (Liège: La Pensée Catholique, 1936), pp. 60-62.

ter 27. Suffice to say here that Fr. Vermeersch's opinion permitting this practice is still solidly probable.

I have indicated the trend of theological discussion with regard to three of the debatable methods of obtaining semen. Another debatable method is the removal of semen from the genital tract of the wife *immediately or very soon after* normal coitus. The italicized words contain the point of controversy. Few, if any, theologians would object to the removal of semen for testing purposes provided a reasonable time has been allowed after coitus for the semen to penetrate the cervical os. And most, I think, would say that about an hour would certainly be a reasonable time. To remove semen immediately or soon after coitus is an interference with the natural processes that are supposed to follow coitus; and the precise point of discussion among theologians is this: is such interference ever permitted? According to one opinion, this interference is an unnatural act, like onanism, and never permissible, even for a good reason. According to the opposite opinion, such interference is somewhat like a mutilation, and permissible for a proportionate reason. The upshot of this difference of opinion is that, if physicians find it necessary for satisfactory testing to remove some semen immediately or soon after intercourse, they may do so.

To sum up the discussion under this heading: All four methods may be used as far as they are helpful. But among the four, the least preferable (because of danger of misunderstanding and abuse) is the use of the perforated condom.

3. Sterility tests are *certainly licit* when the male specimen is obtained in one of the following ways:

*a) the semen is accidentally obtained as a result of an involuntary emission;

b) removal of semen, about an hour after normal coitus, from the genital tract of the wife;

c) expression from the male urethra of the semen remaining there after normal intercourse is completed;

d) the use of a vaginal cup—that is, of a rubber cup which is inserted into the vagina after coitus and which will catch semen that would otherwise be lost.

*e) Testicular biopsy.

Most of the methods mentioned here need no comment. As regards the second, I should like to mention that the Huhner Test (or Syms-Huhner) would very likely be an example of this because it is usually made only an hour or two after coitus. If the test were made immediately after coitus it would be among the methods listed as probably licit. Moreover, I think attention should be called to what seems to me to be a decided improvement over the Huhner Test: namely, the cervical spoon, invented by Dr. Joseph B. Doyle, Director of the Sterility Clinic, St. Elizabeth's Hospital, Boston.[7] Dr. Doyle uses a concave plastic spoon which is inserted into the wife's vagina immediately before coitus so that the spoon itself is close to, and directly beneath, the cervix. After gentle coitus the wife remains supine for 30-60 minutes; the spoon is then withdrawn and its contents used for a seminal test. This procedure furnishes the optimum conditions for sperm migration through the os cervicis; and once this is accomplished the contents of the spoon provide a good testing specimen.

III. THE HOSPITAL AND SEMINAL ANALYSIS

Doctors who are conducting sterility tests sometimes want semen analyzed in our hospital laboratories. This would present no moral problem if we were sure that the specimen had been obtained in one of the ways that I have designated as licit or probably licit. The problem arises from the fact that

---

[7] Cf. "The Cervical Spoon: A New Method of Semen Sampling and Assaying Spermigration; A Preliminary Report," *Journal of Urology,* Dec., 1948, 986-989. See also Dr. Doyle's brief remarks in *The Linacre Quarterly,* May, 1954, pp. 40-41.

some of the specimens submitted for analysis may have been obtained by an illicit method. In fact, a perusal of medical literature indicates rather clearly that the most common means of obtaining the specimen is masturbation. It seems very likely, therefore, that some of the specimens we are asked to analyze can be presumed to have been obtained by this illicit method.

What is the moral problem? In general, it is a problem that might be discussed by moralists under either "cooperation" or "scandal." I prefer to treat it as a problem of scandal: that is, as a question of conduct which might be the occasion of spiritual harm. If the seminal analysis could not be made without creating the impression of approving or condoning evil, then the making of the analysis in our laboratories would be prejudicial to good morals, damaging to the good name and good influence of the Catholic hospital, and harmful to souls who rightfully look to us for sound moral teaching and good example.

I think that generally speaking we sufficiently guard against these dangers by stating clearly in the *Directives* and Codes that we consider some procedures morally objectionable. For this reason our laboratory personnel may usually analyze and report on specimens, without inquiring into the method of procurement.

What should be done in cases in which it is well-known that definite doctors who submit specimens for analysis have obtained these specimens in an illicit manner? The answer to this is a matter of prudential judgment, and perhaps there might be differences of opinion as to how to handle the situation. But I should think that the main thing is to protect the good name of the hospital; hence, I believe that these doctors should have their attention called to the provision of the *Directives,* and they should be told not to submit any more specimens that have been obtained in a morally objectionable manner. If doctors who had been thus warned would later send more specimens, we could usually presume that these specimens had been licitly obtained unless there were some sound reason for questioning the good faith of the doctors.

Before concluding, I should like to refer to one rather delicate aspect of this problem. It happens occasionally that the doctor has his patient bring the seminal specimen for analysis. In this case, since the patient would hardly know what is stated in the *Directives* and Codes, we ought to be certain that his doctor has not instructed him to procure the specimen in an illicit manner. The most prudent way of doing this would be to check with the patient's physician before accepting the specimen for analysis. Obviously, such a check would be unnecessary if it were known that the physician did not use illicit methods to obtain specimens.

chapter |27|

Artificial Insemination

The use of artificial means to enable the natural marital act to be fertile (e.g. the cervical spoon) is permitted. No other form of artificial insemination is in accord with the divine plan for human procreation. Especially objectionable are donor insemination and unnatural methods of obtaining semen.   Directive 39.

THIS DIRECTIVE is based upon two official statements of Pope Pius XII. The first of these was made to the fourth International convention of Catholic doctors, held in Rome in September, 1949. During this convention there was much discussion of artificial insemination. At the conclusion of the convention, the delegates assembled at Castelgandolfo to hear an address by Pope Pius XII. The first part of this address dealt with the attitude of the Christian doctor toward the progress of medicine and the part he is to take in it; the second part was specifically concerned with the judgment of natural and Christian morality on the practice of artificial insemination. An English version of this official statement runs as follows:

We have already had many occasions to speak on a good number of special points regarding medical morality, but now we have here a question of the first order which, with no less urgency than other questions, requires the light of Catholic moral doctrine: that of artificial insemination. We could not allow this present opportunity to pass without indicating briefly, along general lines, the moral judgment that must be made in this matter.

228

1) The practice of artificial insemination, when human beings are concerned, cannot be considered exclusively, or even principally, from a biological and medical point of view, leaving aside the claims of morality and law.

2) Artificial insemination outside of marriage is to be condemned purely and simply as immoral.

According to both the natural law and the divine positive law, the procreation of new life can be only the fruit of marriage. Marriage alone safeguards the dignity of the parties (principally, in the present case, of the woman) and their personal well-being. And it alone, by its nature, provides for the well-being and education of the child.

Consequently, there is no possibility of difference of opinion among Catholics as regards the condemnation of artificial insemination outside the conjugal union. The child conceived under these conditions would be, by that very fact, illegitimate.

3) Artificial insemination in marriage, but effected by means of the active element of a third party, is equally immoral and, as such, is to be summarily rejected.

It is the spouses alone who have a mutual right over their bodies for generating a new life, and this right is exclusive, nontransferable, inalienable. And so it must be also out of consideration for the child. By virtue of this same bond, nature imposes on whoever gives life to a little one the responsibility for its preservation and education. But between the lawful husband and the child who is the fruit of an active element derived from a third party (even should the husband consent) there is no bond of origin, no moral and juridical bond of conjugal procreation.

4) As for the morality of artificial insemination within marriage, let it suffice for the present to recall these principles of the natural law: the simple fact that the desired result is attained by this means does not justify the use of the means itself; nor is the desire to have a child—perfectly lawful as that is for married persons—sufficient to prove the licitness of artificial insemination to attain this end.

It would be false to think that the possibility of resorting to this method might make valid a marriage between persons who are unfit to contract a marriage by reason of the impediment of impotence. Also, it is needless to observe that the active element can never be procured licitly by acts that are contrary to nature.

Although one may not *a priori* exclude new methods for the sole reason that they are new; nevertheless, as regards artificial insemination, there is not only reason for extreme reserve, but it must be

229

entirely rejected. To say this is not necessarily to proscribe the use of certain artificial means designed only to facilitate the natural act or to enable that act, performed in a normal manner, to attain its end.

We must never forget this: It is only the procreation of a new life according to the will and plan of the Creator which brings with it— to an astonishing degree of perfection—the realization of the desired ends. This is, at the same time, in harmony with the dignity of the marriage partners, with their bodily and spiritual nature, and with the normal and happy development of the child.

This was the first official pronouncement of the Holy See since 1897, when the Sacred Congregation of the Holy Office had answered a question with the brief statement that artificial insemination is illicit. And it is undoubtedly the most important of all Catholic statements on the subject. Some time later (Oct. 29, 1951), in his discourse on the moral problems of married life,[1] Pope Pius XII referred to his former address in the following words:

To reduce the cohabitation of married persons and the conjugal act to a mere organic function for the transmission of the germ of life would be to convert the domestic hearth, sanctuary of the family, into nothing more than a biological laboratory. Hence, in our address of September 29, 1949, to the international congress of Catholic doctors, we formally excluded artificial insemination from marriage. The conjugal act in its natural structure is a personal act, a simultaneous and immediate cooperation of the spouses which, by the very nature of the participants and the special character of the act, is the expression of that mutual self-giving which, in the words of Holy Scripture, effects the union "in one flesh."

This is much more than the mere union of two life-germs, which can be brought about also artificially, that is, without the natural action of the spouses. The conjugal act, as it is planned and willed by nature, implies a personal cooperation, the right to which the parties have mutually conferred on each other in contracting marriage.

[1] Pope Pius XII discussed artificial insemination again in his address to participants in the Second World Congress on Fertility and Sterility, which was mentioned in the last chapter. On this occasion he merely confirmed his previous teaching. He did, however, briefly touch on the interesting question of artificial insemination *in vitro,* and he stated unequivocally that this procedure "must be rejected as immoral and absolutely illicit."

230

COMMENTARY

These two papal statements give the essential points on the morality of artificial insemination so completely that a theologian can do little more than supply explanatory background and perhaps indicate more specifically some practical conclusions. This I shall try to do by considering both donor insemination and insemination within the conjugal union itself.

I. DONOR INSEMINATION *(Heterologous Insemination)*

In condemning donor insemination, the Pope was officially confirming the unanimous opinion of moral theologians. Among Catholic moralists, there has never been the slightest disagreement regarding the morality of donor insemination, whether the woman be married or unmarried. From the time when this topic was first brought up for discussion, theologians have consistently opposed donor insemination for the following reasons: it is contrary to the divine plan for marriage; it is the product of a false philosophy of life; it generally involves the immoral procurement of sperm; and its consequences on social life are apt to be disastrous. A word about each of these points.

1. Contrary to The Divine Plan for Marriage:

One way of learning the Creator's plan is to make a careful analysis of the natures He creates. Certainly His plan for human propagation must be judged according to human nature and not according to mere animal nature. And, whatever may be said of cats and dogs and horses, the well-being of the human child normally demands the care of father and mother over a considerable number of years. Moreover, the parents also, if they are to rear their children in a manner consonant with human dignity, need mutual support and security. Because of such facts, Catholic theologians have unwaveringly held to the principle that reproductive acts are permissible only between two persons who are united in the firm bond of

231

marriage. It is the contract of marriage that gives the child the guarantee of father-mother care that his genuine well-being requires and that gives to the parents themselves their much-needed comfort and security. This principle—that the right to generate children belongs only to husband and wife—is not only deduced from an analysis of human nature; it is also an integral part of the Christian tradition. Whatever may have been the lapses in practical life, the principle has never been seriously challenged by Catholics nor—as far as I have been able to discover—by any recognized Christian society.

In a word, the Catholic theologian maintains that the well-being of the parents themselves and especially the well-being of the child demand that generative activity be restricted to the conjugal union. These points were briefly stated by Pope Pius XII in his condemnation of donor insemination. The same points were stated more completely by Pope Pius XI in his encyclical on Christian marriage. As regards the welfare of the child, Pope Pius XI said:

> The blessing of offspring, however, is not completed by the mere begetting of them, but something else must be added, namely, the proper education of the offspring. For the most wise God would have failed to make sufficient provision for children that had been born, and so for the whole human race, if He had not given to those to whom He had entrusted the power and right to beget them, the duty also and the right to educate them. For no one can fail to see that children are incapable of providing wholly for themselves, even in matters pertaining to their natural life, and much less in those pertaining to the supernatural, but require for many years to be helped, instructed, and educated by others.
>
> Now it is certain that both by the law of nature and of God [i.e., by nature and divine positive law] this right and duty of educating their offspring belongs in the first place to those who began the work of nature by giving them birth, and they are indeed forbidden to leave unfinished this work and so expose it to certain ruin. But in matrimony provision has been made in the best possible way for this education of children that is so necessary, for, since the parents are bound together by an indissoluble bond, the care and mutual help of each is always at hand. . . .

232

Nor must We omit to remark, in fine, that since the duty entrusted to parents for the good of their children is of such high dignity and of such great importance, every use of the faculty given by God for the procreation of new life is the right and the privilege of the marriage state alone, by the law of God and of nature, and must be confined absolutely within the sacred limits of that state.

In the encyclical, Pope Pius XI followed St. Augustine's plan of considering marriage according to its three "blessings": offspring, conjugal fidelity, and indissolubility. The words just quoted are in the section dealing with the blessing of offspring, and they show how the true welfare of the child requires that the right to generate children belongs exclusively to the married. The subsequent section explains more in detail the Christian concept of marriage with reference to the welfare of the parents themselves; and it is also pertinent to the question of artificial insemination. It reads in part:

The second blessing of matrimony which We said was mentioned by St. Augustine, is the blessing of conjugal honor which consists in the mutual fidelity of the spouses in fulfilling the marriage contract "so that what belongs to one of the parties by reason of this contract sanctioned by Divine Law, may not be denied to him or permitted to any third person, nor may there be conceded to one of the parties that which, being contrary to the rights and laws of God and entirely opposed to matrimonial faith, can never be conceded."

Wherefore, conjugal faith, or honor, demands in the first place the complete unity of matrimony which the Creator Himself laid down in the beginning when He wished it to be not otherwise than between one man and one woman. And although afterwards this primeval law was relaxed to some extent by God, the Supreme Legislator, there is no doubt that the law of the Gospel fully restored that original and perfect unity, and abrogated all dispensations, as the words of Christ and the constant teaching and action of the Church show plainly.

With reason, therefore, does the sacred Council of Trent solemnly declare: "Christ Our Lord very clearly taught that in this bond two persons only are to be united and joined together when He said: 'Therefore they are no longer two but one flesh.' ". . .

This conjugal faith, however, which is most aptly called by St. Augustine the "faith of chastity" blooms more freely, the more beautifully, and more nobly when it is rooted in that more excellent soil,

233

the love of husband and wife which pervades all the duties of married life and holds pride of place in Christian marriage.

I have given these lengthy quotations because I think it is imperative to note how the Christian concept of marriage insists that the divine law concerning marriage provides for the welfare of both child and parents. This twofold purpose of marriage requires that generative activity be absolutely restricted to man and wife. The inherent wrongness of fornication and adultery are deduced from this principle; and from the same principle we deduce the immorality of donor insemination. It is true that donor insemination is not the same as fornication or adultery in the ordinary sense of these terms. Nevertheless, donor insemination is a generative act—that is precisely the reason why it is used—and the donor and recipient are not man and wife; hence it is immoral for the same basic reason that fornication and adultery are immoral. This idea is quite well expressed, it seems to me, in the following quotation from a speech made by the Archbishop of Canterbury (an Anglican, not a Roman Catholic) in a debate in the House of Lords:

> Adultery is the surrender, outside the bonds of wedlock and in violation of it, either of the sexual organs alone by the use of contraceptives, or of the reproductive organs alone by A.I.D., or, of course, of both, as in normal intercourse. If that be so, A.I.D. is adultery. I do not wish thereby to stigmatize A.I.D. as having the same moral turpitude which attaches to the word adultery in ordinary use . . . there is certainly a moral difference between adultery in the ordinary sense and A.I.D., yet in fact A.I.D. is adultery. Lord Dunedin, in *Russell v. Russell,* said bluntly: "fecundation *ab extra* [which I take to mean from another party] is, I doubt not, adultery." Other legal judgments have supported that. It is a mere fact, whether you like to use the word or not, that by the introduction of semen *ab extra* outside wedlock there is an intrusion into, and a breach of, the natural relations of husband and wife—and that is what adultery means; and the exclusive union set up by marriage between husband and wife is violated—and that is what adultery means.[2]

---

[2] Quoted by Fr. Henry Davis, S.J., in *Artifiicial Human Fecundation* (London: Sheed and Ward, 1950), p. 13. The Archbishop's speech

234

2. Product of a False Philosophy of Life:

I cannot dwell on this reason, but I wish at least to point out that donor insemination makes a logical piece with the false philosophy that has long been working for the degradation of the family. One of the ingredients of this false philosophy is a crude liberalism that claims for every man the "right to be happy" and which really means the right to do as one pleases. A second ingredient is sheer materialism, which denies the spiritual and thus puts man on the same plane as brute animals. The same subversive principles apparently underlie the "proxy" father propaganda. People want a child; they need it "to be happy"; therefore, let them have it in any way they can. And since artificial insemination is a good way of breeding animals, it should be satisfactory for men, too.

3. Immoral Procurement of Sperm:

The point I wish to make here is aptly expressed by an extract from an Anglican paper:

Artificial insemination usually depends on masturbation. This is condemned by all Christian moralists, because it implies the solitary and essentially individualistic use of sexual activities intended to be used in association. It disregards the truth that with those powers God provides physiological means for exercising them in a joint and common act.[3]

The statement that masturbation is condemned by all Christian moralists may be somewhat exaggerated. At any rate, I have seen statements made by supposedly Christian leaders that masturbation is no more immoral than picking the nose. One can hope that these men were merely expressing their own opinion, and not the view of any definite Christian group.

As for the Catholic moralists, they have constantly taught with a practical unanimity that masturbation is against the

---

was given March 16, 1949. Fr. Davis quotes from the official debates in the House of Lords. The letters, "A.I.D.," stand for donor insemination.

[3] Quoted by Fr. Davis, *op. cit.*, p. 13.

natural law and the divine positive law, and that there is no exception to the law. In proving that masturbation is against the natural law, they have advanced various arguments, the simplest of which, I believe, is the one indicated in the Anglican statement just quoted. This argument is based on an analysis of the physical sex mechanism. The very configuration of the male and female bodies and the biological processes pertaining to reproduction make it clear that the psycho-physical processes culminating in orgasm should be directed to and find their fulfillment in coitus. Solitary orgasm makes a mockery of this entire mechanism. Thus runs the principal argument. Besides this there is the plain fact that, if a solitary act is not against nature, then no other sexual act is against nature. In a word, there are no perversions and there is no natural basis for sex morality. That, of course, is just the conclusion that the materialists would like us to draw; but one can reach such a conclusion only by blinding oneself to the divine plan as manifested in human nature.

The argument from revelation is based principally on St. Paul, who says that "effeminates . . . shall not inherit the kingdom of heaven" (cf. I Cor., ch. 6). Early Christian tradition has interpreted "effeminates" (the Latin word is *molles*) to mean those practicing self-abuse; and this interpretation squares perfectly with the context, in which various acts of impurity are enumerated.

4. Consequences on Social Life:

An eminent Jewish scholar speaks thus of donor insemination: "Such human stud-farming exposes society to the gravest dangers which can never be outweighed by the benefits that may accrue in individual cases."[4] Catholic theologians would agree with this general statement, though they might, with a very realistic scepticism, underscore the word "may" and even

---

[4] The Very Rev. I. Jakobovits, B.A., *Problems in Jewish Family Life* (London, 1953), p. 14.

follow it with a very large question mark. Enthusiasts for donor insemination speak and write glowingly about the great happiness that this procedure has brought to many couples. They admit that they cannot prove this because of the secrecy necessarily involved. Moral theologians, who are not mere armchair philosophers but men who must constantly face the realities of life, consider themselves justified in questioning these glowing reports as long as proof is wanting. However, granted for the sake of argument that the reports are true, theologians would still say that the social evils and dangers inherent in the practice are such that there would be no sound moral justification for it, even if it were not in itself contrary to the divine law.

Only rank sentimentalists and the exceptionally boastful "liberals" are willing to plead the case for insemination of an unmarried woman. No one who has had to deal with the problems of unmarried motherhood would seriously argue for insemination of unmarried women. Usually the case for donor insemination concerns the married couple who want a child but cannot have one because of sterility of the husband. The following remarks are made principally with a view to this case.

First of all there is the effect on society when this practice is encouraged and propagated. I have already indicated that the practice is apparently an offshoot of the materialistic attitude that reduces man to the level of the brute animal. It does not stop here; it also fosters the growth of the same attitude. This is aptly expressed by the strong (but not too strong) expression chosen by the Jewish scholar, "human stud-farming."

Then there is the question of the donor. The literature favoring insemination always stresses the splendid qualifications of the donor, his intellect, his character, etc. Alan F. Guttmacher, M.D., a professed advocate of the practice, gives this simple test of the ideal donor: "Is that the kind of a man

I would like my daughter to marry?"[5] Let the readers answer the question for themselves. Personally, I can give my own necessarily conditional answer without any hesitation. If I had a daughter, I would not want her to marry a man whose sense of moral values was such that he could calmly enter a doctor's office or laboratory and ejaculate semen into a glass jar for a sum of money. As a confessor, I can understand and sympathize with the young man who masturbates because of outbursts of passion that he has not yet learned to control; I confess that I have little appreciation of the mentality of the donor. Moreover, to return to the question of my hypothetical daughter, I would not want her to marry a man whose realization of the responsibilities of parenthood was so slight that he would be willing to father a child, or many children, whom he would never see and towards whom he would have no duty —and this, moreover through a woman he does not even know. The donor, whatever be his other qualifications, can hardly be either psychologically or morally normal. The policy of portraying such men as ideal progenitors of human beings is a menace to the true welfare of society.

Next there is the family itself, composed of the lawful husband, the wife and her child conceived through donor insemination. Theologians must admit that they cannot point to actual facts, just as the insemination enthusiasts who claim facts cannot prove them. Nevertheless, from their experience with human beings, theologians can point to some very real dangers inherent in the practice of donor insemination. The child is flesh of his mother's flesh, but not of his supposed father's. He is born a stepson, and worse. To the supposed father he is a constant reminder of the intense humiliation of his sterility.[6] (One wonders, incidentally, how often the hus-

---

[5] See *Transactions of the Conference on Sterility and Fertility of the American Society for the Study of Sterility,* Vol. 3, p. 10.

[6] I mention sterility because it is the most common reason alleged for resorting to donor insemination. Other reasons sometimes advanced are unfavorable genetic history and a previous erythroblastotic fetus.

bands who give "consent" to donor insemination do so merely out of a sense of hurt pride, and not with genuine willingness.) To the mother, the developing child will bring none of the joy that comes to women as they see the characteristics of a beloved husband bud forth in the child; all that she will know about the child's father is that he is the kind of man who will masturbate for a price and assume the function of parenthood with neither the love nor the responsibility that parenthood normally entails. By nature's plan, children should be a bond of union between their parents, and bring them joy and a sense of mutual fulfillment; the donor-child is much more likely to be a source of humiliation, jealousy, and anxiety.

The foregoing are some of the dangers and evils inherent in the practice of donor insemination. With these in mind, the theologian seems perfectly justified in saying that, even if the practice were not wrong in itself, it would still be morally unjustifiable because of its actual and potential effects on society. But, as I have previously pointed out, it is wrong in itself, partly because it usually entails masturbation as the means of procuring the semen and mainly because it is contrary to the divine law which requires that "the procreation of new life can be only the fruit of marriage." It was this divine law that Pope Pius XII stressed in his address to Catholic doctors.

II. WITHIN THE CONJUGAL UNION (Homologous Insemination)

In chapter 26, I spoke of the cervical spoon, invented by Joseph B. Doyle, M.D.[7] One use of the spoon, it will be recalled, is to aid sperm migration through the cervical os. Obviously, this procedure is not artificial insemination in the

---

The first of these would be at least as humiliating to the husband as consciousness of his sterility.

[7] It should be noted that the cervical spoon is not the same as the cervical cap. As regards the latter, cf. M. James Whitelaw, M.D.,

ordinary sense of the expression; it is merely a technique for aiding marital intercourse to be fertile by overcoming certain physiological obstacles. Some might call it "assisted insemination." Another form of assisted insemination sometimes discussed by theologians concerns a case like this: husband and wife have normal coitus, and after coitus the semen is collected in a syringe and placed further into the wife's genital tract. Although there was some theological controversy over the latter method, yet the general practical rule before the papal address to doctors was that the various forms of assisted insemination could be permitted. This practical rule may still be followed, because the Pope made it clear that he wished to make no official statement either for or against assisted insemination when he said: "To say this [that artificial insemination is to be entirely rejected] is not necessarily to proscribe the use of certain artificial means designed only to facilitate the natural act or to enable that act, performed in a normal manner, to attain its end."

As regards homologous insemination, therefore, the Pope's words of warning or condemnation refer only to substitutes for intercourse. Three points call for special attention.

1. The Impediment of Impotence;

Canon 1068 of the Code of Canon Law reads as follows:

"Use of the Cervical Cap to Increase Fertility in Cases of Oligospermia," *Fertility and Sterility,* Jan., 1950, pp. 33-39. In Dr. Whitelaw's article, there is question of artificial insemination between husband and wife, the purpose of the procedure being to place the husband's entire ejaculate close to the cervix. The purpose, therefore, is the same as that of the spoon when the latter is used to promote sperm migration. But there are two pronounced differences from the moral point of view. In the Whitelaw method, the semen is obtained "either by withdrawal or masturbation" and is placed in a cup-like container (the cap), which is then fitted over the cervix. This method is a substitute for intercourse, and it implies the obtaining of semen by illicit methods. The Doyle procedure is merely an aid to natural intercourse.

1. Impotence, antecedent and perpetual, whether on the part of the man or the woman, whether known to the other party or not, whether absolute or relative, invalidates marriage by the law of nature itself.

2. If the impediment of impotence is doubtful either in law or in fact, the marriage is not to be hindered.

3. Sterility neither invalidates marriage nor renders it illicit.

A full explanation of this canon would carry me far beyond the scope of this chapter. I have cited it merely as background for the Pope's statement that the possibility of recurring to artificial insemination would not remove the impediment of impotence. By impotence is understood the inability to have coitus. If this condition certainly exists before a marriage and if it is also certain that the condition is perpetual, and not merely temporary, the person so afflicted is incapable of contracting marriage. An example would be a man whom some accident has permanently deprived of the power of erection. It is quite possible that such a man might have fertile semen and that he could have a child by means of artificial insemination. This would not, according to the Pope, make the man capable of contracting marriage.

2. Acts Contrary to Nature:

With reference to homologous insemination, Stuart Abel, M.S., M.D., once wrote: "The semen specimens for insemination from husband to wife are collected by condomistic intercourse, coitus interruptus, or again, and preferably from a practical standpoint, masturbation."[8] Later in the same article, Dr. Abel pointed out that the Catholic Church would apparently object to all these methods of obtaining germ cells. This observation is correct. And it was undoubtedly to such methods that Pope Pius XII was referring when he said: "Also, it is

---

[8] "The Present Status of Artificial Insemination," p. 4. This is a reprint from *International Abstracts of Surgery*, Dec. 1947, pp. 521-531. The article gives an excellent survey of the medical, legal, and theological aspects of artificial insemination up to 1947.

needless to observe that the active element can never be procured licitly by acts that are contrary to nature."

Why do we consider these methods to be unnatural sex acts? The reason, as I have already explained in the preceding chapter and in this chapter when speaking of masturbation, is that the psycho-physical processes leading to sexual orgasm are used in such a way that the orgasm itself takes place outside of coitus. It is true that there is an appearance of coitus in condomistic intercourse and coitus interruptus. But it is only an appearance. The determining factor of true coitus is ejaculation into the vagina; and that factor is missing in all three procedures.

I realize that some non-Catholics who might agree with all that has been said here about donor insemination would not agree that these methods of obtaining the husband's germ cells for insemination are always immoral. Even among prominent Catholic theologians there have been a few attempts to justify these means of accomplishing homologous insemination. To practically all theologians, however, and certainly to the Pope himself, such attempts mean the sacrifice of principle for the sake of sympathy. It is a basic principle of sexual ethics that an unnatural act is never permitted, even for a laudable purpose; and, if ejaculation into the vagina is not taken as the minimum norm of determining a natural sex act, there seems to be no sound way of determining such an act.

3. Is Any Substitute for Intercourse Justifiable?

The following interesting quotation from the *Year Book of Obstetrics and Gynecology*,[9] can serve as an apt introduction to a final point of discussion:

Adler and Makris (Fertil. & Steril, 2:459, 1951) reported the first case of artificial insemination with use of testicular tissue. A man with aspermia had a testicular biopsy and the wife was prepared for insemination in an adjoining room. The specimen was placed in

---

[9] 1952, p. 337.

Ringer's solution and an emulsion of the tissue made. This showed active spermatozoa. Insemination was performed in the usual way and a healthy baby was delivered.

If I understand this procedure correctly, it is an example of homologous insemination in which the husband's germ cells were obtained without any unnatural sex act and then transferred to the wife. Granted that my interpretation is correct, the case may be used as a concrete illustration of a problem debated by theologians for many years before the Pope's address to the Catholic doctors. The question was: would homologous insemination without intercourse be permissible, provided the husband's germ cells could be obtained in some licit manner? The majority of theologians held that even this would not be permissible. It was their view that husband and wife have no right to generate offspring except through coitus. They contended that coitus is the means established by nature, and the only means of generation in keeping with human dignity and with the traditional notion of the marriage contract. In a word, this majority opinion was that no substitute for conjugal intercourse is permissible. There was, however, a minority opinion that the right of a validly married couple to generate children is not limited to intercourse but might include the use of any artificial means not in itself immoral.[10]

The Pope made no explicit reference to this controversy in his official statements on artificial insemination; but there can be little doubt that the last part of his address on Sept. 29, 1949, and especially his further statement on Oct. 29, 1951, adopt the majority view: viz., that no substitute for intercourse is justifiable.

SUMMARY

The official teaching of the Catholic Church on artificial insemination, as expressed by Pope Pius XII in the statements

---

[10] Those interested in studying the trend of the theological debate should consult *Theological Studies,* March, 1947, pp. 106-110; March, 1949, pp. 113-114; March, 1950, pp. 67-68.

quoted at the beginning of this chapter, may be briefly summarized in these points:

1. Since donor insemination is contrary to the divine law that procreation must be only the fruit of marriage, it is never permitted.

2. The use of acts contrary to nature to obtain germ cells for insemination is always immoral.

3. The possibility of having children by means of homologous insemination does not remove the impediment of impotence.

4. No substitute for intercourse is in harmony with the divine plan that children should be the fruit of a personal union by which the parents become two in one flesh.

5. The use of artificial means to help natural conjugal relations to be fruitful is permitted.

chapter 28

Mutilation:
Some Particular Problems

THE PRESENT CHAPTER will contain a brief explanation of **directives 40, 41, 43 and 48**, with some remarks on particular problems that have a special pertinence to one or more of these directives. The directives themselves read as follows:

40. Any procedure harmful to the patient is morally justified only insofar as it is designed to produce a proportionate good.

Ordinarily the "proportionate good" that justifies a directly mutilating procedure must be the welfare of the patient himself. However, such things as blood transfusions and skin grafts are permitted for the good of others. Whether this principle of "helping the neighbor" can justify organic transplantation is now a matter of discussion. Physicians are asked to present practical cases for solution, if such cases exist.

41. The removal of an apparently healthy appendix while the abdomen is open for some other reason may be allowed at the discretion of the physician.

43. Ghost surgery, which implies the calculated deception of the patient as to the identity of the operating surgeon, is morally objectionable.

48. Unnecessary procedures, whether diagnostic or therapeutic, are morally objectionable. A procedure is unnecessary when no proportionate reason requires it for the welfare of the patient; a fortiori unnecessary is any procedure that is contraindicated by sound medical standards. This directive applies especially, but not exclusively, to unnecessary surgery.

245

DIRECTIVE 40: PRINCIPLES

The first part of this directive is substantially but a brief statement of the principle of totality, which was explained in chapter 1. However, it differs somewhat from the usual formulation and explanation of the principle of totality, because that principle is generally used only with reference to mutilations. The first part of directive 40 is wider: it refers to all treatments which are professedly for the good of the patient; hence, it would include diagnosis, antibiotic therapy, and so forth. But, except for this inclusion of wider subject matter, the principle of totality and this first paragraph of directive 40 are essentially the same. The point to be stressed is that every diagnostic and therapeutic procedure used on the patient should be judged in terms of his total good. This is a basic principle of both good morality and good medicine.

The second part of the directive touches on a topic that is much more difficult: namely, mutilation and other procedures that are primarily *for the good of others*. Examples would be medical experimentation for the advancement of science or for the good of other individuals than the subject of the experiment, blood transfusions, and homografts of various kinds. Experimentation will be discussed in a separate chapter. The present discussion will be limited to procedures which, though not experimental in the strict sense of the expression, are designed to help someone other than the subject.

It may come as a surprise to physicians that theologians should have any difficulty about mutilations and other procedures which are performed with the consent of the subject but which have as their purpose the helping of others. By a sort of instinctive judgment we consider that the giving of a part of one's body to help a sick man is not only morally justifiable but, in some instances, actually heroic. My own opinion is substantially in accord with this instinctive judgment; yet I should be less than fair if I did not indicate here that some eminent theologians are against this and that, as a result, there

246

is considerable controversy today, especially over the subject of organic transplantation: that is, the transplanting of an organ from one living human being to another. To give all the angles of this controversy would take me far beyond the scope of this book. For complete references, see *Theological Studies,* Sept., 1955, pp. 391-396; Dec., 1955, p. 572; Sept., 1956, pp. 333, 341-344; Dec., 1956, pp. 557-561; June, 1957, pp. 228-230; Dec., 1957, pp. 570-572. Here I shall merely state points that are certain and outline reasons for controversy.

In the first place, it is clear from reason and papal teaching that the principle of totality cannot be used to justify the donating of a part of one's body to another person. This principle can be applied only when there is the subordination of part to whole that exists in the natural body. No such subordination exists between human persons or between the individual and society. Each person is a distinct entity, with a distinct finality. No matter how lowly his condition, he is not subordinated to others in the order of being. As for society, it exists for the individuals that compose it; and they do not exist for it. It is true, of course, that they have certain duties to society; but this is quite different from saying that they are parts of the social organism in the same sense, e.g., as the hand is part of the body.

Secondly, it is also clear from reason and papal teaching that, since man is only the administrator of his life and bodily members and functions, his power to dispose of these things is limited. The precise extent of the limitation forms part of the theological debate about organic transplantation.

Thirdly, it is also certain that the making of grafts from cadavers and from legitimately amputated organs is morally justifiable. But, it should be noted that this is not the precise problem we are discussing, for it does not involve the unnecessary mutilation of a living person.

Fourthly, though one or two theologians apparently question it, there can hardly be a reasonable doubt about the moral

247

justification of homografts when they are for the good of both parties involved: e.g., to remedy contrary pathological conditions, as seems to have been the case when ovarian transplants were made by Michael John Bennet, M.D., of Philadelphia. The subjects of his first ovarian isoplasts were two sisters, one of whom was a victim of amenorrhea, and the other, the younger, of hypermenorrhea.[1] These operations were for the benefit of both sisters; hence, there seems to be no solid reason for questioning their licitness. At any rate, they do not come under the very controversial question of organic transplantation, which concerns the case in which a homograft is made from a healthy person solely for the benefit of another person.

Fifthly, it is universally admitted, as indicated in directive 40, that such things as blood transfusions and skin grafts are permitted. Some theologians say these are permitted because the blood and skin restore themselves. This reason is not completely satisfying. Taken by itself, it would seem to justify even the useless letting of blood or removing of skin. A more satisfying reason is found in the law of fraternal charity, according to which one's neighbor is "another self."

The foregoing is a brief outline of the points to be kept in mind regarding the explanation of paragraph 2 of directive 40. More light will be furnished by considering some practical cases; and the complete theological discussion can be found in the references given to *Theological Studies* given on p 247.

SOME PRACTICAL CASES

I have already indicated that, whatever may be the theoretical justification, there is certainly no practical objection to donating blood and skin. In an address given on Oct. 9, 1948, Pope Pius XII praised blood donors for their charity. He obviously would not do this if there were any moral objection

---

[1] Cf. Fr. B. J. Cunningham, C.M., *The Morality of Organic Transplantation* (Washington: The Catholic University Press, 1944), p. 50.

to donating blood. And what is said about giving blood is true both about transfusions given directly to an individual and about donations made to a blood bank.

As regards the Church's attitude on blood transfusions, it might be interesting to note that I have been asked whether the Church had not at one time condemned such transfusions, and if so, what was the reason. The only reference I could find to a condemnation was in the *Enciclopedia Italiana*.[2] According to this account transfusions were attempted in Paris in the latter part of the seventeenth century; but ignorance of antiseptic methods, lack of technical means for making the transfusion, and ignorance of the laws of compatibility led to so many disasters that transfusions were forbidden by an act of the French Parliament and by a papal bull. I have been unable to find any reference to this papal document in available theological sources. However, it is clear that, *if* there was such a condemnation, the reason for it was basically medical—namely, unwarranted risk—and not religious. There is nothing in Catholic teaching that would either condemn or discourage a medically-indicated blood transfusion.[3]

If *corneal transplants* involved the sacrifice of a healthy eye by a living donor, they would serve to exemplify the theological controversy over organic transplantation. This, as doctors well know, is hardly realistic. Corneal transplants are ordinarily made either from the eyes of deceased persons or from eyes that had to be removed because of diseased conditions that did not affect the corneas. Although there can be no moral objection to corneal transplants as thus understood, there are, however, certain precautions to be observed. Pope Pius XII emphasized these precautions in his address on

---

[2] Rome. 1936 ff., Vol. 30, p. 677.

[3] Incidentally, according to another encyclopedia, the first attempt at blood transfusion was probably made on Pope Innocent VIII, who died 1492. Cf. Funk and Wagnall, *The New Standard Encyclopedia*, Vol. 23 (1931), p. 498.

corneal transplants, May 14, 1956. This address was summarized by Fr. John J. Lynch, S.J. After calling attention to the Pope's own statement at the beginning of his address that he did not wish to discuss at that time the problem of corneal transplants from living donors, Fr. Lynch wrote:

Returning then to the problem which Pius chose to discuss, namely, corneal transplants procured from cadavera, we note his moral appraisal of this practice is merely confirmatory of the solution which theologians had previously been giving: considered objectively and merely as a surgical procedure, this type of keratoplasty meets with no moral objection, provided only that certain precautions are observed. The first such precaution refers to an habitual attitude of mind whereby we remain constantly aware of the relative dignity of a human cadaver. As the onetime abode of a spiritual and immortal soul and as temple of the Holy Ghost, the human body—destined itself for resurrection and eternal life—merits even in death a proportionate respect and reverence. Even in the legitimate uses to which a corpse may be put for the benefit of the living, no doctor should allow himself to develop the exclusively clinical mentality which would regard a human cadaver as no more than dead animal tissue.

A further proviso stipulated by His Holiness—one which is not unfamiliar either to theologians or to physicians—is the matter of requisite consent. Apart from exceptional cases, it would usually not be permissible to remove corneas from a corpse, even for the very laudable purpose of transplantation, without the consent of the next of kin (or of others whose right it might be to make proper disposition of a body) or contrary to the explicit refusal of the deceased expressed before death. This condition, as the Pope asserts, is dictated not only by the humane consideration which is due the bereaved; it is also a matter of strict right to be scrupulously respected.

Granted these precautions, however, it is clearly the teaching of Pius XII that the transplantation of corneas from the dead to the living is beyond moral reproach. More than that, he calls it a positively virtuous thing for one to specify before death that his body be used for legitimate medical research and training. Such a decision, however, is usually not of obligation; and His Holiness warns against any intemperate form of propaganda in this regard which would create the false notion that one is ordinarily required in conscience so to dispose of his body for the benefit of others. He insists, too, that this right of choice is no less the prerogative of the poor than it is that of the wealthy or socially prominent. Civil laws on this matter, he concludes, should be so formulated as to guarantee proper respect for the rights of all concerned while at the same time providing for the legitimate requirements of medical science.

The allocution touches also upon an incidental point which sometimes causes concern to doctors and laymen alike. Is it wrong to accept, or even to demand, financial recompense for bequeathing one's body for medical purposes? The Pope's answer again confirms what theologians ordinarily have taught: "It is beyond doubt that grave abuses can occur if compensation is demanded; but it would be going too far to declare immoral every acceptance of recompense or every demand for one. The case is analogous to that of blood transfusion: it is creditable for the donor to refuse recompense; it is not necessarily a fault to accept it."

What the Pope is saying equivalently is that there is nothing intrinsically immoral in accepting payment either for giving one's blood or for agreeing that one's body after death should be used for medical purposes. Circumstances of an individual case could be such as to make this financial consideration mercenary to the point of sin. But the lone fact of monetary recompense does not of itself introduce an element that is necessarily immoral.[4]

In my brief remarks about blood transfusions, I mentioned that there is no moral objection to blood banks. This is true also of *eye banks,* as well as of *skin banks* and *bone banks.* The essence of all these things is the same: tissue or bone that is legitimately removed from a living person or a cadaver is preserved in such a way that it can be grafted on a sick person who has need of it. As I understand it, a bone bank is usually made up of bone removed at operations; cadavers are not used for the purpose. On the other hand, the main, if not the only source of skin for banks is the cadaver. These are but accidental differences; and they have no bearing on the morality of having such banks. The only points of moral significance would be the precautions mentioned by Pius XII in his address on corneal transplants and explained by Fr. Lynch in the words I have quoted.

Renal Homotransplantation. An article in the *Journal of*

---

[4] Cf. *The Linacre Quarterly,* Aug. 1956, pp. 78-80.

the American Medical Association,[5] reported the successful homotransplantation of a healthy kidney from one identical twin to another. To some extent, at least, this operation must be classified as experimentation; and, as such, its morality must be governed according to the principles to be explained in the next chapter. Aside from that, however, renal transplantation is a perfect example of the kind of organic transplantation about which there is theological controversy. It involves the sacrifice of a complete and important organ and it is solely for the benefit of the donee. As long as the controversy is not settled in favor of those who object to organic transplantation, homografts of this kind should be permitted, provided that they are not contrary to good medicine.

DIRECTIVE 41: APPENDECTOMY

This directive deals explicitly only with what is often called "incidental appendectomy": that is, with the removal of an apparently healthy appendix when the abdomen is open for some other reason, e.g., for a cholecystectomy, a cesarean section, and so forth. The directive allows the incidental appendectomy at the "discretion" of the physician. This is not at all the same as the "whim" of the physician, and much less the whim of the patient. Discretion implies the earnest consideration of various factors: e.g., whether appendectomy would increase the risk of the operation, whether it would add any notable inconvenience in convalescence, and so forth. Also, there should be the consent, at least reasonably presumed, of the patient. And finally, the cost, if there be any additional cost, should be reasonable.

Granted the conditions mentioned in the preceding paragraph, there is no moral objection to incidental appendectomy.

---

[5] Jan. 28, 1956, pp. 277-282: "Successful Homotransplantation of the Human Kidney between Identical Twins," by John P. Merrill, M.D., Joseph E. Murray, M.D., J. Hartwell Harrison, M.D., and Warren R. Guild, M.D.

The appendix itself, as far as we know, serves no useful purpose; and its removal at the time of other pelvic surgery precludes the probability of future surgery without undue present risk to the patient. As I understand it, this is fairly routine practice in good hospitals, and it would not be called unnecessary surgery.

It may be interesting to note that Fr. Nicholas Lohkamp, O.F.M., considers that one condition for justifying incidental appendectomy is the probability that the appendix is "here and now in a pathological condition."[6] This is consistent with Fr. Lohkamp's general thesis that a purely prophylactic operation is not permissible. He requires that there always be at least the probability of some *present* pathology or danger. The thesis is interesting, and apparently is held by many theologians, but it cannot be proved either from reason or from papal teaching. It may well be that most apparently healthy appendices are already somewhat diseased; but this is not a requisite either morally or medically, for justifying incidental appendectomy.

It is common knowledge today that appendectomy is among the most frequent of unnecessary operations. But this refers to complete appendectomies, not to the incidental removal of the appendix. According to the American College of Surgeons, an "*unjustified operation* is one in which either the indications were inadequate, or the procedure was one which is contrary to generally accepted surgical practice."[7] As I understand it, the usually accepted indication for a complete appendectomy is appendicitis, either acute or chronic. Certainly, it is wrong for a surgeon to do an appendectomy merely for the fee, or merely because the patient wants it. It is true that, in performing any operation, the doctor is acting for the patient, because it is the patient who has the right and the duty of caring for his health.

---

[6] Cf. *The Morality of Hysterectomy Operations* (Washington: The Catholic University Press, 1956), p. 139, footnote 135.

[7] *Bulletin of the American College of Surgeons,* March-April, 1954, p. 72.

Nevertheless, the surgeon is not the hired man of the patient; he is a professional man who is supposed to use his trained judgment and experience in the interest of the patient.

There are some special cases in which it seems probable that an individual may justifiably ask for an appendectomy, even though no medical indications are actually present, and in which the surgeon might be morally justified in performing the operation. I refer to cases such as these: a missionary is going to a place where he will be for a long time without benefit of expert surgery, or a military man will be going into a similar situation. It seems that in view of such unusual circumstances a man might licitly expose himself to the risk of surgery now in order to avoid the much greater danger of appendicitis when no surgical help could be had. Aside from such special cases, however, accepted medical and surgical criteria should be followed; appendectomies performed without such criteria must be considered as unnecessary surgery, and, as such, morally objectionable.

DIRECTIVE 43: GHOST SURGERY

Ghost surgery may be considered under two forms: a "crude" form, which means that an operation is performed "by a surgeon hired secretly by the patient's own physician who later pretends to have done the job himself,"[8] and a "more refined" form in which, without the knowledge of the patient, a resident surgeon performs the substantial part of an operation and the patient's own physician is present in a supervisory capacity.

That ghost surgery in its crude form is immoral is too obvious to need proof. Not only is it a breach of contract with the patient, but it also includes several other features which are in direct opposition to good medicine and sound morality. Fr. John J. Lynch, S.J., enumerated and explained these objectionable features as follows:

---

[8] *Ibid.*, Jan.-Feb., 1954, p. 36.

(1) *The patient may be exposed to serious and unnecessary surgical risk.* Since the surgeon must of necessity remain unknown to the patient the former has no proper opportunity to make pre-operative examination or to supervise post-operative care. For diagnosis, surgical prognosis, and prudent decision to operate, he must depend entirely upon the competency of another whose reason for summoning a "ghost" is often his own self-acknowledged surgical incompetence. Perhaps only qualified surgeons can fully appreciate so criminal a disregard for human life and limb; but at least they will agree that in too many cases both doctors involved are no less than potential killers—and in some cases killers in fact. The term is used in no rhetorical sense; it is theologically apt.

(2) *The referring physician is paid a surgical fee to which he has no right in justice.* It would be naive to imagine that the referring physician does not profit substantially from ghost surgery. And in some instances either the patient is charged an excessive fee, sufficient to make the operation financially worthwhile for two doctors instead of one; or the ghost surgeon is morally coerced into splitting a normal surgical fee with his surgically idle confrere. In neither case can the referring physician cite any legitimate title to the money he receives. In claiming it from either party, therefore, he is violating justice and acting immorally.

Sometimes, it is true, it is the surgeon who takes the initiative by spontaneously offering a "kick-back" to the referring physician. The latter's honorarium must then be considered as a gift rather than an extortion, and the absence of actual injustice to the surgeon in this case must be admitted. But there still remains a morally reprehensible element in such an agreement insofar as it constitutes a mutual inducement to engaging in or continuing a practice which has many other attendant evils.

(3) *The practice breeds unnecessary surgery and leads to profiteering in the form of excessive fees.* Those who know the unholy facts of ghost surgery need no further proof of its almost inevitable progression towards these patent abuses. Greed is stimulated, never sated, by what it feeds upon; and the more successful the alliance of physician and ghost surgeon, the greater will be the incentive not only to raise the tariff for services needed, but to prescribe surgery where the need is only doubtful or even clearly non-existent. At least that is the partial history of the practice to date.

Theologians would refer to such a situation as an occasion of sin. While still insisting on the immorality of elements intrinsic to ghost

255

surgery in itself, they would decry the practice also because of the additional evils to which it can so easily lead.

(4) *It brings dishonor to an indispensable profession which cannot function properly without the public's esteem and confidence.* Regrettable as is the sensationalism with which the press has publicized the professional derelictions of doctors, it has to be admitted that the charges made were true of *some* and that as a result the profession has suffered seriously in public estimation. And when the medical profession loses face, it is no mere matter of passing humiliation for its individual or collective members. No one will deny that when an essential profession like medicine is dishonored and loses public confidence, it is the common good that suffers, not merely the profession itself.

Fidelity to the ethics of one's profession is not just a question of amenity or *esprit de corps*. It is at times essential to the common good and can on occasion induce a real obligation in conscience.

Briefly then it can be said that ghost surgery is morally unacceptable for two generic reasons: (1) because some of its more common features are intrinsically wrong in themselves; and (2) because inherent in the practice is a threat of further evil effects.[9]

I doubt that any moral theologian or any conscientious and reputable doctor would disagree with the foregoing analysis of ghost surgery in its crude form. But it seems that some very reputable and conscientious doctors have had difficulty in accepting Fr. Lynch's solution to a problem involving the more refined type of ghost surgery.[10] Fr. Lynch states the problem as follows:

Advised by his physician that an appendectomy is imperative, Mr. B engages Dr. X, a surgeon of considerable repute, to perform the operation. Dr. X is present in a supervisory capacity during the entire procedure, but allows Dr. Y, a senior resident with a brilliant record, to perform the appendectomy.

Fr. Lynch points out that this and similar problems have to be solved "in terms of two fundamental rights of the surgical patient: (1) his innate right to be protected from all unneces-

---

[9] *The Linacre Quarterly,* Nov., 1954, pp. 123-125.
[10] "The Resident Surgeon and the Private Patient," *The Linacre Quarterly,* Nov., 1956, pp. 117-122.

sary surgical risk, and (2) his contractual right, if any, to be treated by the surgeon of his own choice." In his solution, Fr. Lynch admits that, in the suppositions of the case—a reputable surgeon, a capable resident, careful supervision, a hospital with a good residency program—there would presumably be no violation of the first right. It is his opinion, however, that the second right is violated. "The patient has contracted with Dr. X only, and cannot be presumed to consent to the substitution of the resident as operator, even under Dr. X's supervision."

I agree with Fr. Lynch and I have not yet seen a contrary argument that impresses me as having any validity. There may be cases in which the patient's consent to this procedure can be presumed; but I think that such cases are so rare that they may not be taken for granted.

In his article, Fr. Lynch shows that his solution is in conformity with the standard approved by the American College of Surgeons. In a later discussion, he mentions that his attention had been called to the following statement, formulated by the Conference Committee on Graduate Training in Surgery and subsequently approved by the American Board of Surgery, the Board of Regents of ACS, the American Medical Association, and the Joint Commission on the Accreditation of Hospitals:

Since the informed consent of the patient is a moral and legal prerequisite to the performance of a surgical operation, every patient about to undergo a surgical operation, or his legal guardian, should have full and complete knowledge of the identity of his surgeon. . . . Private patients can be used honorably and effectively for residency training only when the patient is fully aware of the extent of the resident's responsibility for his care, and is agreeable thereto. . . .[11]

DIRECTIVE 48: UNNECESSARY PROCEDURES

It is worth noting briefly that this directive is not limited to surgery. Despite one's high esteem for the thorough diagnostic

[11] Cf. *Theological Studies*, June, 1957, p. 234. The quotation is taken from *Massachusetts Physician*, Jan., 1957, p. 98.

procedures used in modern medicine, one may legitimately wonder whether tests are not sometimes overdone, with great inconvenience and much added expense for the patient. Then there is the custom that I have seen more than once deplored in medical journals of the needless prescribing of antibiotics. And it seems that today this problem is becoming serious regarding the use of the tranquilizing drugs. These are but examples; and it is somewhat difficult to be more specific. But the point should be stressed that no procedure is either medically or morally acceptable unless it is for the genuine benefit of the patient.

Most commonly, the denunciations of medical societies are leveled against unnecessary surgery; and the operations most frequently branded as unjustifiable are appendectomy, cholecystectomy, cesarean section, fallectomy, hysterectomy, and ovariectomy. It seems that in this chapter or in preceding chapters I have sufficiently discussed all these procedures except cholecystectomy. My subsequent paragraphs will be devoted to this and to a few other operations about which I am frequently questioned.

Cholecystectomy. The reasons for permitting an appendectomy, as explained with reference to directive 41, are the relatively slight value of the organ itself and the genuine statistical probability that an appendectomy may be needed in later life. Neither of these reasons is valid with reference to the removal of a healthy gall bladder. It is an organ with a definite function and, though obviously not indispensable, it is important in the total economy of bodily integrity. Moreover, the probable need of an operation, and especially of an emergency operation, in later life is comparatively slight. The reasonable care of the body, therefore, demands that cholecystectomy be allowed only when medical indications call for it.

Circumcision. There is, of course, no moral objection to circumcision when it is performed for a specific medical reason. But the practice of routinely circumcising all newborn

258

males is certainly open to question. Both Fr. Jules Paquin, S.J.,[12] and Fr. Edwin F. Healy, S.J.,[13] are of the opinion that such routine circumcisions are not medically defensible, hence, morally objectionable. Not a few doctors, however, consider that routine circumcision is advisable unless there are contrary indications. Since the mutilation is slight (in fact, many moralists would not designate it as a mutilation), I believe that our hospitals are justified in adopting a tolerant attitude toward these doctors. By this I mean that we need not oppose the procedure, as long at it is limited to cases in which circumcision is not actually contraindicated.

Cosmetic surgery. By cosmetic surgery I mean an operation to improve one's personal appearance. This might take the form of removing a congenital defect, an extra organ (e.g., sixth finger), a blemish caused by an accident, and so forth. In general, there is no moral objection to such surgery; but special circumstances might make it illicit. For example, it would be wrong to do a face-lifting operation in order to help a dangerous criminal escape detection, or to do any purely cosmetic operation which would involve serious and disproportionate risk for the patient.

Some years ago I discussed an interesting specific case in *Hospital Progress.*[14] The problem concerned a young woman who had to have a breast removed, and after the operation the surgeon inserted sculptured sponges into the cavity in order to preserve the previous form of the breast. In this case, therefore, the mastectomy itself was a surgical necessity; the "cosmetic" part of the operation was the insertion of the sponges in order to restore the normal contour of the breast. I discussed this problem with a group of theologians. All were of

[12] *Morale et médecine* (Montréal: Comité des Hôpitaux du Québec 1957), p. 246.
[13] *Medical Ethics* (Chicago: Loyola University Press, 1956), p. 128.
[14] April, 1955, p. 56.

the opinion that the insertion of the sponges would be licit provided there would be no undue risk of injury either in the operation itself or in its effects. We tried to get information concerning the possible injurious effects of such surgery, but we found nothing. In the absence of such information, it should be presumed that the surgeon would not insert the sponges if their presence would be a source of harm to the patient.

It has been suggested that such an operation would be "catering to vanity"; also, that it would be unnecessary surgery because the patient could use some kind of "external appliance" to preserve the appearance of a normal breast. None of the theologians with whom I discussed the problem considered these to be sound objections to the operation. As regards the first suggestion, one can hardly consider a woman vain merely because she wishes to preserve her normal appearance. As for the second, the use of an "external appliance" is certainly an inconvenience. If it can be avoided by a harmless operation there can be no reasonable objection to the operation on moral grounds.

Tonsillectomy. I have heard it argued that the same reasons that justify incidental appendectomy would also apply to the routine removal of healthy tonsils. This is not correct. When an incidental appendectomy is performed, the probability of having to re-open the abdomen at some later date is removed. But the tonsils can be easily reached at any time; hence, there seems to be no sound reason for removing healthy tonsils, especially routinely. It may be true that they apparently have little use; also that the operation can be performed with minimum risk. Nevertheless, there is some risk; hence, a tonsillectomy without medical indication creates risk without proportionate cause. This is unnecessary surgery and morally objectionable.

260

chapter 29

Experimentation on Human Beings

Experimentation on patients without due consent and not for the benefit of the patients themselves is morally objectionable. Even when experimentation is for the genuine good of the patient, the physician must have the consent, at least reasonably presumed, of the patient or his legitimate guardian. Directive 42.

EVEN MEDICAL TREATMENTS of proved worth are sometimes accompanied by risk because of the unpredictable reactions of the patient. Avoidance of such risks for the patient is one purpose of the careful diagnosis required by medical societies; and avoidance of similar risks for others is one purpose of the autopsy. Yet, even the utmost care cannot completely eliminate such risk; and it is not to this kind of risk that the expression "medical experimentation" refers. Rather, experimentation usually means either the use of treatments not sufficiently established or the use of procedures which have for their precise purpose the discovery of some truth or the verification of some hypothesis. In the present chapter I am following this usual meaning, and I am supposing that the experimentation involves some degree of inconvenience or risk for the subject.

In general, the purposes of medical experimentation are two: to benefit the subject (e.g., the patient) or to advance medical science and thus benefit others. When we speak of experimen-

261

tation for the good of the patient, we mean *primarily* for his good, because it is obvious that the results of such treatments may and should be used for the benefit of others. Ordinarily, experimentation in our hospitals should be limited to procedures that are primarily for the good of the patient; and that is the meaning of the first part of directive 42. The directive does not, however, absolutely rule out experimentation which is primarily or even exclusively for the good of others, provided the patient consents and the precautions to be explained later are observed. My subsequent remarks will be concerned with both kinds of experimentation: namely, for the good of the patient; and for the good of others.

I. FOR THE GOOD OF THE PATIENT

Experimental procedures are, by supposition, of dubious efficacy. Theology manuals generally give three rather simple rules for the use of such procedures: (1) they may not be used if a certainly effective remedy is available; (2) when the only available treatments are of dubious efficacy, then the one most likely to help the patient should be used; and (3) the consent, at least reasonably presumed, of the patient or his legitimate representative must be had.

Only the third of these rules is an absolute. The first two rules are subject to exceptions. For example, if the one certainly effective remedy for a disease is a long, difficult, and very expensive procedure, the patient may try to avoid these inconveniences by resorting to a less certain, but also less inconvenient, treatment. In a word, the patient may take the risk of a less certain remedy provided there is a proportionate reason for it. This is in keeping with the general principle enunciated in the first part of directive 40: "Any procedure harmful to the patient is morally justified only insofar as it is designed to produce a proportionate good." And it is also in conformity with the provision of directive 42 that experimentation must be "for the genuine good of the patient." If this principle of proportionate reason or genuine good is conscientiously observed, there should be no great difficulty in determining when experimentation may be used in the interests of the patient.

II. FOR THE GOOD OF OTHERS

The literature, both medical and theological, on experimentation for the good of others is so vast that I could not even attempt to cover it in a short chapter. My plan is to review one representative set of scientific articles and to compare the conclusions with the teaching of Pope Pius XII. I shall add some remarks on abuses and on standards of the medical profession.

1. Articles in "Science"

The articles that I have chosen as representative of scientific literature, were published in *Science* under the general title, "The Problem of Experimentation on Human Beings."[1] These articles, four in number, are based on a symposium held at the University of California School of Medicine. They are mainly concerned with experimentation for the advancement of science on normal healthy persons or on the incurably and fatally ill. As regards healthy individuals, it is conceded that no experiment should be conducted until the experimenters are in possession of the most thorough information available from animal and clinical studies; and in the case of the incurably ill, palliation must be the first medical consideration. Experimentation, therefore, must be understood within these limits.

In the first article, "The Research Worker's Point of View," Michael B. Shimkin outlines the whole problem, cites the rules for human experimentation formulated by the Tribunal at Nuremberg, refers to similar rules adopted by medical committees, and says:

---

[1] *Science,* Feb. 27, 1953, pp. 205-215.

Analysis of the rules shows that they can be reduced to two primary principles: First, the investigators must be thoroughly trained in the scientific disciplines of the problem, must understand and appreciate the ethics involved, and must thus be competent to undertake and to carry out the experiment. Second, the human experimental subject must understand and voluntarily consent to the procedure, and must not be selected upon any basis such as race, religion, level of education, or economic status. In other words, *the investigators and the subjects are human beings with entirely equal, inalienable rights* that supersede any consideration of science or general public welfare.

Giving "The Physician's Point of View," Otto E. Guttentag explicitly discusses the type of experiment on the sick which "is of no immediate value to the patient but is made to confirm or disprove some doubtful or suggested biological generalization." He believes such experimentation to be necessary; yet he points to the fact that the conducting of the experiment conflicts with the traditional role of the physician as the friend and helper of the sick man, and the physician must be extraordinarily careful to preserve the attitude of "utmost concern" for the patient's welfare.

The lawyer's side of this question is given by Alexander M. Kidd in the third article, "Limits of the Right of a Person to Consent to Experimentation on Himself." He stresses the legal need of consent by any subject for experimentations; suggests that it is not a matter of good public relations for physicians to use any procedure on a patient that is not for the patient's benefit; and states two general limits to the rights of persons to permit experimentations that are not for their benefit: i.e., one may not consent either to one's own death or to an injury amounting to a maim. In the last article, "Civil Rights of Military Personnel Regarding Medical Care and Experimental Procedures," Colonel W. H. Johnson cites a military regulation which he believes might be the basis for authorizing the use of volunteer military personnel for experimentation, but he adds: "Needless to say, the Medical Department would not receive volunteers in this field if it considered the experimentation unduly hazardous or unnecessary."

264

The foregoing paragraphs express the main lines of thought in the *Science* articles. They lead, I believe, to a conclusion which may be expressed thus: experimentation on the healthy or incurably ill should, or at least may, be permitted for the good of others and the advancement of science, provided *(a)* that the subject freely consents, *(b)* that no experiment which directly inflicts grave injury or death is used, and *(c)* that all reasonable precautions are taken to avoid even the indirect causing of grave injury or death.

2. Teaching of Pius XII:

In his address to the histopathologists (Sept. 13, 1952) and later in his discourse to delegates to the Eighth Congress of the World Medical Association (Sept. 30, 1954), Pope Pius XII spoke at great length about experimentation which is primarily or exclusively for the good of others. It will be interesting to compare his teaching with the conclusion drawn from the *Science* articles.

The Pope laid great stress on the dignity of the individual and on his personal responsibility for the care of his health. From this it follows that the individual's consent, at least tacit, must be had for any medical treatment, whether therapeutic or experimental. On this point there is perfect agreement between the *Science* articles and the papal teaching.

The individual, said the Pope, is only the administrator of his life and bodily members and functions; and, because he is only the administrator, his power to dispose of these things is limited. Thus, even as regards treatments for his own good, he must observe the law of "hierarchy of values"—for example, he may not permit an operation which would deprive him of the use of his higher faculties, such as freedom and intellectual cognition, merely to cure some bodily or emotional ailment. And, as regards experimental procedures for the good of others, no individual has the right to permit things

265

which would "entail, either immediately or subsequently, serious destructions, mutilations, wounds, or dangers." These words were used in the address to the histopathologists. More comprehensive and more detailed is the following statement taken from the discourse of Sept. 30, 1954:

> What goes for the doctor in regard to his patient goes also for the doctor in regard to himself. He is subject to the same great moral and juridical principles. He cannot, therefore, submit himself to scientific experiments or practices that entail serious harm or threaten his health. Still less is he authorized to attempt an experiment which, according to authoritative information, may involve mutilation or suicide. The same must be said, furthermore, of male and female nurses and of anyone who may be disposed to give himself to therapeutic research. They cannot submit themselves to such experiments.

From the foregoing it is clear that the papal teaching sets limits to what the subject of an experiment may permit and that it condemns the attitude of extreme individualism which holds that, granted a person freely consents to an experiment, there is practically no limit to what may be done. There may be some differences of opinion as to the precise limits permitted by the Pope; but it seems to me that there is no conflict between his teaching and the limitations defined by the *Science* articles.

It is very important that those engaged in medical research and experimentation have sound philosophical attitudes toward man, his nature, his rights, and his destiny. Pius XII emphasized this and strongly condemned two false attitudes. One of these attitudes is the extreme individualism mentioned in the preceding paragraph. Another is the totalitarian attitude, the view that the individual exists for the community and is subordinated to it as part to whole. The most glaring example of this disastrous attitude is the experimentation carried on by the Nazi doctors. Civilization looks with horror on these experiments; nevertheless, as Pius XII has very often said or implied, the totalitarian attitude did not die with the execution of the

War criminals. In condemning this attitude, the Pope clearly taught that the individual is not a subordinate part of society in the same way, e.g., as the hand is a part of the physical body; and, as a consequence of this, it is wrong to invoke the principle of totality to justify medical experimentation for the advancement of science or for the good of others.

The *Science* articles do not, of course, make explicit mention of the principle of totality, because that expression is a strictly theological one. Nevertheless, they do insist on the dignity of the individual and on the fact that he has inalienable rights that supersede any considerations of science or general public welfare. This is substantially the same, it seems to me, as saying that the individual is not subordinated to society as part to whole; hence, on this point, there is no difference between the philosophy underlying the article and the papal teaching.

My conclusion from a comparison of the *Science* articles with the papal teaching is that they do not differ substantially;[2] hence, the points previously given as the conclusion of the articles may also be used as concrete statements of the teaching of Pius XII.

3. Abuses Versus Standards:

What I have written should not be taken as a "whitewashing" of abuses by clinical investigators and research workers. That there are real abuses is clear to me both from my reading and from what I have been told by doctors. These abuses mainly consist in doing things without consent or in practically forcing the consent of "charity" patients; but in some cases risks are apparently taken that would not be justified even with consent. For example, some small things done without consent might be making certain tests with a needle or practicing

---

[2] I say "substantially," because there are some *obiter dicta* concerning abortion, euthanasia, and sterilization that are not above suspicion.

with some instrument such as a proctoscope. These things are done, not for the good of the patient, but to build up statistics or to give young doctors practice. Such things do the patient no harm but they do annoy him. Other abuses concern more serious matters: transfusions with blood from a person with a serious blood disease; giving hormones or vaccine to one group that might be harmed and withholding the same from a group that may need them—all for the purpose of having "control groups" for research projects. I would not want to say that these or similar abuses are common, but I have good reason to believe that they are not entirely uncommon. And that the Pope was conscious of such abuses, and perhaps much more serious ones, is evident from his address to the histo-pathologists.

In fairness to the medical profession, it should be said that these abuses must be attributed to individuals' attitudes and conduct and not to published professional standards. I have read many professional statements and have found in them little or nothing that could be considered morally objectionable. For example, the rules for experimentation on human beings used at the Nuremberg medical trials contain such points as these: the absolute need of the enlightened consent of the human subject; the preliminary use, as far as possible, of animal experimentation and other methods of study; the sound hope of fruitful results, with due proportion between this and the risk involved; avoidance of any experiment when there is an *a priori* reason to believe that death or disabling injury will occur; the use of all possible precautions against injury; the complete liberty of the human subject to terminate the experiment at any time when he thinks his physical or mental state requires it; and the sincere willingness of the scientist to terminate the experiment at any stage when its continuation is likely to result in injury, disability, or death for the subject. It seems to me that there is no conflict between these provisions and the teaching of Pius XII; rather, they seem to make his teaching more concrete.[3]

<hr>

[3] The text of the ten rules is given in *The Linacre Quarterly*, Nov., 1953, pp. 114-115. Rule 5 reads as follows: "No experiment should be conducted where there is an *a priori* reason to believe that death or disabling injury will occur; except, perhaps, in those experiments where the experimental physicians also serve as subjects." This tentative admission that the moral limits might be extended when the experimenters themselves are the subjects is the only point that seems to conflict in any way with the teaching of Pius XII.

$\boxed{30}$

Psychosurgery

Lobotomy and similar operations are morally justifiable when medically indicated as the proper treatment of serious mental illness or of intractable pain. In each case the welfare of the patient himself, considered as a person, must be the determining factor. These operations are not justifiable when less extreme remedies are reasonably available or in cases in which the probability of harm to the patient outweighs the hope of benefit for him. Directive 44. (Cf. Canadian Code, art. 41; U. S. Code, "Other Special Directives," n. 2.)

B̲Y̲ PSYCHOSURGERY I mean cerebral surgery employed for the purpose of treating mental illness and pain. In the booklets on medico-moral problems there were four discussions of psychosurgery.[1] It is hardly necessary to incorporate all that material into the present chapter of the revised *Medico-Moral Problems*. It seems better to give here merely a commentary on directive 44, so that all will know its meaning. In this commentary, I shall say something about: (1) the operations; (2) indications; (3) effects; (4) medical evaluation of the individual case; (5) consultation; (6) permission; and (7) the moral decision.

---

[1] These were: "Lobotomy," "More about Lobotomy," "Lobotomy for Pain Relief," and "Pope Pius XII and Psychosurgery"—which were published in booklets I, II, III, and V, respectively. The original articles are in *Hospital Progress:* Dec., 1948, pp. 427-428; Aug., 1949, pp. 254-256; Feb., 1950, pp. 56-57; and Feb., 1954, p. 66.

1. The Operations

The first successful psychosurgical operation was performed by two Portuguese physicians, Egaz Moniz and Almeida Lima. The operation was a prefrontal lobotomy, which consists essentially in severing the white nerve fibers connecting the frontal lobes of the brain with the thalamus. The Portuguese doctors accomplished this by making two small holes in the skull, one at each temple, and inserting a dull, rounded knife called a leucotome. Because this operation could not be performed under direct vision, it is often called a "closed" lobotomy; and, because of the instrument used, the operation has been designated a leucotomy.

Since the original operation, there have been many variations of technique. There is "open" lobotomy, in which enough of the skull is removed to allow for operating under direct vision. There is a transorbital lobotomy, in which a sharp instrument that looks very much like an ice pick is inserted along the nose and through the eye socket and the fibers are thus cut from below. Still another variation is "coagulation" lobotomy, which is accomplished by inserting insulated electrodes into the frontal lobes from above. And there are, as every physician knows, numerous other procedures: for instance, lobectomy and topectomy, which consist in removing parts of the brain substance; thalamotomy, in which a wire electrode is passed down into the thalamus and a small portion of this part of the brain is coagulated; and selective cortical undercutting, which involves cutting the white fibers in one of the main areas of the frontal lobes. Finally, there is the growing tendency to restrict formerly extensive operations by doing only a partial cutting, e.g., unilateral instead of bilateral lobotomy.

The foregoing may not be a complete list of psychosurgical procedures; but they are the operations most frequently mentioned in the literature. Each operation has its defenders and its critics. The obvious purpose of directive 44 is to take no

271

sides in a controversy over techniques but simply to give the general rule that, granted the conditions outlined in the directive, any of the techniques may be used. As for the choice of technique in an individual case, a good working rule is enunciated by Fr. Thomas J. O'Donnell, S.J., as follows: "The only moral directive here is that the surgeon select that method which he considers safest in his hands and in the best interest of the patient."[2]

2. Indications

The directive gives only the very general indications for psychosurgery: namely, serious mental illness and intractable pain. The main reason, of course, for keeping to a general statement was the need of brevity. Yet, even if space allowed for a development of these points, it would not be wise to enumerate specific indications for the operations in a directive. As is the case regarding the operative techniques, there are differences of opinion among specialists concerning the precise indications for psychosurgery. For instance, some would limit it to psychoses; many others would extend it to certain forms of neurosis. The directive simply requires that the mental illness be serious: that is, an illness which is chronic and truly disabling. Granted this, and granted the other conditions to be explained later, the directive would allow the operation for mental illness, regardless of the technical classification of the illness.

As regards pain, the cases considered intractable in the sense of the directive would be great and unbearable sufferings complicated by an anxiety state that makes them similar to a mental illness.

Even though the directive is purposely phrased in a general way, there seems to be no objection to citing some of the statements of specialists concerning the indications for psychosur-

---

[2] *Morals in Medicine* (Westminster, Md.: The Newman Press, 1956), p. 88.

gery. I cite these, however, merely as illustrations and not as qualifications of the meaning of the directive. For instance, one doctor, writing in 1949, had this to say:

Today most observers see the best outlook for prefrontal lobotomy in long-standing depressive illnesses, particularly the involutional type, and in incapacitating obsessive-compulsive neuroses. Also, certain schizophrenic patients, especially the catatonic subgroup, have benefitted from the operation. Contraindications for lobotomy are present when the emotional tone has become chronically flattened (the operation would only "flatten" it all the more); and the advisability of operation is also questionable in those cases where antisocial traits were evident in the previous personality.[3]

Two years later (in 1951) another specialist, after having described the effects of lobotomy in certain cases of mental illness, concluded:

It is considerations such as these which convince us that leucotomy is morally permissible in cases of serious psychasthenia, schizophrenia, and morbid attacks of depressive anxiety, provided these patients cannot be cured in some other way.

On the other hand, we do not consider that leucotomy is permissible in psychopathic cases where the structure of the personality reveals, on serious examination, no still healthy core on which to work. In this connection, we are thinking of certain groups of psychopaths who, as we know from experience, are completely lacking in any development of the emotions, intelligence and will, beyond the sphere of simple essential relations. Leucotomy cannot achieve its purpose with such individuals, psychically ill-developed and deformed, because the faculties which the intervention aims at liberating are completely faulty.[4]

Another, and more general, statement of the indication for psychosurgery, is that "it presupposes that the brain of the patient remains more or less intact, and that as a result of

---

[3] C. Charles Burlingame, M.D., "Psychosurgery—New Help for the Mentally Ill," *The Scientific Monthly*, Feb., 1949, pp. 140-144; words quoted are on p. 142.

[4] Prof. J. J. G. Prick, in *The Ethics of Brain Surgery* (Chicago: Henry Regnery Company, 1955), p. 28. The articles translated in this book originally appeared in *Cahiers Laënnec*, March, 1951.

273

delusions, hallucinations, or obsessions, the mental tension is such that the patient cannot carry on a normal life."[5] And, as a final sample of this interesting literature, let me quote this paragraph:

Our patients are selected for lobotomy only after a thorough evaluation of the factor of anxiety, regardless of the clinical diagnosis. The beneficial effects of any type of prefrontal lobotomy are to be explained solely in terms of release of tension generated by repression. The chief symptom of such tension is anxiety in all its undisguised forms, such as guilt, self-condemnation, self-punishment, and fear, and in its masked forms such as phobias, obsessions, compulsions, hallucinations and delusions, hostility, and aggression. In this connection, it is well to remember that hypomanic and manic behavior is frequently a cloak for anxiety and in such instances represents a masked form of anxiety. If the symptoms of tension with resulting anxiety are prominent in a psychotic or neurotic patient, a varying measure of relief may be expected from lobotomy. The converse is also true, the less the anxiety the poorer the therapeutic result. Patients should then be selected on the basis of the anxiety symptom and the results of lobotomy appraised in terms of relief of anxiety and tension, rather than by the percentage of so-called remissions or cures in various diagnostic categories.[6]

3. Effects

As regards mental illness, the principal good effect of psychosurgery is relief from emotional tension: for example, a patient may be relieved from a crippling anxiety and, with proper help, may begin to lead a more or less normal life. Just how this relief is brought about has been and still is a matter of speculation. One explanation often accepted as very probable is that psychosurgery effects a sort of divorce between cog-

---

[5] Quoted from *The Transactions of the Catholic Medical Guild of St. Luke* (Australia), Jan. 1954. This number of *The Transactions* contains a symposium on leucotomy held at Sancta Sophia College, University of Sydney, March 1, 1953. The symposium covers pp. 19-42. The statement quoted in my text is by Dr. S. J. Minogue, p. 37.

[6] Howard D. McIntyre, M.D., Frank H. Mayfield, M.D., and Aurelia P. McIntyre, M.D., "Ventromedial Quadrant Coagulation in the Treatment of the Psychoses and Neuroses," *American Journal of Psychiatry*, Aug., 1954, pp. 112-119; see p. 119.

nition and emotional response. In other words—to use an example—a thought or suggestion which might have caused the patient a veritable panic before the operation would scarcely trouble him after the operation.

There is a heavy price to pay for the desired release from tension. According to various specialists, psychosurgery induces personality changes of many kinds. For instance, here are some of the changes observed: inertia, lack of ambition and initiative, a tendency to be satisfied with little or no work or with work of a very inferior quality, lack of human-respect, some degree of moral degeneration, reduced capacity for prolonged attention, inferior planning ability, impairment of creative ability, lack of foresight and concern for the future, tactlessness, crude social behavior, lessening of affection, fatigue and excessive sleep, indifference to pain. To these personality changes may be added such things as failure to control toilet habits, and the risks of brain surgery in terms of mortality rate. Estimates of mortality rate vary somewhat, but, with some qualifications according to techniques, 2% to 3% is often given.

At first glance, this seems to be a grim picture, and one might easily conclude that psychosurgery does more harm than good. There are, however, some mitigating factors. For one thing, not all these effects are noticed in the same person. Also, there are degrees: some changes are very slight. Moreover, it is possible to preclude or avoid many of them by proper postoperative care. Furthermore, a careful selection of patients will avoid some of the worst effects: e.g., the probability of immoral acts and of antisocial behavior. Finally, there is the plain fact that, despite the unjustifiable experimentation that has sometimes been carried on in this field, the overall picture is that at least half the patients have been improved by the operations, and of the others, comparatively few were made worse. When patients are carefully selected, the operations

275

properly performed, and postoperative care is properly given, the percentage of success is much greater.

It must be remembered that "improvement" both in mental cases and in cases of intractable pain must be measured in terms of the morbid state and not in terms of the premorbid personality. Precisely for this reason, some of the effects of psychosurgery that may be undesirable in themselves and for normal persons, may be actually good for those who are mentally ill or distraught with pain. I might illustrate this by a few citations from conscientious specialists. The first quotation concerns a woman patient, with generalized metastases from carcinoma of the rectum. The other two quotations concern mental patients in general. I shall merely give the quotations here, reserving comment to the next section:

> The extreme pain, anxiety and despair were not controlled by a total of 122 grains of morphine, 70 grains of luminal and 12 ampules of cobra venom, during the month prior to neurosurgical consultation.
> She was obviously terminal. Her demands for relief, the disturbance she set up, taxed everyone, house officers as well as nurses. Medication was as frequent as every two hours. She was too far gone physically to attempt a procedure such as chordotomy.
> Under pentothal anesthesia, a bilateral prefrontal lobotomy was carried out on March 6, 1947. Following this procedure the patient, after the usual period of inertia of about four to five days duration, was alert, visited pleasantly with her family. She was affable, quiet and content. Subsequently only 2 grains of luminal and ¼ grain of morphine were required until time of death approximately one month later.[7]

Although it is difficult to predict in each individual case, the balance-sheet of profits and losses, current practice demands that the *gravity* and *incurability* of the mental disease should be taken as criteria for deciding in favour of this intervention [leucotomy]. When the true human personality appears to be buried, in no uncertain fashion, under the action of affective pathological mechanisms, the positive outcome of

---

[7] Edmund A. Smolik, M.S., M.D., F.A.C.S., "Surgical Methods for the Management of Intractable Pain," *Mississippi Valley Medical Journal and Radiologic Review,* March 1948. Quotation from a reprint without page numbers.

the intervention will more than compensate for the accompanying losses; for it will be a liberation—modest, indeed, but qualitatively significant—of the power of abstract thought, of the will, and of a certain interior freedom.[8]

It is essential that we should maintain our perspective and keep the whole picture before us. Here is a psychotic patient, hopeless, irrational, illogical, submerged in a psychotic quagmire. He has a successful leucotomy. He becomes rational, logical and responsible. He works efficiently in an office, in the home, for the council, as the presented cases showed us tonight. Indeed, he once more becomes capable of human acts.

It is true that leucotomy has reduced his capacity to become an Ignatius Loyola, but it has lifted him out of the aimless psychotic impotence. At least he is now capable of intelligently striving to reach the lower storeys within the celestial hierarchy.[9]

4. The Individual Case

According to the directive, psychosurgery is morally justifiable when it is medically indicated. This preoperative medical judgment, though especially difficult as regards psychosurgery, is made along essentially the same lines as in other serious surgical procedures. For instance, no competent and conscientious doctors would decide for or against any serious surgery merely on the basis of general statistics and results in other cases. The judgment must be made in terms of the particular patient's condition; the good and bad effects are weighed as they will probably occur in this case; and the final judgment to operate or not operate is concerned with a comparison of these probable effects on the patient. All this may seem too obvious to mention; yet I have seen some literature, both medical and moral, which at least implies that important surgical decisions should be made merely on the basis of statistics. This, of course, is not correct. The doctors' ultimate

---

[8] *The Ethics of Brain Surgery,* p. 28.

[9] The *Transactions* (see footnote 5), p. 41; statement by Dr. F. J. Kyneur.

responsibility must always be concerned with the individual case.

Another consideration common to all preoperative decisions concerns the possibility of obtaining the same good effects in some more conservative manner. Thus, in our particular problem, everyone would admit, I think, that the ideal treatment for mental illness and pain is psychotherapy, because psychotherapy is completely constructive. And, when psychotherapy is not feasible, the next consideration must be given to the possibility of producing the good results by means of chemical therapy. In the treatment of pain, this is the most common way of dealing with the situation: that is, by means of drugs, the use of which can be carefully controlled. As I write this chapter, there are already some indications that the use of various forms of chemical therapy may supplant the more drastic measures that have been used in the treatment of mental illness and intractable pain. Even the most enthusiastic supporters of psychosurgery would welcome further progress along these lines.

Physicians and moralists who write about psychosurgery usually stress the idea that it is a procedure "of last resort." This is the meaning of the directive when it says that psychosurgery is not justifiable "when less extreme remedies are reasonably available." Article 41 of the Canadian Code is more specific and more helpful on this point. It states that psychosurgery is permitted "when other treatments have failed, or are unavailable or deemed medically inexpedient."

Theoretically, the choice of therapeutic measures is always made in terms of the best interests of the patient. Other considerations such as the advancement of science and the help of other people are secondary. Every medical society would subscribe to these statements. The directive, in calling attention to the primary place of the patient's welfare, emphasizes the fact that he is a *person*. There are several reasons for this emphasis. It is easy to lose appreciation of the true human

278

dignity of some mentally ill persons; and this can lead to experimentation for the good of others at the expense of the patient. It is my impression that such experimentation is more common in public institutions than in private hospitals and that it is less common in our country than in some others.

Failure to appreciate the personal dignity of the patient can also lead to psychosurgery just to make him more manageable. If this means merely to reduce the work of those who care for him, it is completely unjustifiable. I say "merely," because in some instances it is actually for the patient's own good to make him "more manageable." I refer to cases in which the psychosurgery protects him from himself by reducing a suicidal impulse, and makes it possible for him to have greater liberty by reducing dangerous antisocial traits.

In the human person, there is a hierarchy of values, as Pope Pius XII has pointed out.[10] The highest value, of course, is spiritual: the power to think and to use free will. No good of the merely corporeal order is sufficient to compensate for the loss of these spiritual powers. Yet, when those treating the mentally ill forget their personal dignity, they may also forget this order of values and sacrifice the spiritual for the corporeal. Thus, we hear at times that patients have been dehumanized, turned into vegetables, by psychosurgery. Very likely such things have happened chiefly because of unintentional mistakes in predicting results or in unintentionally making an operation too extensive. Yet, they can also be the result of a materialistic mentality that does not recognize the true dignity of the human person.

The specialists quoted in the previous section show a fine appreciation of true values. Those who speak of the mentally ill make it clear that their aim is to liberate the spiritual powers. And, though the doctor does not mention the spiritual aspect explicitly, it seems clear that the woman who had the

---

[10] Cf. his statement in the concluding section of this chapter.

279

prefrontal lobotomy for pain was better able to prepare herself for death after the operation than she was before. In her case, as in all terminal cases, the ability to pray and to cooperate with grace should be considered as especially precious. In terms of the human person and his destiny, it is the supreme value.

5. Consultation

The Canadian Code explicitly requires the serious consultation of specialists before psychosurgery. Our directive supposes this. Moreover, as I explained in chapter 7, this is a case in which special care must be taken to protect the interests of the helpless.

6. Permission

Also presupposed here is the necessity of due permission before psychosurgical intervention. If the patient is capable of making his own decisions, he has the inviolable right to give or to refuse consent. To perform the operation through deception or against his will is an invasion of his rights. If he is incapable of making the decision, his parents or guardians have the right to make it for him. Here, too, as I pointed out in chapter 7, special care to protect the patient is necessary. Hospital authorities should see that no undue influence is brought to bear on the patient or his guardians and that guardians do not make the decision through selfish interests. Competent and conscientious medical consultants can do much to prevent such dangers.

7. The Moral Decision

Granted the conditions explained in the foregoing sections of this chapter, psychosurgery is, as the directive states, morally justifiable. It is hardly necessary to elaborate on this. However, I should like to add a word about a papal statement that has caused some misunderstanding. In his address of Sept. 13, 1952, Pope Pius XII said that a man may not submit to medical procedures which alleviate physical or psychic illness, but at the same time "involve the destruction or the diminution to a considerable and lasting extent of freedom—that is to say, of the human personality in its typical and characteristic functions. In that way man is degraded to the level of a purely sensory being—a being of acquired reflexes or a living automaton. Such a reversal of values is not permitted by the natural law."

When that statement first appeared, some doctors asked me whether it was a condemnation of psychosurgery. They were much concerned over that. Actually, there was no sound foundation for such concern. The Pope was simply indicating in rather broad, general terms a case in which the harm to the patient would outweigh the benefit, because no merely material benefit would compensate for the loss of freedom "to a considerable and lasting extent." I think this point was explained sufficiently in section 4 of this chapter.

chapter 31

Narcoanalysis and Hypnoanalysis

The use of narcosis or hypnosis for the cure of mental illness is permissible with the consent at least reasonably presumed of the patient, provided due precautions are taken to protect the patient and the hospital from harmful effects, and provided the patient's right to secrecy is duly safeguarded. **Directive 45.**

IN TREATING SOME CASES of mental illness, it is especially important to discover the incident that precipitated the illness. One diagnostic tool for this purpose is psychoanalysis. Other tools, which might be called short-cuts in the psychoanalytic method, are hypnotism (hypnoanalysis) and the use of drugs such as sodium Amytal and sodium Pentothal (narcoanalysis, or narcosynthesis). The present directive is concerned with the use of hypnotism and drugs; directive 46 deals explicitly with psychoanalysis.

The most recent of the techniques to get the psychiatric patient to talk freely is, I believe, the use of sodium Pentothal. This technique is graphically described by Doctors Grinker and Spiegel in their book *Men Under Stress.*[1] A typical example of the treatment, as recommended and practiced by these doctors would be somewhat as follows:

---

[1] R. R. Grinker, M.D., and J. P. Spiegel, M.D., *Men Under Stress* (Philadelphia: The Blakiston Co., 1945).

Suppose the psychiatrist's patient is suffering from some neurotic illness. By means of interviews the psychiatrist first establishes a relationship of confidence with his patient and learns all that he can about the repressed emotional situation or situations that brought on the neurotic condition. When the psychiatrist realizes that further recall would require too much time or that it is too difficult, or perhaps impossible, he resorts to the Pentothal treatment. Pentothal is given intravenously, and the patient is told to count backwards from 100. When the counting becomes confused, the injection is discontinued. In this narcotic condition the patient usually talks freely about himself. Sometimes his talking will spontaneously follow lines pertinent to his illness; sometimes he must be skillfully directed by the psychiatrist. Very often the patient will literally relive an entire frightening experience, verbally, emotionally, dramatically. Often, too, as the effects of the drug begin to wear off, the patient begins unconsciously to gain an insight into his troubles and to make appropriate readjustments. After that, the psychiatrist's task is simply to aid the patient to a completion of the insight and readjustment. Because their treatment not only enabled the physician to diagnose the illness but also helped the patient toward self-understanding and adjustment, Drs. Grinker and Spiegel preferred to call it narcosynthesis rather than merely narcoanalysis.

It is obvious that some moral problems could be involved in the use of narcoanalysis and hypnoanalysis, and that certain conditions must be fulfilled for such treatments to be licit. Directive 46 outlines the conditions. In the following paragraphs I shall give the conditions separately and a brief explanation of each one.

1) *If the patient has the use of reason, the treatments should not ordinarily be used without his explicit consent.*

We must remember that in the ordinary psychiatric interviews, the patient is always free to refuse to answer a question. He may be unreasonable in thus refusing to cooperate in his cure, but this refusal is his natural right. Under narcosis or hypnosis he loses this freedom; hence the induction of such states without his consent is ordinarily an invasion of his rights.

I have stressed the word "ordinarily" here, because I think there may be occasions when the psychiatrist may legitimately presume the patient's consent to the treatments: for instance, when the psychiatrist knows that the patient really wishes to do everything necessary to get well but would nevertheless shrink from narco- or hypnotherapy because of some exaggerated and unfounded fear.

If the patient has not the use of reason, the consent of his guardian or guardians should be obtained before the treatments are used. Ordinarily this consent should also be explicit; but I believe that such consent might be legitimately presumed under the same circumstances that would justify the treatments without the explicit consent of a rational patient. Furthermore, from a merely moral point of view, a guardian's explicit refusal might even be ignored if it were manifestly unreasonable and therefore detrimental to the health of the patient.

2) *There should be no unjustifiable risk of harm for the patient.*

This condition hardly needs explanation, as it is always necessary for the licit use of any procedure. I include it here merely for the sake of completeness.

3) *The psychiatrist must take the necessary means of protecting himself, and particularly the hospital, from harmful effects.*

I am referring to the danger of unsavory lawsuits and of derogatory gossip. For instance, in certain cases of presumed consent of patient or guardian, or in cases of extraordinary risk of harmful effects to the patient, there might be serious legal complications. And if the patient is a woman, certain precautions may be called for to prevent harmful gossip. The hospital has a right to know of such risks and to refuse to become involved in them.

4) *Professional secrecy must be rigidly observed concerning the information gleaned in the course of the treatment.*

Here again we list a condition which pertains to all medical practice, nevertheless the point deserves special emphasis for several reasons. In the first place, the patient under narcosis or hypnosis is unable to direct the course of his speech; hence his revelations are even more inviolable than those made in a wakeful state. Furthermore, we live in an age of "case histories," and this is particularly true of social work and psychiatric practice. Perhaps I am too meticulous, but I certainly get the impression that many of these case histories are veiled so thinly that anyone who really wanted to do so could easily identify the subject. If that impression is correct, I can see no justification for the recounting or publishing of the histories without the consent of the patient.

Finally—a third reason for stressing the need of professional secrecy—we live in a "clinic" age. Patients are examined before large groups of specialists, students, and so forth. Perhaps this is necessary for the advancement of science; yet one wonders at times if the poor are not unduly humiliated in the process. With regard to narcoanalysis or hypnoanalysis, the examination of a patient before a group means the revelation of the patient's secrets (sometimes very embarrassing secrets) to the entire group. An examination of this kind should never be forced on the patient; and, if such an examination is judged useful and permissible, all who are present should keep in mind that they are bound by the professional secret.

Generally speaking, if the four conditions I have just explained are observed, narcoanalysis and hypnoanalysis may be considered as morally unobjectionable, and the treatments may be allowed in Catholic hospitals. Before concluding the subject, however, I should like to mention two other factors that are sometimes brought up for discussion.

For instance, I have been asked if there is any danger that a patient under narcosis might re-enact some sexual sin that he had committed. I can give no definite answer to the question; but several psychiatrists have told me that, in their opinion, this will not happen.

The second factor is indicated by these words of Fr. Francis J. Connell, C.SS.R.: "The patient may submit to the treatment at the hands of a competent and *conscientious* physician who believes that it will probably be helpful."[2] I have italicized the word "conscientious." Readers who are familiar with Catholic moral treatises on hypnotism will probably recall that these usually specify that the hypnotist also be conscientious. The same idea would very likely be included in any Catholic statement of the morality of psychotherapy or narcoanalysis.

Why this insistent demand that the psychiatrist be conscientious? As I understand it, there is no intention here of discriminating against the psychiatrist. As a matter of fact, it is dangerous to consult other physicians, especially obstetricians, who are not conscientious. Nevertheless, there seems to be a special need of such emphasis with regard to psychiatrists, because not infrequently psychiatric help must include the influencing of the patient's conscience: for example, in cases of scrupulosity. Where such influence is called for, the psychiatrist can hardly avoid applying his own standards of morality to the case—at least, so it seems to me.

Psychiatrists will say that they do not try to influence the conscience of the patient—that they merely try to aid him to understand his own problems and to solve them according to his own conscience. I am willing to concede that this is generally true; but it does not apply to all psychiatrists, and it can hardly apply to the treatment of all patients.

The presumption is that all physicians who belong to the

[2] Cf. "The Morality of Narcotherapy," *American Ecclesiastical Review,* Dec., 1945, pp. 448-449.

staffs of our Catholic hospitals are sufficiently conscientious; and this presumption includes the psychiatrists. Hospitals may act on this presumption unless there is a positive reason for suspecting some morally harmful practice. And I might add that much of the suspicion and difficulty that may arise with regard to various medical practices can be avoided by fostering sympathetic contacts between priests and physicians. In my own experience with physicians of various special fields, including psychiatry, I have found that even those who have no personal religious convictions are quite willing to respect the conscience and religious tenets of their patients and that they welcome the friendly advice and cooperation of priests in treating Catholic patients. Perhaps this experience is not typical; but there is no sound reason why it should not be.

chapter 32

Hypnosis as Anesthesia

DIRECTIVE 45, which was explained in the preceding chapter, contains the principles relative to the use of hypnotism in psychiatric treatments. Since that directive was formulated, we have been faced more and more frequently with the problem of using hypnosis as an anesthetic, especially in obstetrics, dentistry, and surgery. It is not yet time for any kind of final and comprehensive statement on this problem. It seems advisable, however, to outline some pertinent considerations.

As regards obstetrics in particular, hypnosis is mentioned frequently in the medical literature of recent years; but a careful perusal of this literature shows that the meaning of "hypnosis" is not always clearly defined. It may mean "light hypnosis" or "deep hypnosis," or it may mean "natural childbirth," as explained by Grantly Dick Read. That this last method satisfies the demands of good morality was clearly stated by Pope Pius XII in his address to doctors, Jan. 8, 1956.

Incidentally, it may be noted that, at the beginning of the address of Jan. 8, 1956, the Pope referred to deep hypnosis in delivery and suggested that one danger of this method might be emotional indifference of the mother toward her child. He was careful to add, however, that some doctors thought this indifference need not be attributed to the use of hypnosis. Moreover, the danger could be avoided. It seems to me that the very manner in which the Holy Father spoke of hypnosis in this context showed that he considered this as primarily a medical question and that the judgment of its morality would ultimately be based on sound medical opinion. His subsequent address on anesthesia, Feb. 24, 1957, confirms this interpretation. On this occasion, he said:

> But consciousness can also be reduced by artificial means. It makes no difference from the moral standpoint whether this result is obtained by the administration of drugs or by artificially produced sleep (hypnosis)—which can be called a form of psychic pain prevention. But hypnosis, even considered exclusively in itself, is subject to certain rules. May We recall a brief reference We made to the medical use of hypnosis, at the beginning of the address of Jan. 8, 1956, on natural painless childbirth?
>
> In the matter which engages Us at present, there is question of hypnosis practised by the doctor to serve a clinical purpose, while he observes the precautions which science and medical ethics demand from the doctor as much as from the patient who submits to it. The moral judgment which We are going to state on the suppression of consciousness applies to this specific use of hypnosis.
>
> But We do not wish what We say of hypnosis in the service of medicine to be extended to hypnosis in general without qualification. In fact, hypnosis, insofar as it is an object of scientific research, cannot be studied by any casual individual, but only by a serious scientist, and within the moral limits valid for all scientific activity. It is not the affair of some group of laymen or ecclesiastics, who might dabble in it as an interesting activity for the sake of mere experience, or even as a simple hobby.[1]

If we consider these quoted paragraphs in reverse order, we note three cardinal points: (1) Hypnotism is a serious scientific matter, and not something to be "dabbled" in. (2) In its scientific use, the precautions dictated by both science and morality are to be heeded. (3) Under the aspect of anesthesia, it is governed by the same principles as any other form

---

[1] Translation from *The Catholic Medical Quarterly*, April, 1957, p. 60. This issue of the *Quarterly* contains a complete English version of the papal address (pp. 51-66), with some helpful preliminary remarks by the editor (pp. 49-50).

of anesthesia. The first of these points needs no explanation here. The second was already sufficiently explained in the preceding chapter. When I say, "sufficiently explained," I realize that in that chapter I said very little about the dangers in either narcosis or hypnosis. That omission was deliberate. It seemed to me that doctors know these dangers much better than I; and I would be venturing into a field of which I have very little definite knowledge were I to attempt a full discussion of these dangers.

The third point is of greatest importance here: hypnotism is to be governed by the same principles as the use of other anesthetics. This is tantamount to saying that the rules of good medicine apply to the use of hypnotism as an anesthetic; and, insofar as its use conforms to these rules, it is in conformity with good morality.

MEDICAL OPINION

A report published in the *Journal of the American Medical Association,* Oct. 20, 1956, p. 769, announced the setting up of an *ad hoc* committee, "to review the present status and use of hypnosis in American medicine." It was hoped that from the work of this committee the Board of Trustees of the American Medical Association would be able to "take official action toward adopting a policy regarding medical use of hypnosis that will reflect the opinion of American medicine generally."

At the time I write, I have not seen any further official statement on this topic; and, lacking this official statement, it would be imprudent to suggest anything more than a tentative and limited conclusion concerning the medical status of hypnosis as an anesthetic. The same *Journal,* however, has published enough material to allow for at least the tentative conclusion that hypnosis can be wisely used either as a substitute for chemical anesthesia or as an adjunct to chemical anesthesia.

In an article entitled "Hypnotism in Pregnancy and Labor,"[2] Sol T. DeLee, M.D., reviewed the history of hypnotism, evaluated its medical advantages and disadvantages as a procedure to be used in pregnancy and labor, illustrated how it should be used in prenatal care and parturition, and concluded as follows:

During the past decade, as a result of the interest of the medical profession in suggestive relaxation methods for painless childbirth, a marked increase in the scientific applications of hypnosis has become apparent. It has been a belated but welcome recognition of the usefulness of hypnoanesthesia, either as an anesthetic agent or as an adjunct to chemoanesthesia. Hypnosis in parturition is far from a panacea nor will it ever supplant chemoanesthetic agents. Nevertheless, its applications are growing daily, and it is proving a powerful ally in alleviating other functional conditions in obstetrics and gynecology; this is also true in other clinical fields. Seminars by qualified scientists to teach all aspects of clinical hypnosis are increasing rapidly, and the British Medical Association recently recommended that all physicians be grounded in the basic principles of hypnotherapy. It must be emphasized that in order to successfully employ hypnotic techniques for psychotherapy, one must be oriented or trained in psychodynamics. More active participation and education in hypnotic methodology will help dispel misunderstanding and apprehension among the laity. Thus, if judiciously employed, another valuable technique will be available to more physicians who wish to mitigate the pain of parturition.

Later, in collaboration with William S. Kroger, M.D., Dr. DeLee described a case in which hypnosis was the only anesthesia used in a cesarean section with hysterectomy.[3] In the course of their article, the doctors state: "We wish to empha-

---

[2] *Journal of the American Medical Association,* Oct. 22, 1955, pp. 750-754. There is a summary of the article in the *Year Book of Obstetrics & Gynecology,* 1956-1957 Series, pp. 155-157. In some remarks appended to this summary, Dr. J. P. Greenhill observes: "Any unbiased physician will find that there is a definite field of usefulness for hypnosis in many branches of medicine."

[3] "Use of Hypnoanesthesia for Cesarean Section and Hysterectomy," *Journal of the American Medical Association,* Feb. 9, 1957, pp. 442-444.

size that hypnosis is never going to be a substitute for chemoanesthesia, because it can be utilized in only about 10% of carefully selected patients." And, among their concluding paragraphs is the following:

Hypnoanesthesia per se is recommended only for certain patients. These constitute less than 10% of selected patients requiring major surgery. It has a much wider field of application when used as an adjunct to chemoanesthesia. In this capacity, it can decrease the quantity of anesthetic required and facilitate induction of anesthesia, due to marked muscular relaxation. Additionally, anoxia is greatly diminished. In many patients, the use of hypnosis can obviate the traditional use of preanesthetic medicaments and thus lessen the tendency to the development of respiratory depression. Employed postoperatively, with or without chemoanesthesia, hypnosis can often prevent pulmonary complications, postoperative pain, and vomiting. As a result of improved nutrition the healing of wounds is facilitated.

Harold B. Crasilneck, Ph.D., E. James McCranie, M.D., and M. T. Jenkins, M.D.,[4] say that the use of hypnoanesthesia, in preference to chemical anesthesia, "should be reserved for cases with special indications, because there are definite psychological hazards to its indiscriminate use and in most uncomplicated cases its use is neither practical nor economically feasible." As for the special cases in which it might be indicated, their own experience has prompted them to suggest the following:

First, it is indicated in cases in which chemical analgesics and depressants are contraindicated or dangerous because of respiratory or cardiac disease. . . . Second, it is indicated in cases in which the preferred anesthetic agent cannot be used because the patient has demonstrated sensitivity to it. . . . Third, hypnoanesthesia should be used in cases in which the repeated use of anesthetics tends to have a debilitating effect on the patient with an already disturbed physiology. This is frequently a problem with severely burned patients who require frequent painful changes of dressings, débridement, and skin grafts. . . . Fourth, it is indicated in patients whose apprehension and fear of general anesthesia are so great as to interfere with its

---

[4] "Special Indications for Hypnosis as a Method of Anesthesia," *ibid.*, Dec. 29, 1956, pp. 1606-1608.

smooth application or even to result in serious anesthetic risks. . . . Fifth, hypnosis should be utilized in patients whom it is desirable to free of some of the neurophysiological effects of the anesthetic.

The preceding articles were mainly concerned with some specific uses of hypnoanesthesia. More general in its approach is "The Role of Hypnosis in Anesthesiology," by Milton J. Marmer, M.D.[5] Like Dr. DeLee, Dr. Marmer gives a short history of medical hypnosis. He then discusses its use in modern anesthesiology, describes how it was used in conjunction with chemical agents in a case of thoracic surgery, and concludes:

> Hypnosis has much to offer the anesthesiologist. It minimizes fear and apprehension and is valuable as an adjunct to the measures commonly employed in sedation before and after operation. It can be attempted when chemical anesthetics are contraindicated. Posthypnotic suggestion has proved to be of great value in the postoperative course, namely, in reducing or eliminating nausea, vomiting, and pain. Hypnosis is a successful auxiliary measure for inducing anesthesia and can effect anesthesia alone. Patients vary in their susceptibility to hypnosis, and a deep hypnotic level cannot be reached in every instance. Ideally, hypnosis should be used in combination with chemical agents to achieve anesthesia. . . .

One who reads the articles I have cited will be impressed by the fact that the authors are earnest, scientific men who are not interested in exaggerating the benefits of hypnoanesthesia or in minimizing its limitations. The articles themselves, which in turn contain abundant references to other scientific discussions, lead to the conclusion that hypnoanesthesia can be wisely used by responsible physicians in properly selected cases. Pending the final report of the Board of Trustees of the American Medical Association, our hospitals may safely follow this conclusion.

[5] *Ibid.*, Sept., 29, 1956, pp. 441-443. In the course of this article, Dr. Mermer says: "It should be mentioned that hypnodontia is a well-recognized and highly useful field of dentistry." For a development of this statement, one might read "Hypnosis in Dentistry," by George F. Kuehner, D.D.S., in *Hypnosis and Its Therapeutic Applications* (New York: McGraw-Hill Book Company, Inc., 1956), edited by Roy M. Dorcus, Ph.D. Dr. Kuehner's contribution is Chapter 12.

chapter 33

Electro-Shock Therapy

**Shock-therapy is permitted when medically indicated.
Directive 47.**

Cavanagh and McGoldrick briefly describe electro-shock therapy as "the induction of convulsions by the use of electrical current sent through the frontal lobes of the brain from electrodes placed over the temples."[1] The principle for judging the morality of this therapy is easily phrased: it is permitted when it offers the patient the hope of needed benefit without incurring the risk of some disproportionate harm. In a word, as directive 47 puts it, it "is permitted when medically indicated." Obviously, one cannot apply this principle to individual cases without knowing the condition of the patient, the indications and contraindications of electro-shock therapy, the possibility of producing the same or greater benefit by other therapies, and so forth. It is the province of the medical expert, not the moralist, to determine and evaluate such points; and one can say about shock therapy just what is said about other procedures: that good medicine is good morality.

According to Cavanagh and McGoldrick, electro-shock therapy is, or can be, indicated in involutional melancholia and the depressions of later life, in the depressed phase of manic-depressive psychosis, in the excited phase of manic-de-

---

[1] *Fundamental Psychiatry* (Milwaukee: The Bruce Publishing Co., 1953), p. 360.

pressive psychosis, and in schizophrenia. The degree of benefit varies considerably according to these indications. VanderVeldt and Odenwald state that the treatment "is valuable in cases of depression, especially those of involutional melancholia, and for slight prepsychotic conditions."[2] Report No. 15 of the Group for the Advancement of Psychiatry gives a somewhat detailed evaluation (in outline form) of these various indications.[3]

Incidentally, two of the reports published by the Group for Advancement of Psychiatry deal with electro-shock therapy. The first of these (GAP Report No. 1; Sept. 15, 1947) begins by referring to "the reported promiscuous and indiscriminate use of electro-shock therapy"; and the predominant tone of the report is rather negative, stressing such things as lack of evidence for certain claims, abuses, etc.[4] The revised report is more positive, as these opening words of the first point indicate: "Electro-shock therapy (perhaps better named electro-convulsive therapy or electro-cerebral therapy) is of unquestioned benefit in certain psychiatric conditions. When indicated it is a valuable part of the overall psychiatric treatment program and in many cases is the major therapeutic procedure." Despite the positive tone, however, the revised report cites certain abuses that the committee considered to be widespread: e.g., the use of shock therapy without adequate evaluation of the patient's needs, without proper safeguards (especially with non-hospitalized patients), without consideration of other forms of therapy, by unqualified persons, etc.[5]

It is not my intention, in giving the preceding paragraphs,

---

[2] *Psychiatry and Catholicism* (New York: The McGraw-Hill Publishing Company, 1952), p. 68.

[3] The Group for the Advancement of Psychiatry has a membership of approximately 150 psychiatrists. Its reports are published at 3617 W. Sixth Ave., Topeka, Kansas.

[4] GAP Report No. 1, Sept. 15, 1947.

[5] GAP Report No. 15, Aug., 1950.

to make any judgment on the indications for, or abuses of, electro-shock treatments. The paragraphs merely scratch the surface of the professional literature. However, even though superficial, they illustrate the points to be considered when a moral appraisal of electro-shock therapy must be made. The treatment is unquestionably justified when it is preceded by adequate diagnosis, administered by competent persons, accompanied by necessary safeguards, and supplemented, when necessary, by other forms of therapy. The precise moral obligation of hospital authorities and physicians is to see that these conditions are fulfilled.

Lest the summary rule I have just given be misunderstood, let me add that by "adequate diagnosis" I mean not merely an analysis of the patient's condition but also a consideration of other methods of treatment. Obviously, it would be neither good medicine nor good morality to use shock therapy if an equally good result could be produced by a less drastic measure. For example, it now seems clear that the judicious use of such drugs as the tranquilizers can reduce, and perhaps totally eliminate, the use of shock therapy. Insofar as this is true, shock therapy ceases to be medically indicated and becomes morally objectionable.

On a Pregnant Patient

I have been asked more than once whether electro-shock therapy may be permitted on a patient who is pregnant. Before answering this question, one would have to know whether any harm might be done the fetus or whether there would be any special danger for the mother that would not be incurred if she were not pregnant. If no special risks are involved, the morality of the treatments would be judged in the same way as I have indicated above. If there are special risks, the precise problem would be to judge whether these might be justified— for instance, by the application of the principle of the double effect. Cavanagh and McGoldrick say that pregnancy was

296

formerly regarded as a contraindication to electro-shock therapy, but there is considerable evidence accumulating that this procedure does not affect pregnancy. Within the past few years several psychiatrists and an experienced psychiatric nurse have told me that pregnancy creates no special risk either for mother or for child. On one occasion, when a woman aborted after the sixth electro-shock treatment, all the experts consulted said that the treatment was not a causal factor in the abortion. An abstract in a recent number of the *Journal of the American Medical Association*[6] concerns a child that was born approximately three months after the completion of shock treatments and which at the age of 32 months was found to be mentally deficient. The doctors think that the mental deficiency is probably not due to the shock treatments; but it is suggested that attention be paid to the incidence of mentally deficient children of mothers who have received electro-convulsive therapy during pregnancy.

These few points indicate that medical opinion is predominantly in favor of the view that pregnancy adds no special hazard to electro-shock therapy, but the matter is not without obscurity. In practice, there is certainly no reason for a blanket prohibition of shock treatments during pregnancy. Hospitals and patients may safely abide by the judgment of their own physicians and consultants regarding the need or advisability of the treatments.

---

[6] March 27, 1954, p. 1132. For the original article, cf. *Minnesota Medicine*, Dec., 1953, p. 1260.

chapter 34

An Instruction on Baptism

I T HAPPENS very often in hospitals that emergencies arise when those who are not priests must confer baptism. The purpose of the present instruction is to give in very brief form the points that ought to be kept in mind in such emergencies. To explain these points fully would defeat the purpose of the instruction; hence, it would be wise for all to read these points over from time to time and to ask for explanations of the points they do not understand.

1) *Ordinary method of baptizing:*

Water is poured on the head in such a way that it will flow on the skin, and not merely on the hair; and while the water is being poured these words are pronounced: "I baptize you in the Name of the Father, and of the Son, and of the Holy Ghost."

The water will more easily flow on the skin if it is poured on the forehead. The same person who pours the water should pronounce the words.

2) *Conditional baptism:*

The subject for valid baptism should be a living person, not yet validly baptized, and (if an adult) willing to receive baptism. When there is a doubt about any of these three requisites (i.e., life, previous baptism, or willingness), the baptism should be conferred *conditionally.* The condition in all cases is, "if you can be baptized"; and the complete formula is: "If you can be baptized, I baptize you in the Name of the Father, and of the Son, and of the Holy Ghost."

It may be well to note that it is not strictly necessary to put this condition into words. It suffices that the person baptizing (e.g., nurse or doctor) has the intention of conferring the sacrament if it can be validly received. Hence, if a nurse or doctor should be somewhat upset because of the emergency, it would be sufficient merely to use the ordinary formula, "I baptize you in the Name of the Father, and of the Son, and of the Holy Ghost," with the intention of making the baptism conditional if that be necessary. In fact, as far as the condition goes, it would suffice in these emergencies to have the general intention of conferring baptism according to the mind of the Church. This holds not only for the doubts mentioned here but for all emergency cases when there is some doubt about the conditions required for the validity of the sacrament.

In a word, it is better to use the proper formula for conditional baptism; but if there is any confusion about the formula, such expressions as "if you can be baptized," "if you are alive," etc., can be dropped. The main thing is to say the essential words and to pour the water (or immerse) correctly, with the desire to baptize according to the mind of the Church.

3) *Conscious adults:* (Canon 752, par. 2.)

[N.B. All the points briefly outlined here and in 4 are fully explained in the next chapter.]

A conscious adult who wishes to be baptized should be helped to make acts of faith and of contrition for his sins before the baptism is conferred. The act of faith should embrace at least these four truths: the existence of God, the fact that God rewards the good and punishes the wicked, the mystery of the Blessed Trinity, and the mystery of the Incarnation. Excellent prayers for this use, as well as on other occasions, may be found on the card published by the Apostolate to Assist Dying Non-Catholics.

4) *Unconscious adults:* (Canon 752, par. 3.)

a) If an unconscious dying adult has already asked for baptism, he should be baptized absolutely.

b) If he has not clearly asked, but has given some probable sign that he wanted to be baptized (e.g., by showing interest in the Church), he should be baptized conditionally.

c) If he is unconscious and entirely unknown—i.e., if nothing is known about his desire for baptism or whether he has ever been baptized, it is at least commendable to baptize him conditionally.

d) Even a person who has refused baptism may, when unconscious and dying, be given conditional baptism.

5) *Dying babies:*

All babies who are in danger of death should be baptized. In cases in which one or both parents are Catholics, there should be no difficulty about this, even though the parents cannot be consulted. But, even when the parents are not Catholic, the right of the baby to the fruit of the sacrament should normally transcend any other consideration. Should difficulty with non-Catholic parents be anticipated, the chaplain should be consulted, if possible, about the prudent course of action: e.g., whether to ask the parents, whether to notify them about a baptism conferred, and so forth.

6) *Baptism of fetus that cannot survive:*

a) Every such fetus, even an embryo, if visible at all, must be baptized immediately, unless it is certainly dead. (Cf. canon 747.) *For this purpose,* the only certain sign of death is noticeable corruption (putrefaction, decomposition, offensive odor, maceration, discoloration of flesh, etc.). If there is no clear sign of corruption, the fetus should be considered as at least probably alive and should be baptized conditionally.

b) If a fetus is delivered enclosed in the membranes, the membranes must be ruptured before baptism is conferred.

c) If there is time and opportunity, baptism by *immersion*

is the surer way of baptizing a fetus expelled during the early stages of pregnancy. This is accomplished by immersing the fetus completely in water and, after breaking the membranes, pronouncing the words of baptism, conditionally or absolutely, as the case requires, and at the same time moving the fetus in the water.

7) *Baptism during difficult delivery:*

a) Baptism should be conferred immediately when there is danger that the child will not survive complete delivery.

b) In the case of head presentation, baptism should be conferred on the head, and unconditionally.

c) In the case of other presentation, baptism should be conferred conditionally on the part presented, and then repeated conditionally on the head after delivery. The reason for this is that baptism is considered certainly valid only when conferred on the head.

d) In these cases of difficult delivery the baptism should be conferred by the doctor, nurse, or sister, as may be judged best according to circumstances.

8) *Intrauterine baptism:*

a) When there is danger that the fetus will die before it can be even partially delivered, it should, when possible, be baptized conditionally while in the uterus. If it is later successfully delivered, or if there is at least a head presentation, the baptism should be repeated conditionally on the head, because there is always some doubt about the validity of baptism within the uterus.

b) Intrauterine baptism can be conferred only after the membranes have ruptured.

c) For baptizing a fetus within the uterus, a sterile bulb syringe containing sterile water is inserted so that the water will flow directly on the fetus. The words of conditional baptism should be pronounced by the same person who is causing the water to flow and while the water is flowing. The person who baptizes should have the medical knowledge necessary to eliminate the danger of infection.

9) *When a pregnant mother dies:*

a) Granted the consent, at least reasonably presumed, of the other parent or guardian, a fetus that is at least probably alive should be immediately extracted and baptized.

b) Even without consent of parent or guardian, a cesarean section may be performed to extract a living, viable fetus. It seems that only one state, Oklahoma, makes explicit provision for this; but lawyers tell me that the practice of other states would very likely be the same. The reason is that our legal tradition recognizes the right of the viable fetus to life outside the uterus. If there is any doubt about this in any particular state, legal advice should be sought.

Once the viable fetus is delivered, the ordinary rule about baptism should be followed: if the baby is in danger of death (as many premature infants would be), he should be immediately baptized.

c) When there is question of delivering an inviable fetus merely to baptize it, there may be serious legal difficulty. Hence, unless the required consent is had, it seems better to attempt an intrauterine baptism.

10) *Monsters:*

a) The general rule is that a monster is to be treated in the same way as a normal fetus.

b) If there is some doubt whether a monstrosity is more than one person, one being should be baptized absolutely (if certainly alive), conditionally (if doubtfully alive) and the other possible beings should be baptized conditionally (Cf. canon 748).

When there is difficulty about applying the rule just given, the problem can be solved this way: Pour water over the entire monstrosity, or immerse it (moving it in the water), and pronounce the words of baptism *with the intention of baptizing as many persons as are present.* For example: a nurse immerses the monstrosity in water and, while moving it in the water, she says: "I baptize you (meaning 'all of you, if there be more than one') in the Name of the Father, and of the Son, and of the Holy Ghost."

chapter 35

Baptism of Adults

WITH REFERENCE to the reception of baptism, the Church considers anyone who has not yet attained the use of reason to be an infant and anyone who has attained the use of reason to be an adult. Obviously, the attainment of the use of reason differs somewhat according to individuals. It is not something that can be mathematically and absolutely set at any definite age—e.g., 5, 6, 7, or 8. However, in the absence of any special signs to the contrary, it is sound theological practice to consider children below the age of seven to be infants in the canonical sense, and others to be adults.

In chapter 34, nn. 3 and 4, I gave brief rules stating when adults should or may be baptized. Because of the great practical importance of the topic, however, I think it should be thoroughly explained. The explanation will entail first a commentary on the provisions of canon 752 of the Code of Canon Law, and secondly, a discussion of some special cases that are at least partially outside the scope of this canon.

I. CANON 752

This canon formulates several clear, crisp rules concerning the baptism of adults. In general, these rules cover three distinct cases: (1) the baptism of adults who are not in danger of death; (2) the baptism of adults who are in danger of death, but conscious; and (3) the baptism of adults who are in danger of death and already unconscious. I have designedly said that the Code *formulates* these rules; for the rules them-selves are not merely disciplinary laws of the Church but are rather statements of, or corollaries from, sound theological principles.

No Danger of Death

The first part of canon 752 prescribes that adults who are not in danger of death are not to be baptized unless they ex-pressly desire it; moreover, before they are baptized they are to be given complete catechetical instructions and are to be warned to make an act of contrition for their sins.

Such are the regulations for what we may term the ordinary case: that is, the preparation for baptism of converts who are not in danger of death. The reason for the first prescription is obvious. Everyone who has attained the use of reason must decide for himself whether he wishes to receive baptism; God will not force His gifts on him. Hence, in the case of all but infants, a requisite for valid baptism is the *willingness* of the subject. And, of course, the minister of the sacrament must know of this willingness before he confers baptism.

The need for complete instruction in this case is also evident. The convert is being prepared to lead a Catholic life. He should know the doctrines and laws of the Church that per-tain to normal Catholic living; and before his baptism he should accept these doctrines through an act of faith and be willing to fulfill the duties of a Catholic. Finally, the act of contrition is necessary because even baptism cannot take away his personal sins unless he repents of them.

We need not delay further on this part of the canon. Ordi-narily these cases of "complete instruction" would not occur in a hospital; and, if they did (e.g. in the case of a permanent invalid), the chaplain would take care of them. I might add, however, for the benefit of religious and lay nurses who may be occasionally privileged to instruct converts, that it is very important to teach them how to go to confession. This knowledge will be an immense help to them after their baptism.

Dying, But Conscious

The second part of the canon deals with the case of a person who is in danger of death, but still conscious and in possession of his faculties. In this case there is no change with regard to the requisite intention and act of contrition. The person is not to be baptized unless he wishes it; and, if he is baptized, he is to be cautioned to make an act of contrition for his sins.

With regard to the instruction, there must be some modification. The complete instruction of a convert takes several weeks, or even several months, depending on the convert's capacity and on the frequency and duration of the instructions. Evidently such complete instruction is impossible when death is imminent. The canon recognizes this and indicates the minimum essentials of instruction to be given in these urgent cases: namely a sufficient explanation of the principal truths of the Catholic Faith so that the sick person can give some assent to these truths and profess his willingness to live up to the obligations imposed by the Christian religion (in case he should recover).

The principal truths of our faith, belief in which is necessary for salvation, are four: the existence of one God, the fact that God rewards the good and punishes the wicked, the mystery of the Blessed Trinity, and the mystery of the Incarnation. These truths are aptly expressed in simple acts of faith by Msgr. Markham in the prayers he composed for the assistance of dying non-Catholics.

I believe in one God. I believe that God rewards the good and punishes the wicked. I believe that in God there are three divine Persons—God the Father, God the Son, and God the Holy Ghost. I believe that God the Son became Man, without ceasing to be God. I believe that He is my Lord and my Saviour, the Redeemer of the human race, that He died on the Cross for the salvation of all men, that He died also for me.

Such is one brief statement of the four truths that everyone must believe in order to be certain of saving his soul. If at all possible, something should be said about each of the truths so that the dying person can make his act of faith in all of them. This can generally be done in a few minutes; hence there is usually no great difficulty in at least outlining the truths. In the rare cases in which all four truths cannot be mentioned, we should at least help the patient make an act of faith in the first two truths: namely, in the existence of one God and in the fact that God rewards the good and punishes the wicked. It is probable, though by no means certain, that faith in these two truths is sufficient for salvation; and that probability can be acted upon when further instruction is impossible.

In assisting dying non-Catholics we should not place too much confidence in the mere words, "I believe." In Catholic doctrine, the words "faith" and "believe" have technical meanings. When we say we believe, we mean we accept a truth, not because we see it or understand it, but because God revealed it. In other words, we take God's word for it. It is important for us to bear this in mind and to impress this point on the dying non-Catholic, because many of them have very vague notions of "faith" and "belief." Msgr. Markham's card, after giving the acts of faith cited above, adds this brief prayer: "I believe, on God's authority, everything that He has taught and revealed." If a nurse is using this card, these words would give the opportunity for a brief explanation of the true meaning of faith.

Fr. William Bowdern, S.J., suggests that the nurse explain the meaning of faith and the truths necessary to be believed in the following simple manner:

> You believe that there is a very good and loving God, don't you? You know that he could not tell a lie or teach us anything wrong. He told us some things about himself, and because he only tells the truth, you and I believe what he has told us. We take his word for it, don't we?

He told us that there is only one God and three divine persons; the Father, the Son, and the Holy Ghost. And he said that the Son came down on earth and took on himself our human nature, and then died on the cross to save us, because he loved us so much. And he told us that he wants us all to be happy with him forever in heaven when we die. And he told us that the only ones who will not be with him in heaven are those who insist on going to hell where they will suffer and never see him. We believe these things because God told us, don't we?[1]

The foregoing are ways of helping the dying person make the necessary acts of faith. Every nurse ought to have some simple, clearly-planned way of doing this. Having helped the patient make the acts of faith, she should then help him to say the other prayers, particularly the act of contrition. Msgr. Markham's card is also a great aid to this, as it contains, besides the acts of faith, also brief acts of hope, charity, and contrition.

What we have said thus far pertains to the preparation of a dying person for baptism. This is equivalent to saying that we are preparing him for admission into the Catholic Church; hence, the canon cautions us to have the patient express a willingness to observe the precepts of the Christian religion. This does not mean that we have to recount all these precepts in detail; but, when we are dealing with a conscious person and there is time, we should at least be sure that he wants to keep the commandments of God and live up to the obligations that the Church imposes on him. If he expresses this willingness, he is to be baptized without delay. The canon supposes that the baptism will be conferred while the recipient is still conscious, if this is possible. However, should he lose consciousness before receiving the sacrament, but after having requested it, it should be administered unconditionally.

Dying, But Unconscious

The third part of canon 752 gives us some practical rules about dying adults who are either wholly or partially

---

[1] *The Catholic Nurse and the Dying* (St. Louis: The Queen's Work, 1934), pp. 6-7

unconscious. Such persons are to be baptized conditionally if, before becoming unconscious, they gave some probable sign that they wanted baptism, or if, in their present state (when partially unconscious) they give a probable indication that they wish to be baptized. The baptism is administered conditionally—the condition being: "If you wish to be baptized." Later, if the subject recovers and manifests a clear desire to be baptized, he is to be re-baptized conditionally ("if you are not baptized"), unless it is certain that the first conditional baptism is valid. Such certainty would seldom be had.

Each of the conditions mentioned in the preceding paragraph —"if you wish to be baptized," and "if you are not baptized"— can be expressed by the more general formula, "if you can be baptized." Moreover, as I explained in chapter 34, n. 2, it is not strictly necessary to put the condition into words.

Such are the prescriptions of the canon. In themselves, these prescriptions are clear and admit of no controversy. However, with regard to one point there is evidently room for differences of opinion. I refer to the interpretation of the words, "a probable sign that he wishes to be baptized." Theologians can and do dispute over what constitutes a wish to be baptized, and also over what constitutes a manifestation of such a wish. Because of this possibility of differences of opinion, it may be well for us to consider some of the cases likely to arise.

Mr. X belongs to no particular religion; but his wife is a Catholic and his children are Catholics. He has never said openly that he intended to join the Catholic Church, but he has manifested such general good will that those who know him feel rather confident that he had "leanings" in that direction. Cases like this are not infrequent. One who is assisting at X's deathbed has good reason to conclude: "It is probable that this man intended to join the Catholic Church before his death." Evidently, an intention to join the Catholic Church

309

includes an intention to receive baptism; hence we have here a probable sign of the will to be baptized. I doubt whether any one would question the fact that such a person should be given conditional baptism, if he were unconscious and dying.

Mr. Y presents a somewhat different case. He has never manifested that he wanted to be a Catholic, but he has shown a disposition to be a "Christian," that is, to belong to one of the sects that profess Christianity. In other words he has given some indication that he wants to belong to "Christ's religion," whatever that is. Actually, of course, there is only one true Church of Christ. A person may be mistaken as to which is the true one; but if he does want to belong to Christ's Church, he also wants baptism, because our Lord made baptism the sacrament of entry into His Church. Hence, anyone who has given an indication that he wants to be a Christian should be conditionally baptized when he is unconscious and dying, unless it is certain that he is already validly baptized.

Mr. Z presents a still different and more difficult case. He belongs to no Christian body; but he has been a "good man" in the sense that he wanted to do the right thing, or at least he has manifested that he was sorry for all his sins and that he wanted to do what was necessary to save his soul. This, of course, is a much more general disposition than that of X or Y. And the question arises: can such a disposition—that is, sorrow for sins and desire to do what is necessary for salvation— be construed as a wish to receive baptism, or is something more definite demanded? Theologians do not agree in their answer to the question. Many hold that this disposition is entirely too general; others consider that it implicitly includes the wish to receive baptism, because this sacrament is the ordinary means of salvation instituted by God.

Because of the controversy just mentioned, we cannot say with certainty that a man who has indicated that he wants to do everything necessary to save his soul has the requisite intention for baptism. But we can say, at least because of the authorities behind the opinion, that it is probable that such a person wishes to be baptized; hence we are justified in conferring conditional baptism when the man is in danger of death and unconscious.

II. SOME SPECIAL PROBLEMS

The foregoing comments cover all the explicit provisions of canon 752. But there are some further special problems that seem to lie outside the scope of the canon and that occur rather frequently in hospital practice. My purpose in this section is to give some useful information about the theological discussions of these problems and to state some practical conclusions that may be safely followed by priests, physicians, and nurses who may be faced with the problems.

Unconscious and Unknown

Suppose a patient is brought into the hospital in an unconscious and dying condition, and nothing is known about him. Perhaps he is baptized, perhaps not; perhaps he desires to be baptized, perhaps he does not. May we, or should we, give him conditional baptism?

There are two opinions concerning this problem. Many theologians hold that we neither should nor may baptize the unknown person, even conditionally. They argue that baptism is a sacramental rite which incorporates a person into the Church and makes him subject to many definite obligations. Because of these serious consequences the rite is not to be conferred on anyone unless there is some positive indication that he wishes it. These theologians believe, moreover, that the very fact that the canon law says nothing explicitly about this case confirms their opinion; for, if the Church wanted us to confer baptism on unknown dying persons it would say so. Finally, the defenders of this opinion can point to a number of decisions of the Holy See which apparently favor their severe view.

311

According to the first opinion, therefore, the Church *forbids* the baptism, even conditional, of a dying person *unless* he has given some positive indication that he wishes to be baptized. In other words, canon 752 tells us not only everything that we should do, but also everything that we *may* do.

Many theologians reject this first opinion as unnecessarily severe. They point to the probable opinion that every unbaptized person who sincerely desires to save his soul at least implicitly wishes to be baptized, and they say that the presumption of such good will should favor every unknown dying person. But, though one may presume that the unknown person has good will, one may not presume that he is already baptized, because we know that vast numbers of people are not baptized. It follows from this that every unknown and unconscious dying person is probably an apt subject for baptism, and that it is permissible, if not obligatory, to give him the benefit of conditional baptism.

The theologians who sponsor the second opinion obviously will not admit that the canon law forbids us to confer even conditional baptism on dying adults who are unconscious and unknown. They say that the canon law simply does not touch the case. It was a matter of debate before the publication of the Code of Canon Law, and it may still be debated.

Speaking of the more lenient opinion, which he styles "sufficiently probable to be followed safely," Fr. Francis J. Connell, C.SS.R., says: "The best argument for the opinion seems to be that on the law of averages there is some probability that every unknown individual is an unbaptized person who either explicitly or implicitly desires baptism."[2] I think Fr. Connell's words summarize the matter very well. Sound reasons, as well as eminent authorities, allow us to confer conditional baptism on the unknown and unconscious dying adult. We may safely

---

[2] *American Ecclesiastical Review,* April, 1948, p. 258.

follow this practice unless some new pronouncement of the Holy See would clearly forbid it.

Refused Baptism

Suppose an unconscious dying person is not unknown, but rather it is known that he has never showed the slightest inclination to receive baptism, in fact, that he led a life of sin and even refused baptism. It seems that the majority of theologians would say that such a person is not a fit subject even for conditional baptism. According to them, all we may do is pray for him and leave him to God. However, there are some milder views, and it may be well to indicate them.

Fr. Henry Davis, S.J., says:

Cases arise, especially in missionary countries, when a dying person has never manifested a desire for Baptism; it may even be that such a person has positively refused to become a Christian and has given orders that a missionary should not be allowed to come near him in his last moments; furthermore, he may even have rejected, before loss of consciousness, all ministrations of the priest. Nevertheless, since such a person may have changed his mind in the last stage of consciousness, and since indeed there is every hope that he did so, under the universal salvific will of God, and since the very presence of a priest must be considered to be a manifest act of divine providence, conditional Baptism may and, we believe, should be given to such a one. It must, however, be admitted that Baptism may not be given in such cases if the Christian religion would thereby be contemned and thought magical or superstitious by numbers of pagans present. The wise missionary will know how to administer the Sacrament secretly without giving scandal.[3]

Somewhat similarly, Fr. Edwin F. Healy, S.J., writes:

If on the other hand a person has never shown any inclination to become a Christian nor given any indication of repentance for his seriously sinful life, may he, while dying and unconscious, be baptized conditionally? It would seem that the essential requisites are certainly lacking. Nevertheless, because there is some slight probability that the

---

[3] *Moral and Pastoral Theology*, Vol. 3 (London: Sheed and Ward, 1943), pp. 54-55.

required dispositions are present, one may baptize him under the condition, "If thou art capable, I baptize thee, etc."[4]

Another illustrative quotation may be given from Fr. Matthaeus Conte a Coronata, O.M.C., an author distinguished for his ability to weigh the values of conflicting opinions. In the first volume of his treatise on the Sacraments, he writes:

Many authors teach that both on the missions and in our own lands, baptism is to be administered with the condition, if you are capable, to all unconscious dying persons, not excepting those who, while they were able, seemed to resist their conversion. The reason [for baptizing them] is the probability that God gives to the dying special graces of illumination that move them to desire baptism. This milder opinion does not seem to be against the Code, because the Code does not deal directly with this question.[5]

Finally, I should like to refer to an excellent article, "Ministering to Dying Non-Catholics," by Fr. L. L. McReavy.[6] This article contains a comprehensive discussion, on the theological level, of the problems pertaining to the administration of sacraments to dying non-Catholics; and at the end of the discussion the author states some conclusions which can be "regarded as probable enough for practice." The first of these conclusions is: "All three sacraments, Baptism, Penance and Extreme Unction, may be given conditionally to the unconscious, *whatever their previous dispositions may have been,* provided always that scandal can be avoided" (italics added).

Certain points should be noted about the opinion held by the authors just cited and others whom they represent. In the first place, they are not saying that we may baptize a person when it is certain that he does not want to be baptized. They

---

[4] *Christian Guidance* (Chicago: The Loyola University Press, 1949), p. 67. Father Healy reiterates this opinion in *Medical Ethics* (Chicago: The Loyola University Press, 1956), p. 368-369, and gives a concrete illustration on p. 372.

[5] *De Sacramentis,* Vol. 1 (Turin: Marietti, 1943), p. 95, n. 131.

[6] Cf. *The Clergy Review,* Feb., 1955, pp. 79-90.

would all admit that to attempt to baptize an adult, even conditionally, when it is clear that he does not want it is a sacrilege. Their position, therefore, is that there is some probability that the dying person has the required intention.

Secondly, they do not claim any great probability that the baptism would be valid. Rather, they admit the probability is slight, but they contend that in an extreme case we may act even on very slight probability. Their principal reason for hope is the probability that God gives the dying especially powerful graces. But they might add other reasons which would cover some cases. For instance, sometimes a conscious person refuses baptism because he does not understand it, yet he really wants what baptism would give him. In other words, he implicitly wants what he explicitly rejects. Moreover, some people resist conversion because of fear or other emotional difficulties that often disappear when life is ebbing away. Since it would be impossible always to examine these and other avenues of hope, the authors appeal to a more universal principle: the salvific will of God.

Finally, all these authors realize that the conferring of conditional baptism in some of these extreme cases might create the impression that we force baptism on people or that we use the sacramental rite as a sort of magic; hence, they caution us to administer the conditional baptism quietly and secretly, insofar as that is necessary to avoid such scandalous impressions.

I have suggested previously that the lenient opinion held by the authors cited here is a minority opinion. Nevertheless, if I were in the presence of a dying unconscious person, I would follow this opinion with a safe conscience, and I am convinced that others may do likewise if they wish. As a practical conclusion, therefore, I would say: even when it is known that a person never showed any inclination to receive baptism, and even when he has actually led a life of sin and refused baptism, we are justified in baptizing him conditionally when he is unconscious and dying.

I cannot insist too strongly on our *right* both to teach and to follow the practical conclusion I have just enunciated. As Fr. John J. Lynch, S.J., stated at the conclusion of a survey of articles (including Fr. McReavy's) dealing with the administration of sacraments to the unconscious, especially those who had refused to receive the sacraments while conscious:

> It is difficult for me to understand the reluctance of some priests to acknowledge our right to follow this opinion in practice. Perhaps they are simply not aware of the number and stature of those theologians who espouse it, or have not really considered the reasons adduced in its defense. But neither intrinsic reason nor extrinsic authority is lacking to justify the conclusion, most recently reiterated by L. L. McReavy, that "all three sacraments, Baptism, Penance and Extreme Unction, may be given conditionally to the unconscious, whatever their previous dispositions may have been, provided always that scandal can be avoided."[7]

Protestants

Suppose that an unconscious dying person is known to be a Protestant who has never showed any inclination to become a Catholic or who has even refused to become a Catholic. There is substantial agreement among theologians on this case. The fact that the person is a Protestant usually not only indicates an intention of receiving baptism but also creates a presumption that he is already baptized. However, unless it is already known that he has been baptized *and* that his baptism was valid, it is considered advisable to baptize him conditionally when he is unconscious and dying.

CONCLUSION

We can briefly summarize these various cases by a citation from Fr. Arthur Vermeersch, S.J., for many years professor of moral theology at the Gregorian University, Rome, and certainly one of the outstanding moralists of this century. After having thoroughly examined all the arguments for and against

---

[7] *Theological Studies,* June, 1956, p. 196.

baptizing unconscious dying persons, Fr. Vermeersch reached this conclusion: "If scandal is avoided, one may confer conditional baptism on any unconscious dying adult who is not known to be already baptized."[8]

Priests, physicians, nurses, and others are justified in using Fr. Vermeersch's conclusion as a norm for their spiritual ministrations to unconscious dying adults. This means that whenever it is not certain that the unconscious dying person is already validly baptized, one may secretly baptize him conditionally. The condition to be used is, "if you can be baptized." This condition would mean "if you are not baptized, and if you wish to be baptized."

The same Fr. Vermeersch has another maxim that should mean even more to those who minister to the dying. "I could not resign myself," he said, "to permit a single soul to be lost that might have been saved by my ministrations." It should be noted that these words are applicable not merely to the case of giving conditional baptism to unconscious persons, but also, and even especially, to the preparation of conscious persons for death. After all, the baptism of many of the unconscious persons mentioned in this chapter is of very dubious efficacy, as even the staunchest defenders of the practice will admit. It is simply the seizing of a last plank of hope, the use of a last desperate remedy. We seldom, if ever, know whether it produces the desired result.

But when a patient is conscious, no matter what be his religion, we accomplish results that are definitely fruitful, even to a high degree, by encouraging him to make devout acts of faith, hope, charity, and contrition. Nurses have special opportunities in this regard because of their close association with their patients, and those nurses who help patients to say the prayers composed by the Apostolate to Assist Dying Non-Catholics are performing a work of supreme spiritual value.

---

[8] Cf. Vermeersch-Creusen, *Epitome juris canonici,* II (Rome: The Gregorian University, 1940), n. 35.

ADDED REFERENCES

The footnotes of this chapter on adult baptism contain several references to helpful books and articles. A few more references may increase the utility of the chapter.

1. In my discussion of the problem concerning the unknown and unconscious dying person I mentioned that many eminent theologians are of the opinion that conditional baptism may be conferred. The list of authorities favoring this view would include Bucceroni, Cappello, Davis, Genicot, Iorio, Lehmkuhl, Piscetta, Sabetti, Vermeersch, and Wouters. These names, of course, would mean little or nothing to nurses and physicians; but to the priest who is conversant with books of moral theology the list should be highly significant.

2. *Theological Studies,* March, 1952, pp. 94-97, contains a brief, but sufficiently comprehensive, discussion of the authorities and intrinsic reasons for conferring the sacraments conditionally on unconscious persons. Chaplains who have doubts concerning any of the conclusions expressed in this chapter could profitably consult this number of *Theological Studies.* Another very worthwhile reference is: "Administration of the Sacraments to Heretics and Schismatics," by John J. Danagher, C.M., in *The Jurist,* Oct., 1953, pp. 357-381.

3. *Routine Spiritual Care Procedures,* by Gerald H. Fitz-Gibbon, S.J., is a pamphlet prepared especially to help laymen, doctors, and nurses in the spiritual care of the dying. It is published by The Catholic Hospital Association of the United States and Canada. Fr. FitzGibbon has also composed a leaflet entitled *Spiritual First Aid Procedures* which gives some essential points to be observed in the care of the dying. This leaflet is published by The Queen's Work.

4. In my text I have mentioned the Apostolate to Assist Dying Non-Catholics. This apostolate was founded by the Rt. Rev. Raphael J. Markham, of the Archdiocese of Cincinnati. The Apostolate uses prayers composed by Msgr. Markham especially for non-Catholics who are seriously ill and with

whom a conversion to the true faith is not very likely. A brochure explaining the work of the Apostolate, and cards containing the prayer may be obtained from:

Sisters of the Poor of St. Francis, St. Clare Convent, Hartwell, Cincinnati 15, Ohio, and Sister M. Carmelita, R.S.M., Convent of Mercy, 1409 Freeman Avenue, Cincinnati 14, Ohio.

chapter 36

Calling a Non-Catholic Minister

While avoiding odious proselytism, we must not be indifferent to the spiritual needs and desires of non-Catholics; and everything consonant with our principles must be done for them. In particular, when a non-Catholic patient asks to have his minister or rabbi called this request should be honored. Directive 58. (See also the U.S. Code, "Religious Supplement," n. 5; and the Canadian Code, art. 53.)

IN PRECEDING CHAPTERS I have already indicated some ways of giving religious help to non-Catholics. The present chapter will be mainly concerned with the special problem of calling a non-Catholic minister. On this point, three questions are of very frequent occurrence: (1) May the minister be called by a Catholic nurse or sister? (2) May the call be made if the request comes, not from the patient, but from his relatives? (3) May a minister who visits the hospital be supplied with a list of patients registered under his denomination?

Before giving definite answers to these questions, I should like to say that throughout the chapter the expression, "non-Catholic minister," means not only a Protestant minister, but also a Jewish rabbi and a schismatic priest. In a word, I am talking about all official ministers of non-Catholics, whatever be their denomination. And let me note also that my answers concern conditions as they exist generally in the United States and Canada. If there are special difficulties in some localities, these should be solved by the local authorities, e.g., by the bishop or his representative.

1. *Who may make the call?*

Canon lawyers follow a principle which may be roughly translated thus: "When a law makes no distinction, neither should we distinguish." A similar principle may be applied in explaining the provision of the Codes and *Directives* that ministers are to be called when non-Catholic patients request it. No qualification is made as to who may do the calling: hence, we should make no qualification. Anyone in the hospital may make the call.

As a matter of fact, one reason for including this provision in the U.S. Code and the revised *Directives* was to clear up a misunderstanding relative to the calling of a minister by a religious or a Catholic nurse. The basis for this misunderstanding seems to be at least partially that our Catholic textbooks of medical ethics formerly stated that, when a non-Catholic patient requested his minister, a Catholic should not make this call personally but it should be made through someone of the same religious affiliation as the patient. It is true that the Holy See itself gave this ruling in practical answers to questions from Cologne in 1848, from Egypt in 1872, and from Rome in 1898.

Practical answers given by the Holy See are not the same as universal principles; they are rather the applications of principles to concrete situations. These applications, unlike principles, can differ according to circumstances of time and place. For this reason it is hardly possible to give an adequate explanation of such practical answers without a complete knowledge of those factors of time and place. Actually, we do not know all the factors pertinent to these particular replies of the Holy See. To the theologians who worked on our U.S. Code and *Directives,* it seemed that the replies of the Holy See were very likely based on the judgment that in those circum-

321

stances the calling of a minister by a religious or Catholic nurse would readily be open to misinterpretation: e.g., it might create the impression of religious indifferentism (that all religions are equal before God), and this would be equivalent to a denial of the Catholic teaching regarding the one true Church of Christ.

It was the considered judgment of our theologians that there would be no danger of such misrepresentation if the Catholic hospitals in our country followed the simple rule that a religious or Catholic nurse (or any other member of the hospital staff or personnel) may call a minister at the request of a non-Catholic patient. Among us this action would merely be taken as a professional courtesy, the denial of which might be reasonably resented by non-Catholics. I presume that the theologians who worked on the formulation of the new Canadian Code were of the same mind.[1]

It will be worthwhile to make two further observations before going on to the next question. I referred above to the Catholic doctrine of the one true Church. Our non-Catholic friends know that we hold this doctrine and that, in keeping with it, Catholics must avoid conduct which fosters the impression that all religions are equal before God. They also know that this doctrine does not exclude from salvation those who through their own sincere convictions are not actual members of the Church. Nevertheless, not only our non-Catholic friends but also Catholics themselves often have difficulty in harmonizing these apparently contradictory doctrines: namely, that there is only one true Church, yet those who are not actually members can be saved. A very clear explanation of this matter has been given in a letter sent by the Sacred Con-

---

[1] For a more complete discussion of the replies of the Holy See and of the theologians' opinions, see *Theological Studies*, March, 1949, pp. 71-74.

gregation of the Holy Office to Archbishop Richard J. Cushing.[2]

Another observation concerns a practical suggestion that is sometimes made by moralists who treat the present question. They say that the fact that a non-Catholic patient is visited by his minister should not keep the nurse from carrying out her own spiritual ministrations, e.g., of praying with the patient, and especially of helping him to make acts of faith, hope, charity, and contrition. I would not only agree with this suggestion; I would add that it should be followed also in the case of Catholic patients who have been visited by a priest. The nurse is in a special position to pray with the patient. I can say from my own experience as a patient that when I was critically ill I was deeply grateful to the sisters and other nurses who prayed with me and for me, by making the salutary acts mentioned above, as well as by saying the rosary and various aspirations. Other patients, no doubt, would be similarly grateful. It is difficult, if not practically impossible, to pray verbally when one is in great pain, has an oxygen mask, etc.; but even in these circumstances one can listen to the prayers and by his intention "make them his own."

2. *Request by relatives:*

The same principle which justifies the calling of a minister at the request of a non-Catholic patient would justify a similar courtesy when the patient's desire is expressed by his relatives. A practical man, however, might wonder why the relatives do not themselves call the minister, as it would usually be much easier and more natural for them to do so—just as a Catholic family that wishes its own parish priest would generally call him personally and not ask the hospital to do so. Perhaps this question refers to a case in which the non-Catholics are strang-

---

[2] For the text of the letter, see *The Catholic Mind*, Dec., 1952, pp. 749-752.

ers, e.g., a family that lives in a rural district and has just brought a patient to a hospital in a city.

3. *Supplying a list:*

In general, I see no difficulty about supplying the list for a minister who wishes to visit patients of his denomination. Obviously, if patients object to this it should not be done; but I should think that any patient who had registered as a "Lutheran," "Methodist," etc., would not object to a visit by a minister of that particular denomination.

37

Disposal of
Amputated Members

Major parts of the body should be buried in a cemetery when it is reasonably possible to do so. Moreover, the members of Catholics should, if possible, be buried in blessed ground. When burial is not reasonably possible, the burning of such members is permissible. Directive 59. (See also the U.S. Code, "Religious Supplement," n. 3; and the Canadian Code, art. 54.)

THE FORMULATION of this directive required considerable study of textbooks and periodicals, as well as a knowledge and appraisal of local diocesan customs. This chapter will indicate how the study was made and the conclusions drawn from it. The material given here is not only interesting as the background for the directive; it is also essential to the proper understanding of the directive.

THE GENERAL LAW

The only general law of the Church pertinent to the present topic is succinctly stated in canon 1203, the first of the canons on Christian burial: "The bodies of the faithful deceased must be buried; and their cremation is reprobated."

This law expresses an ancient Christian custom. From earliest times the Christians buried their dead because they considered this the most respectful way of treating the human body, especially a body that had been a temple of the Holy Ghost. Cremation was looked upon as unbecoming. Moreover, at various times cremation acquired anti-Christian and heretical connotations. For instance, some of the early persecutors had the bodies of martyrs burned to express contempt for the hope in the resurrection; hence Christian burial acquired the opposite connotation, namely, of profession of faith and hope in the resurrection. In more recent times, according to a strong statement of the Congregation of the Holy Office (June 19, 1926), the enemies of Christianity have praised and propagated the practice of cremation in order to pave the way to the acceptance of materialism.

This law, commanding burial and forbidding cremation, is the ordinary rule. The cremation of bodies is permitted when the public welfare demands it, for example, in time of pestilence—an exception which is explicitly mentioned in the instruction of the Holy Office just referred to. It is understood, of course, that in such cases cremation is divested of its anti-Christian and heretical connotations.

The law refers primarily to entire bodies. However, in the sources of canon 1203 we are referred to a reply of the Holy Office which dealt specifically with the disposal of amputated members. Since we shall be particularly concerned with this reply during the remainder of our discussion, it will be well to consider carefully both the circumstances that occasioned it and the wording of the response itself.

REPLY OF HOLY OFFICE

The reply was given in August, 1897, to the superior general of the Sisters of the Sorrowful Mother, a papal congregation with motherhouse in Rome and with many hospitals in the United States. The superior general presented this problem to the Holy See: In many of the hospitals conducted by her sisters in North America amputations of arms or legs are of frequent occurrence. In the past, the sisters' practice has

326

been to bury these amputated limbs in a corner of the hospital grounds that is not blessed, or sometimes, on the advice of the doctors, to burn them. Some of the persons who undergo these amputations are Catholics; others are baptized non-Catholics; and still others are unbaptized. The superior general is disturbed about these practices and seeks an official directive from the Holy See. That the case may be perfectly clear, however, she adds that the burial of such amputated members in a cemetery would very often be morally impossible, and not infrequently physically impossible.

An accurate, though somewhat rough, translation of the reply of the Holy Office, runs as follows:[1]

With regard to the amputated members of non-Catholics, the sisters may safely continue their present practice. They should try to have the amputated members of Catholics buried in blessed ground; but if serious difficulties stand in the way of such burial the sisters need not be disturbed about their present practice. As for the burning of members, if the physicians demand this, the sisters may keep a tactful silence and carry out their orders. And note: the mind of the Sacred Congregation is that, if it can be done, a small part of the hospital garden should be blessed and set aside for the burial of the amputated members of Catholics.

MANUALS AND PERIODICALS

The approved manuals of moral theology and canon law and the comments in ecclesiastical periodicals usually help us to understand the pronouncements of the Holy See. In the present instance this is hardly true of the manuals. Many of them do not even mention the disposal of amputated members. And most of those that do treat the subject are content with a brief reference to, or perhaps citation from, the response of the Holy Office; and they do this in such a way as to make the reply seem much more rigorous than a careful study of the text and background seems to justify.

---

[1] The reply was drawn up by the Holy Office on Aug. 3, 1897, and was officially approved by Pope Leo XIII on Aug. 6. For the Latin text, see *Fontes Codicis*, Vol. 4, pp. 494-495.

The periodicals are slightly more helpful. One Italian periodical for the clergy expresses the view that only notable parts of the body need to be buried. The theoretical distinction between notable (or major) and minor parts of the body seems quite reasonable; yet it is not easy to determine a practical norm for applying the distinction. Perhaps the distinction lies in this: a major part is one that retains its "human quality" even after the amputation. An arm or a leg usually retains this characteristic; whereas internal organs, even though very important, usually lose it after removal.

Fr. S. Woywod, O.F.M., makes two useful observations.[2] First, he calls attention to the fact that the very tenor of the response makes it clear "that the Church does not urge the burial of amputated limbs in consecrated ground in the same manner as the burial of the bodies of the faithful." This is an important point, and one that the manuals tend to obscure. As a matter of fact, we should naturally expect a certain modification of the law, even with regard to cremation, for amputated members are quite likely to be so diseased as to require cremation; and the practice of cremating them would seldom, if ever, have the anti-Christian connotation which makes the cremation of bodies particularly odious.

Another opinion expressed by Fr. Woywod is that limbs that are so crushed as to be simply a mass of flesh and bones may be burned without hesitation. I imagine that theologians in general would agree with this opinion; and I believe that the same may be said with regard to limbs that have been greatly distorted by disease.

The *Review for Religious*[3] also stresses the fact that the response of the Holy Office is quite moderate in tone; and it ventures the opinion that the Church is not opposed to the saving of amputated parts for scientific purposes.

---

[2] Cf. *The Homiletic and Pastoral Review*, Dec., 1933, pp. 291-292.
[3] May, 1947, p. 247.

DIFFICULTIES

In her petition to the Holy See the superior general stated that the burial of amputated limbs in a cemetery is often impossible, at least morally. The Holy Office did not question this statement; rather it seemed to assume the frequent existence of such difficulty and for this reason suggested the setting aside of the small plot of blessed ground in the hospital garden.

What are the difficulties? For the sisters themselves, one excuse for burning members is mentioned in the reply itself: namely, when the doctors insist on it the sisters may quietly acquiesce. The implication here, it seems to me, is that even when doctors are not justified in their demand the sisters need not oppose them. This relieves the consciences of the sisters; but one might ask: what about the doctors? In other words, we should like to have a norm that can be conscientiously followed, not only by the sisters, but by all others who wish to observe the law of the Church.

One difficulty often mentioned in questions concerning the disposal of amputated members has to do precisely with the suggestion made by the Holy Office that a small plot of ground be set aside in the hospital garden. Some urban hospitals do not have a garden. And in some places the sanitary codes would not permit this procedure. And as for burial in a cemetery, it is often alleged that the formalities to be observed make this a practical impossibility. For example, at least in some places, an undertaker must be procured, a burial permit obtained, and a grave opened. Collectively, such formalities impose a financial burden that is too much for many patients; and in large hospitals the repetition of the formalities for numerous amputations would be a great drain on time and personnel.

I am not prepared to say how common the foregoing inconveniences are; I have merely cited them as examples of the

329

difficulties that have at various times been called to my attention.

DIOCESAN SOLUTIONS

In a matter of this kind, it is important to know the approved practices in various dioceses. Official instructions in some places imply that burial has been found feasible; but in other places it is apparently taken for granted that burial is a practical impossibility. In many places the custom seems to be to ask the patient or his relatives to see to the decent burial of the amputated limbs. But the customs of the hospitals when the patients or relatives show indifference seem to vary considerably. My impression is that burning is the more common procedure in such cases; but I am not sure of it.

These various items, vague as they are, are at least "straws in the wind." They show us that conditions vary greatly from place to place; and they warn us against making sweeping generalizations. I think it is important to insist on this point: the judgment of excusing causes concerns actual facts, and facts (that is, the existence of actual difficulties) are not the same in all places. Some hospitals seem to have found that they can arrange for burial without much inconvenience; others have found it too difficult.

CONCLUSIONS

In the preceding discussion, I have compiled all pertinent information that I have been able to gather from ecclesiastical documents, textbooks, periodicals, correspondence, and discussion with other moralists and canonists. We are now ready for some definite conclusions, but before giving them I wish to say that they are presented here only for the benefit of those hospitals which do not already have official diocesan instructions, and as a possible aid to diocesan authorities who wish to establish some definite and workable procedure which is in harmony with the mind of the Holy See. The conclusions are as follows:

1. The ecclesiastical law commanding burial and forbidding cremation applies only to the bodies and amputated members of Catholics. However, the general tenor of ecclesiastical documents indicates that even in the case of non-Catholics the burial of amputated members (in unblessed ground) is preferable to cremation when the latter is not necessary.

2. Even with regard to the amputated members of Catholics, the law applies only to such portions of the body as are reasonably considered notable or major. Perhaps the question —does the amputated member retain its "human quality"?— may be of service in determining what is a major part.

3. The duty of seeing to the decent burial of major amputated parts falls primarily on the patient or his family; when these are willing and able to fulfill this duty the hospital authorities have no further obligations in the matter. It does not seem necessary, however, or even advisable to urge this duty on patients or their families when it is known that the prescribed legal formalities or the expense would be a source of great inconvenience to the persons involved. And certainly hospital authorities are excused from even suggesting this procedure when there is a well-founded fear that it would prejudice people against Catholic hospitals.

4. When the patients or their families are unwilling or unable to see to the decent burial of the amputated members, the hospital authorities should provide for the disposal of the members according to the provisions of directive 59. If arrangements can be made for burial without much inconvenience, this should be done. Cremation of such members is permissible when health or sanitation demands it; also when burial is not feasible because of expense, inability to observe prescribed formalities, inability to provide a suitable place and so forth.

331

chapter $\boxed{38}$

Cooperation in
Illicit Operations

IN A CATHOLIC HOSPITAL, there should be no illicit
operations; hence, there should be no problem about assisting at such operations. But many of the nurses trained in our
hospitals are later employed in institutions where such procedures take place and they are sometimes called upon to assist by
preparing the patient, handing instruments to doctors, and so
forth. This situation gives rise to a number of problems, of
which the following questions are typical: (1) May Catholic
nurses ever take such part in illicit operations? (2) Are the
nurses obliged to ask to be excused from this work? (3) If
their request is refused, must they resign rather than assist?

These questions concern the problem which moralists technically class as "cooperation in evil." The doctor who performs
the operation is called the "principal agent," and all who assist
him are called "cooperators." I shall not try to cover this subject completely, but shall content myself with briefly answering
the questions.

1) *May Catholic nurses ever take such part in these
operations?*

In itself, the work done by the nurses is not morally wrong.
It is exactly the same work that they would do at a perfectly
moral operation; hence, it would come under the classification
of indifferent or morally good actions. To render this kind of

332

assistance to one who is performing or about to perform an evil action, while at the same time disapproving of his evil action and evil purpose, is called material cooperation. Such cooperation is permissible under certain conditions to be explained in the answers to the other questions.

2) *Are they obliged to ask to be excused from such work?*

I mentioned in the answer to the first question that material cooperation presupposes disapproval of the evil action and evil purpose of the principal agent. In itself, "disapproval" is an internal act; and the nurses are certainly obliged to that. But they must do more than internally disapprove; they must show in some way that they do not approve of these operations. This certainly means that, if the nurses' request to be excused from assisting at the operations would be reasonably heard and granted, they are obliged to make the request; otherwise their unprotesting assistance would *imply* approval.

If the nurses judge that their request would be futile but that it would not be held against them, they ought to make the request as a definite way of showing their disapproval. But if they foresee, or know from past experience, that the request would not only be futile but would also be a source of serious inconvenience to them, they could omit the request and show their disapproval in some other way.

I might add here that nurses in public institutions should not be too ready to judge that their conscientious requests will not be honored. Very often not only are their requests honored but they themselves are highly esteemed for asserting their principles.

3) *Must they resign rather than assist?*

The essential condition for merely material assistance in an evil action is a "proportionate reason." In other words, such unwilling assistance is licit when it cannot be avoided without incurring some proportionately serious inconvenience. All Catholic moralists agree on the principle; but there seem to be differences of opinion in the various estimates of the inconvenience sufficient to justify nurses' assistance at illicit operations.

Most authors would agree that the danger of losing one's position without the hope of getting another would certainly be a sufficient reason to justify material cooperation at the illicit operations. On the other hand, many authors seem to think that if the nurse could get an equally good position, she would have to resign rather than assist at the operations. I think that these latter authors are overlooking a very important point; they are judging the case only in terms of the personal inconvenience to the nurse and are failing to take account of what may be even more important considerations.

Relative to the point I am making, Fr. Edwin F. Healy, S.J., gives the following example of a sufficient reason for permitting a Catholic nurse to remain in a state institution, even though she must occasionally be a material co-operator at illicit operations:

> If nurse Ann leaves this state hospital, she could find work at St. Joseph's Sanitarium. However, at this state hospital she is doing much spiritual good in summoning the priest for Catholic patients, in helping the dying to make their peace with God, in baptizing dying babies, etc. If she is replaced at this hospital by a non-Catholic, this good will not be done.[1]

Fr. Healy's words deserve careful consideration. We should not be too ready to insist or suggest that Catholic nurses leave public institutions merely because they could get equally good or even better positions elsewhere. The conscientious and exemplary nurse can do much spiritual good in these institutions; and this good more than compensates for occasional and unavoidable material cooperation in evil.

It should be noted that, in answering these questions, I have had in mind the nurse who is willing to assert and live up

---

[1] Cf. *Moral Guidance* (Chicago: The Loyola University Press, 1942), p. 320.

to her Catholic principles. Nurses who are merely nominal Catholics might do more harm than good in public institutions. Moreover, I have considered the cases in which the material cooperation in illicit operations is only occasional. If demands for such cooperation were very frequent it might be necessary, or at least advisable, for even the good Catholic to withdraw.

In view of the foregoing, I would say very briefly: (1) There are certainly some situations in which nurses can assist in these operations without incurring any guilt. (2) As a general rule, nurses should ask to be excused from assisting at such operations; although circumstances might arise in which the request could be legitimately omitted. (3) Seldom, it seems to me, would a nurse find herself in a situation in which resignation would be her only legitimate choice.

STATEMENTS OF THE HOLY SEE

This appendix contains some pertinent data concerning all the statements of the Holy See mentioned or quoted in this book. The chronological order is followed. The data is arranged as follows: author of the statement; to whom given; brief indication of contents; and references to: (1) official, or quasi-official, sources; (2) pamphlet translations; (3) other publications, mostly periodicals, which contain complete translations or abstracts or summaries of the statements. These references are abbreviated as follows:

1. Official and Quasi-official Sources:

AAS—*Acta Apostolicae Sedis.* This is the official publication of the Holy See since 1909.

ASS—*Acta Sanctae Sedis.* This was begun as a private publication in 1865. Its purpose was to make readily available the text of the more important statements of the Holy See. In May, 1904, it was declared to be an organ of the Holy See to the extent that all documents printed in it could be considered "authentic and official." It ceased publication when the AAS was begun.

DR—*Discorsi e Radiomessaggi di Sua Santità Pio XII.* A quasi-official publication of the Vatican Press, containing the discourses and radio messages, as well as other statements, made by Pope Pius XII. References to all these are by volume and the first page of the text containing the statement.

2. Pamphlet translations.

The following abbreviations refer to publishers of pamphlets:

AP—The America Press, 70 E. 45th St. New 17, N.Y.

NCWC—The National Catholic Welfare Conference. 1312 Massachusetts Ave., N.W., Washington 5, D.C.

PP—*The Paulist Press.* 401 W. 59th St., New York 19, N.Y.

References to pamphlets are made only by the abbreviations given above. When pamphlet translations are abundant (as in the case of *Casti connubii* and *Mystici Corporis*) no references are given to translations in periodicals.

3. Other Publications.

CD—*Catholic Documents.* The purpose of this publication is to give English translations of some of the recent pronouncements of the Holy Father. It was begun in 1950. It appears at irregular intervals, in the form of small brochures numbered consecutively. In the references given below the first number stands for the brochure, the other number for the page on which the translation begins. It is published for the Pontifical Court Club by: The Salesian Press, Surrey Lane, Battersea, S. W. 11, London, England.

CLD—*The Canon Law Digest*. It contains exceptionally good translations of official documents of the Holy See. To date, there are three bound volumes compiled by T. Lincoln Bouscaren, S.J. Since the publication of the third volume, there have been annual loose-leaf supplements, beginning with 1953. The supplements are co-authored by James I. O'Connor, S.J. The Bruce Publishing Company, Milwaukee 1, Wisconsin.

CM—*The Catholic Mind*. This is now in its fifty-sixth year. Formerly published monthly, it is now published six times a year. It contains not only papal statements, but also addresses, statements, and articles by bishops, priests, religious, and laity. Published by The America Press, 70 E. 45th St., New Your 17, N. Y.

CMQ—*The Catholic Medical Quarterly*. This was formerly *The Catholic Medical Guardian*. It contains material of value to Catholic doctors. Published by the Guild of St. Luke, SS. Cosmas and Damian: 29 Blenheim Road, London, S.W. 20, England.

LQ—*The Linacre, Quarterly*. Official journal of The Federation of Catholic Physicians' Guilds in the United States and Canada. Also contains material of special value to Catholic doctors. Publishing address: 1438 South Grand Blvd., St. Louis 4, Missouri

PS—*The Pope Speaks*. This quarterly began publication in 1954. It contains the most complete papal documentation in English that we have. Publishing address: 3622 12th St., N.E., Washington 17, D.C.

In the references to the last five publications, the first number refers to the volume, and the second to the page where the translation begins For one number of *The Linacre Quarterly* it was necessary to add the month because in that volume of *LQ* the pages were not numbered consecutively.

★　★　★　★

May 28, 1884. H.O. Reply to Cardinal Archbishop of Lyons: It cannot be safely taught in Catholic schools that destructive craniotomy is permitted, even when this operation on the fetus would save the life of the mother, and when, without the operation, both mother and child would die.—ASS, 17:556. CLD, 3:669.

Aug. 19, 1889. H.O. Reply to Archbishop of Cambrai: It cannot be safely taught in Catholic schools that any operation which is a direct killing of either the child or the pregnant mother is permitted—ASS, 22:748. CLD, 3:669.

July 24, 1895. H.O. Reply to Archbishop of Cambrai: Direct abortion is not allowed; and this is included in the previous replies of 1884 and 1889.—ASS, 28:383. CLD, 3:669.

March 26, 1897. H.O. Decree: Artificial insemination is illicit.—ASS, 29:704.

Aug. 3, 1897. H.O. Reply to a religious superior in North America: Amputated members should be buried if reasonably possible.—ASS, 30:630.

May 4, 1898. H.O. Reply to Bishop of Sinaloa, Mexico: Premature induction of labor is licit; abortion is not. Laparotomy for removal of ectopic fetus is permitted, when life of fetus, as well as of mother, is protected.—ASS, 30:703. CLD, 3:669.

March 5, 1902. H.O. Reply to a question from the Archdiocese of Montreal: The extraction of an immature ectopic fetus is illicit.—ASS, 35:162. CLD, 3:669.

June 19, 1926. H.O. Instruction on cremation.—AAS, 18:282. CLD, 1:564.

Aug. 2, 1929. H.O. Reply that direct masturbation is illicit.—AAS, 21:490. CLD, 1:156.

Dec. 31, 1930. Pius XI. Encyclical letter, *Casti connubii:* On Christian Marriage.—AAS, 22:539. AP. NCWC. PP.

March 21, 1931. H.O. Decree: On eugenics and sex education.—AAS, 23:118. CLD, 1:677.

Feb. 24, 1940. H.O. Decree: Direct sterilization is against the natural law.—AAS, 32:73. CLD, 2:96.

Dec. 2, 1940. H.O. Decree: Direct killing of innocent persons by order of the public authority is contrary to the natural law.—AAS, 32:553. CLD, 2:96.

June 29, 1943. Pius XII. Encyclical letter, *Mystici corporis:* On the Mystical Body of Christ.—AAS, 35:193. AP. NCWC. PP.

Nov. 12, 1944. Pius XII. Address to Italian Medical Guild of St. Luke. On the moral and social duties of the medical profession.—DR, 6:183. LQ, 23:109.

Oct. 9, 1948. Pius XII. Address to the National Congress of the Italian Association of Voluntary Blood Donors: To give blood to one's neighbor is to imitate the charity of Christ, the Redeemer.—DR, 10:253.

Aug. 8, 1949. H.O. Letter to Archbishop of Boston, Richard J. Cushing: Explanation of the axiom, "Outside the Church there is no salvation."—CLD, 3:525. CM, 50:749.

Sept. 29, 1949. Pius XII. Address to the Fourth International Congress of Catholic Doctors: On artificial insemination.—AAS, 41:557. CLD, 3:432. LQ, 16: Oct., 1949, p. 1.

Aug. 12, 1950. Pius XII. Encyclical letter, *Humani generis:* On some false opinions which threaten to undermine the foundations of Catholic doctrine.—AAS, 42:561. NCWC. CD, 3:28. CM, 48:688.

Oct. 29, 1951. Pius XII. Address to members of the Congress of the Italian Association of Catholic Midwives: On childbirth, marital duties, and sexual ethics.—AAS, 43:835. NCWC ("Moral Questions Affecting Married Life"). CD, 6:1. CLD, 3:*passim.* CM, 50:49.

Nov. 26, 1951. Pius XII. Address to the Family Front: On ethical aspects of marriage and childbirth.—AAS, 43:855. NCWC ("Moral Questions Affecting Married Life"). CD, 6:28. CM, 50:307.

March 23, 1952. Pius XII. Radio address: On the formation of a right conscience in the young.—AAS, 44:270. CD, 8:1.

Sept. 13, 1952. Pius XII. Address to delegates to the First International Congress on the Histopathology of the Nervous System: On the moral limits of Medical Research and Experimentation.—AAS, 44:779. NCWC. CD, 10:12. CM, 51:305. LQ, 19:98.

Oct. 8, 1953. Pius XII. Address to the Twenty-sixth Convention of the Italian Society of Urology: On the excision of a healthy organ, especially castration for cancer.—AAS, 45:673. LQ, 20:107.

Sept. 30, 1954. Pius XII. Address to delegates to the Eighth Congress of the World Medical Association: On the prevention of atomic warfare; preservation of peace; medical ethics; and human experimentation.—AAS, 46:587. CD, 21:1. CM, 53:242. PS, 1:347.

Jan. 8, 1956. Pius XII. Address to a group of Catholic obstetricians and gynecologists: On natural painless childbirth.—AAS, 48:82. CD, 22:1. CM, 54:280. PS, 3:25.

May 14, 1956. Pius XII. Address to oculists and cornea donors: On corneal transplants.—AAS, 48:459. CD, 24:4. CM, 54:579. PS, 3:198.

May 19, 1956. Pius XII. Address to delegates to the Second World Congress on Fertility and Sterility: On marriage, parenthood, artifcial insemination, and sterility tests.—AAS, 48:467. PS, 3:191.

Feb. 24, 1957. Pius XII. Address to delegates to the Ninth National Congress of the Italian Society of the Science of Anesthetics:On religious and moral aspects of pain prevention in medical practice.—AAS, 49:129. CD, 23:27. CM, 55:260. CMQ, 10:51. PS, 4:33.

Index

A

Abdominal pregnancy, 111-114
  contrasted with tubal pregnancy with reference to double effect, 112
Abel, Stuart, on homologous insemination, 241
Aborted fetus, baptism, 67
Abortion, association with electroshock therapy, 297
  complete, definition, 86
  direct, 63, 67, 69, 70, 71
  ergot and, 84-89
  incomplete, definition, 86
  inevitable, definition, 87
  involuntary, 84-89
  spontaneous, 84-89
  therapeutic, 68-83
    medical aspects, 75-82
  threatened, definition, 86
  use of ergot, morality, 84
Abstinence, continuous, 174
  from marital intercourse, natural birth control, 169
  periodic, the rhythm, 169
Abuses, elective induction of labor open to, 143
  of electro-shock therapy, 295
  of marriage, 154
  prevention, 58
  versus standards in experimentation, 267-269
Acts contrary to nature, 241-242
Adrenalectomy, medical or surgical, in prostate cancer, 201
  for palliation in cancer of breast, 203
  in palliation of prostate cancer, 200
Adultery, comparison of donor insemination to, 234
  definitions, 234
  possible result of practice of rhythm, 170
  wrongness deduced from Christian concept of marriage, 234

Adults, baptism, 304-319
Advertising of contraceptives contrary to natural law, 160
Aertnys, on fetus as aggressor, 72
Affirmative law, 4
Age of adulthood for baptism, 304
Allred, Vincent C., on legal philosophy favoring euthanasia, 119
Alvarez, Walter C., on arguments favorable to euthanasia, 125
  example of extraordinary means of prolonging life, 135
American College of Surgeons, panel discussion on indications for therapeutic abortion, 79
American Hospital Association on medical consultation, 51
Amputated members, disposal, 325-331
  parts, saving for scientific purposes, 328
Amytal sodium, use in narcoanalysis, 282
Anesthesia, hypnosis as, 288-293
Animal experimentation, preliminary use, before human experimentation, 268
Anoxia, reduction with hypnosis as adjunct to anesthesia, 292
Antibiotics, needless prescription, 258
  substitution for vasectomy, 190
Anxiety symptom as chief indication for psychosurgery, 274
Appendectomy, 252-254
  as unnecessary surgery, 254
Appendicitis as indication for appendectomy, 253
Appendix, incidental removal, permissible, 245

Archbishop of Canterbury on donor insemination as adultery, 234

Artificial birth control, 169
prevention, official Catholic teaching on, 153-157
insemination, 228-244
means of preserving life, differences of opinion on, 140

Aspiration for hydrocephalus, 99-102
method of obtaining semen specimen, approval by Vermeersch, 223
of semen from testicles for test specimen, 221

Assisted insemination, permissibility, 240

Atrocities of totalitarianism and euthanasia, 116

Authorities, duty, 18

Avoiding evil and doing good, distinction in use of ordinary and extraordinary means, 131

B

Babies, dying, baptism, of, 300

Baby, maturity, criterion for elective induction of labor, 147
of non-Catholic parents, baptism of, 300

Baird, Dugald, on risk of elective induction of labor, 144

Banks of body organs, morality of, 251

Baptism of aborted fetus, 67
of adults, 304-319
of fetus extracted after mother's death, 302
instruction on, 298-303

Belief, meaning to Catholic and non-Catholic, 307

Bender, Louis, on hysterectomy a direct sterilization, 215

Benedict XIV, repudiation of euphonic castration, 185

Bennet, Michael John, ovarian transplants made by, 248

Bertke, Stanley, on ignorance of natural law, 166

Biopsy, testicular, licit method of obtaining semen specimen, 225

Birth control, artificial, Catholic views on, 150
and natural, 169
continence only acceptable form, 168
prevention, artificial, Catholic thought on, 149
rate, reduction, by practices of birth limitation, 171

Blackstone, William, 1
Commentaries, citations on legal aspects of euthanasia, 119
on natural law, 3

Bladder, internal sphincter, effect of prostatectomy, 195

Blakely, Paul L., on sentimental writings of euthanasians, 120

Bleeding, excessive, indication for hysterectomy, 209
uterine, and ovarian function, 187-188

Blessed ground, burial of members of Catholics in, 325
plot for burial of amputated limbs, 327, 329

Blood banks, morality of, 251
transfusions, early condemnation for medical reasons, 249
permissible for good of others, 245
permissibility, 248

Board certification and qualifications of consultant, 55

Bodies, burial of, 325
natural right of spouses over, for generating life, 229

Bodily integrity, human life and, 5-6

Body of Christ, Mystical, feeble members, honor to, 117
giving of part to help another, theological views on, 246
individual as administrator of, 265
major and minor parts, distinction, 328
members and functions, nature and purpose, 6
part, donation to another, contrary to principle of totality, 247
right to dispose of for benefit of others, 250
time of infusion of soul into, 66
whole, threat to, by functioning of healthy organ, in prostate carcinoma, 202

Bone banks, morality of, 251

Bonnar, A., on attempt to legalize euthanasia in England, 120

Bouscaren, T. L., on intervention in abdominal pregnancy, 114
on principle of double effect, 15
on termination of abdominal pregnancy, 111
on therapeutic abortion, 69
translations of decrees on eugenic theory and direct sterilization, 167

Bowdern, William, on explanation of faith and truths necessary for salvation, 307

Bragg, J. C., on cases of full-term abdominal pregnancy, 114

Brain surgery, 270-281

Breast cancer, oophorectomy in, 12-14
castration for, 203-205

Burial of amputated limbs of non-Catholics, 327
of members, 325

in blessed ground, difficulties, 329
of bodies, 325

Burch, John C., on lack of absolutes in pelvic surgery, 208

Burleson, R. J., on cases of full-term abdominal pregnancy, 114

Burlingame, C. Charles, on indications and contraindications for prefrontal lobotomy, 273

Burning of amputated members, 325

C

Cadaver, human, relative dignity of, 250

Calling non-Catholic minister, 320-324

Cambo, Miguel, on morality of removal of badly damaged uterus, 215

Campbell, Elmore M., on repeat cesarean section, 93

Cancer of breast, oophorectomy in, 12-14, 164
castration for, 199-205
dread, educational policy to reduce, 49
incurable, application of principle of informing the dying to, 47
patient, curable, 49
incurable, 49
reaction to, 47
should he be told, 46-50
problem in telling dying patient, 44
of prostate, castration for, 12, 199-202
orchiectomy in, 165

Canon Law, Code, on following advice of counselors, 56
on baptism of unconscious unknown adults, interpretation, 312

Canterbury, Archbishop of, on donor insemination as adultery, 234

Cap, cervical, method, substitute for intercourse, 240

Carcinoma (*see* Cancer)

Carter, Patricia A., on elimination of indications for therapeutic abortion, 78

Case histories, meticulous anonymity of patients, requirements, 285

Cassidy, Louis, on aspiration for hydrocephalus, 100

Castration for cancer, 199-205
of prostate, 12
of criminals, 187
euphonic, 184-186
to preserve chastity, 186-187
and sterilization, distinction, 205
therapeutic pretexts, in Middle Ages, 185

Catechetical instruction before baptism, 305
modification for conscious dying person, 305

Catholic Church (*see* Church)
codes, non-Catholics and, 26-35
doctrine, way of teaching, 32
ethics, application to all human beings, 153
learned by reason alone, 150
faith, principal truths, 306
hospitals, incidence of hysterectomy in, 207
ideal, large family, 177
nurses, cooperation in illicit operations, permissibility, 332
position on saving life of mother and child, 70
on therapeutic abortion a life-saving principle, 75
objections, 71-75
principles, assertion by nurses in public institutions, 335
observance in Catholic hospitals, 18
standards of family living wage, 173
teaching on contraception and sterilization, 149-167
viewpoint of natural law, 31

Catholics, burial of amputated members of, 327

Cavanagh and McGoldrick on electro-shock therapy in pregnancy, 296
indications for electro-shock therapy, 294

Cemetery, burial of amputated members in, 325

Cerebral surgery, moral justification, 270

Certification, board, and qualifications of consultant, 55

Cervical cap method, substitute for intercourse, 240
spoon and cap procedures, comparison, 240
technique for aiding fertility of marital intercourse, 239

Cesarean hysterectomy, indications and prohibitions, 213
section, 90-95
hysterectomy with, in Catholic hospitals, 207
mother's desire for, 92-93
postmortem, legality of, 302
primary and repeat, distinction, 90
repeat, 92-95, 213
"previous section" as indication, 93
sections, no definite number as indication for hysterectomy, 206

Chaplain, decision on extreme unction, 44
duty of informing dying patient, 44

Character, better development in large family, 171, 177

Charity, fraternal, law of, moral basis for transfusions and skin grafts, 248

Chastity, castration to preserve, 186-187
danger to, by practice of rhythm, 170

Chemical therapy in treatment of mental illness and pain, 278

343

Chemoanesthesia, hypnoanesthesia as adjunct, 291
indications for use of hypnoanesthesia in preference, 292

Child born of donor insemination, status, 238
life of, and life of mother, 63, 64
safety, cesarean section necessary for, 91
unborn, indications for killing, 63, 64
a person, 66-67
well-being dependent upon married parents, 231

Childbearing, duty, suspension, 172
further, dangerous to health, physician's advice concerning, 178
in marriage, obligations, 131

Childbirth, avoidance, spiritual counselor concerning, 179
natural, as hypnosis, 288
pathological sequelae, indication for hysterectomy, 210, 212

Children, begetting and rearing, primary purpose of marriage, 178
boon to community and nation, 177
chief blessing of marriage, 171
number of, beyond the call of duty, 174

Cholecystectomy, permissible only on medical indications, 258

Christian attitude, moderate standard of preserving life in accord, with, 139
concept of marriage, 234
custom, burial of dead, 325
ideal of family, 177
marriage, encyclical on, 153-155
religion, precepts, acceptance by dying patient, 308

tradition, right of husband and wife only to generate children, part of, 232
wish to be, indication for baptism, 310

Church, admission by baptism, 308
attitude on blood transfusions, 249
baptism according to mind of, 299
the sacrament of entry, 310
Catholic conception, 31
competence, 30-32
guidance in adequate knowledge of natural law, 153
instruction in doctrines and laws before baptism, 305
interpreter of natural moral law, 31
lawmaking power, 31
laws made by, human laws, 31
no pronouncement on time of infusion of soul, 66
obligations, acceptance, requirement for baptism, 308
official business conducted by Congregations, 33
custodian of divine revelation, 152
teaching on artificial insemination, 243
position on euphonic castration, 185
teaching authority, 31
necessity for knowledge of natural law, 153
true, Catholic doctrine of, 322
ways of teaching, 32-35

Circumcision as mutilation, 259
permissible for medical reasons, 259
routine, morality of, 259

Civil law and consent of patient, 37

Clavicle, fracture, intentional, on living fetus, 97

Cleidotomy, 97-99
as life-saving procedure, 98
on living fetus, morality, 97

Clifford, John J., on use of perforated condom to obtain semen specimen, 222

Clinic examination of patients, violation of privacy, 285

Closed lobotomy, description, 271

Codes, Catholic, non-Catholics and, 26-35

Coitus, fulfillment of psycho-physical processes leading to orgasm, 236
unnatural, with use of condom, 160
true, determining factor, 221, 242

Collar bone, breaking, to effect vaginal delivery, 97

Commandments, Ten, instructions concerning human nature, 29

Competence of Church, 30-32

Conception, avoidance, 169

Conditional Baptism, 298
of dying unconscious persons, 308
secret, of unconscious dying person, 317
of unconscious and unknown person, 311

Condom, perforated, use to obtain semen specimen, 221
controversial theological opinions on, 222
unperforated, use to obtain semen specimen, 221

Confession, instruction on, before baptism, 306

Confessor as counselor concerning requirements for practice of rhythm, 173

Confidence, lack, in medical profession engendered by ghost surgery, 256

Conflict of rights, principle, applied to therapeutic abortion, 73

Congregation, Sacred, of Holy Office (see Sacred Congregation of Holy Office)

Congregations, Roman, functions, 33

Conjugal act, nature of, 230
intercourse, no substitute permissible, 243
union, restriction of generative activity to, 232

Conlin, John F., exposure of fallacies on euthanasia, 123

Connell, Francis J., on baptism of unknown unconscious adult, 312
on psychiatric treatment by conscientious physician, 286
on removal of damaged uterus as contraceptive measure, 215
on use of perforated condom to obtain semen specimen, 222

Connery, John R., on permissibility of removal of badly damaged uterus, 216

Conscience, decision by, in doubtful cases, 24
observance of directives, matter of, 18
of patient, influence by psychiatrist, 286
perplexed, as justification for therapeutic abortion, 74
solution by moralists, 24
physician's, guide in emergency, 18

Conscientious objection of non-Catholic personnel, 27

Conscientiousness, special importance in psychiatrists, 286

Conscious adults, baptism of, 299
dying patient, baptism of, 306

Consciousness, suppression, by hypnosis, morality of, 289

Consent, enlightened, of human experimental subject, need for, 268
forced or lacking, of charity patients, abuse in experimentation, 267
of individual for any medical treatment, 265
of patient, 36-41
   or guardian, requisite for experimentation, 261, 262
   to publication of case history, 285
   required for narcosis and hypnosis, 282
presupposes knowledge, 37
reasonable presumption, 38
refusal of, cases against natural law, 40
right of, to experimentation, papal limitations of, 266

Consequences, undesirable, of cesarean section, 91

Conservatism as good medicine, 78
vs. therapeutic abortion as lifesaving measure, 76

Consultant as censor, 56
definition, 54
meaning, 54-56

Consultants, majority, action contrary to, 56-58
obstetrical, on elective induction of labor, 142

Consultation, disagreement in, 56-58
in doubtful cases, 18
on local level in puzzling cases, 23
medical, 51-58
moral, 24
in primary cesarean section, 90
before psychosurgery, 280

Conte a Coronata, Matthaeus, on baptism of persons who resisted conversion, 314

Continence, acceptable form of birth control, 168
continuous, 181-182
not contraception, 176

Contraception as abuse of marriage, 154

Catholic teaching on, 149-167
and ectopic operations, stand of Church on, comparison, 109
no justification for, 154
practice, advising not permitted, 176

Contraceptive measure, hysterectomy not permissible as, 206
procedure, cutting fallopian tubes, 207

Contrition, act of, requisite for baptism of conscious dying person, 306
acts of faith and, before baptism, 299
for sins, act of, before baptism of adult, 305

Control groups, abuses involved in setting up, 268

Controversial indications for hysterectomy, 208

Convenience as criterion of ordinary means of preserving life, 134
of doctor or mother, elective induction of labor for, 142

Convulsions, induction, in electroshock therapy, 294

Cooperation in evil, moral problem, 332
in illicit operations, 332-335
material, definition, 333

Corneal transplantation from dead to living, beyond moral reproach, 250
transplants, morality of, 249

Corporeal, sacrifice of spiritual values for, in treating mentally ill, 279

Corruption, only certain sign of death precluding baptism, 300

Cortisone, medical adrenalectomy, in prostate cancer, 201

Cosgrove, Samuel A., on aspiration for hydrocephalus, 101

on maternal death rate with and without practice of therapeutic abortion, 77

Cosmetic surgery, morality of, 259

Cotter, A. C., translation of *The Encyclical "H u m a n i Generis,"* 166

Council of Trent, declaration on marriage, 233

Counselor, consultation with, on requirements for practice of rhythm, 173
spiritual, on avoidance of childbirth, 179

Courtesy, professional, calling of non-Catholic minister considered as, 322

Cranial operations on fetus, permissible, 101

Craniotomy, aspiration for hydrocephalus, 100
definition, 103
pronouncement on, 69, 70

Crasilneck, Harold B., on indication for use of hypnoanesthesia, 292

Cremation, anti-Christian connotation. 326
of bodies, 325
of limbs, permissible cases, 328

Criminals, castration, 187

Criteria for elective induction of labor, 143

Cunningham, B. J., on mutilation, 7-8

Cunningham, J. F., on aspiration for hydrocephalus, 103
on inevitable abortion, 89
on repeat cesarean section, 94

Curable cancer patient, 49

Cure in carcinoma of prostate, 199

Curettage, permissibility of, 53

Cushing, Richard J., letter to, on salvation of non-Catholics, 323

Cycle of sterile and fertile periods, use of knowledge, 177

D

Danagher, John J., on administration of sacraments to heretics and schismatics, 318

Dangers, personal, of rhythm method, 171
social, inherent in donor insemination, 238

Davis, Henry, on baptism of person who rejected Christianity, 313
on craniotomy vs. aspiration for hydrocephalus, 100

Dead, burial, Christian custom, 325
fetus, emptying uterus in case of, 85
morality of destructive operations on, 97

Death, baptism of adults not in danger of, 305
consent to one's own, prohibition, 264
by failure to preserve life, 128
or injury, avoidance of experimentation leading to, 268
preparation for, 42
by non-Catholics, 43
spiritual, 43
temporal, 43
rate, maternal, in hospitals with and without practice of therapeutic abortion, 76-78

Debatable questions, 21-22

Deceit, damage to patient through, 47

Defeatism, avoidance by strict standard of preserving life, 138
and moderate standard of preserving life, 139

Defectives, psychic and physical, killing of, 116

DeLee, J. B., on cleidotomy on dead fetus, 99

DeLee, Sol T., on hypnotism in pregnancy and labor, 291

Delivery, difficult, baptism during, 301
  premature, rules applicable to abdominal pregnancy, 111
  successful, cesarean section necessary for, 91
  vaginal, vs. cesarean section, safety, 91

Dentistry, hypnosis as anesthetic in, 288

Depression, indication for electroshock therapy, 295

Design and purpose of human nature, 29

Destruction or risk of life: principles, 62-67

Diagnosis, adequate, need of, before electro-shock therapy, 296

Diagnostic procedures to determine cause of infertility, 218-227
  unnecessary, morally objectionable, 245

Differences of opinion recognized in *Directives*, 22

Difficulties of burial of amputated limbs in cemetery, 329

Diocesan solutions to difficulties of burial of amputated limbs, 330

Direct killing, 62-65

Directives (Special Index of Directives, p. 375)
  ethical, to prevent abuses, 27
  and religious, 17-25
  vitality, 19-21

Disapproval of evil act, evidence of, requirement, 333

Disciplinary action in breach of code, 61

Diseased member, removal for good of the whole, 9

Disposal of amputated members, 325-331

Distance from hospital, indication for elective induction of labor, 146

Divine law, 30
  laws, 1-3
  positive law, 2
  revelation, communication of truth to man by God, 151
    teaching authority of Church concerning, 31

Doctor (*see also* Physician)
  baptism by, 299, 301
  duty and patient's wishes, 136
  obligation to use means of preserving life, 134
  as principal agent in performance of illicit operation, 332
  and rhythm, 176-182
  subject of same moral and juridical principles as patient, 266
  and supervisor, 59-61

Doctor-patient relationship, doctor's prerogative in, 92
  and use of extraordinary means, 137

Doctors, submission of illicitly obtained semen specimens by, warning to, 226

Doctrine, Catholic, of one true Church, 322
  ways of teaching, 32

Donnelly, James F., on indications for tubal ligation, 163

Donor insemination, 231-239
  objection to, 228

Double effect, principle, 12-16
  application to termination of abdominal pregnancy, 112
  application to tubal pregnancy, 109
  in justification of electroshock therapy in pregnancy, 296
  standard not permitted in Catholic hospitals, 26

"Doubt of fact," 22

Doubts and freedom from obligation, 22
  unforeseen, 22-25

348

Doyle, Joseph B., method of obtaining semen specimen, 225

Doyle and Whitelaw procedures, comparison, 240

Drastic measures, obsolescence by new remedies, 20

Drew, J. E., on ordinary and extraordinary means of preserving life, 128

Drinan, Robert F., on history of euthanasia movement, 126

Drugs, safeguards to use, in elective induction of labor, 147
and vasectomy, comparative effectiveness, 197

Duty of authorities, 18
of childbearing, suspension, 172
doctor's, and patient's wishes, 136
of individual to take ordinary means of preserving life, 130
of medical personnel to use extraordinary means of preserving life, 135
neglect in connection with use of rhythm, 169
of parents, importance of, 233
of physician to inform dying patient, 42
of preserving life, limits, estimate of, 132
of supervisor, 59

Dying, care of, no clear-cut professional standard regarding, 140
conscious patient, baptism of, 306
patient, informing, 42-45
unconscious patient, baptism, 308

Dysmenorrhea and stilbestrol, 189

E

Eastman, Nicholson J., on status of therapeutic abortion at Johns Hopkins Hospital, 81

Ecclesiastical law on burial of Catholics, 331

Economic indications for suspension of duty of childbearing, 172
reasons for family limitation, defects in society, 173

Ectopic fetuses, immature, removal, permissibility, 108
operations and contraception, stand of Church on, comparison, 109
morality of, 105-110
removal of fallopian tube in, 12-14

Education of children, procreation and, primary purpose of marriage, 178
of offspring, provided by matrimony, 232

Educational policy to reduce dread of cancer, 49

Effect, double, principle, 12-16
in justification of electroshock therapy in pregnancy, 296

Effects of psychosurgery, 274-277

Ejaculation outside vagina to obtain semen specimen, prohibition, 221

Ejaculatory ducts, damage by prostatectomy, 194

Elective induction of labor, 142-148

Electro-convulsive therapy, 294-297

Electro-shock therapy, 294-297

Embryo, baptism of, 300

Emergency baptism, 298
decisions, conscience guide in, 24

Emotional indifference of mother toward child, danger of hypnosis, 288
nature of arguments in favor of artificial birth prevention, 158
tension, relief, chief good effect of psychosurgery, 274

Encyclical on Christian marriage, 153-155

Encyclical *Humani Generis,* 150

End, good, as justification of evil means, 4

Endocrine control of prostate cancer, 200
function of ovaries, suppression, in carcinoma of breast, 204
of reproductive organs, 6

Epididymes, infection, vasectomy for, 190

Epididymitis, incidence, 193-194
seriousness, 194

Ergot and abortion, 84-89

Estrogen therapy, palliation, in prostate cancer, 200

Ethical Directives, 17-25

Ethics, Catholic, application to all human beings, 153
learned by reason alone, 150
of experimental problem, appreciation by investigators, 264
medical, applicable to all human beings, 153
some issues not clearly defined, 35
science, competence of Catholic moralists in, 34
sexual, basic principle, 242
truths concern natural law, 150

Eugenical indications for suspension of duty of childbearing, 172

Euphonic castration, 184-186

Euthanasia, 115-127
avoidance, by strict standards of preserving life, 138
by failing to preserve life, 128
and moderate standard of preserving life, 139
neglect of ordinary means of preserving life equivalent to, 130
reference material, 119-127
voluntary, 115

Evil, avoiding, and doing good, distinction, in use of ordinary and extraordinary means, 131
negative law, 4
cooperation in, moral problem, 332
doing, form of sin, 168
moral, prohibition, 4
physical, justification under some circumstances, 4
social, reduction of birth rate by birth control practices, 171

Excuse from assistance at illicit operation, necessary request, 333

Expectancy treatment of unruptured tubal pregnancy, 106

Expense, reasonable limits, in preserving life, 132

Experimental operations for cancer therapy, justification, 204

Experimentation, abuses versus standards, 267-269
for good of others, 263-269
of patient, 262-263
on human beings, 261-269
alleged justifications, 10
on mentally ill persons, 279

Extraordinary means of preserving life, 128, 135-141

Extrauterine pregnancy, 105-114

Extreme unction, administration to unconscious dying patient, 314, 316
by whom decided, 44
condition of patient for reception, 43

Eye banks, morality of, 251

F

Fact, doubt of, 22

Failure to save life, principle, application to therapeutic abortion, 74

Faith, act of, in accepting Catholic doctrines before baptism, 305

Catholic, principal truths, 306
and contrition, acts of, before
baptism, 299
meaning to Catholic and non-
Catholic, 307

Falk operation, not direct sterilization, 163

Fallacies concerning euthanasia,
answers to, 124

Fallectomy, less drastic procedure
than oophorectomy, 205

Fallopian tube, pregnancy in, morality of operations for,
105-110
removal in ectopic pregnancy,
12-14
rupture due to pregnancy,
treatment of, 106
tubes, cutting, contraceptive
procedure, 208
ligation or resection, direct
sterilization, 163-164

False assumptions on therapeutic
abortion, 76

Family, 235
large, Catholic ideal, 177
living wage, Catholic standards,
173
restriction of size by rhythm
method, 174
wishes, concerning use of extraordinary means, 136

Fertile marriage, Pope Pius XII
on, 171
period, abstinence during, 169
sexual desire during, 170
periods, cycle of sterile and,
177

Fertility, destruction by prostatectomy, 194
loss, indirect, in therapy of prostate cancer, 201
use of Ogino-Knaus discoveries
to promote, 177

Fertilized ovum, living, treatment
as human person, 67

Fetus, aborted, baptism, 67
dead, emptying uterus in case
of, 85
morality of destructive operations on, 97

ectopic, immature, removal, permissibility, 108
extraction, immediate, upon
death of mother, 302
harm to, by electro-shock therapy, 296, 297
inviable, baptism, 302
not a materially unjust aggressor, 72
that cannot survive, baptism,
300
viability, definition, 111

Finality, natural, argument from,
against contraception,
157

Finney, P., on cleidotomy on living child, 99

FitzGibbon, Gerald H., on spiritual care of the dying,
318

Ford, John C., on moral arguments for removal of
damaged uterus, 216
on morality of euthanasia, 126
on ordinary and extraordinary
means of preserving life,
128

Formula for baptism, 298

Formulation of principles, striving
for improvement, 19

Fornication, inherent wrongness
deduced from Christian
concept of marriage,
234

Fraternal charity, law of, moral
basis for transfusions
and skin grafts, 248

Frugal support, economic condition for duty of child-
bearing, 173

Functions, bodily, suppression, 6
endocrine, of reproductive organs, 6

G

Generative act, contraception contrary to natural purpose,
157
activity, restriction to conjugal
union, 232

faculty, unnatural use, unlawful even for laudable purpose, 221

organ, diseased, excision, indirect sterilization, 161

Ghost surgery, 254-257
morally objectionable, 245
objectionable features, 255

Golden rule in doctor's decision concerning use of extraordinary means, 137

Good, doing, affirmative natural law, 4
and avoiding evil, distinction, in use of ordinary and extraordinary means, 131
not doing, form of sin, 168
of others, experimentation for, 263-269
on mentally ill for, 279
mutilations and other procedures for, morality of, 246
of patient, experimentation for, 262-263
proportionate, justification for mutilating procedure, 245
spiritual, done by Catholic nurses in state institutions, 334
will, presumption, 60-61

Gorman, Arthur J., on intraventricular tap in case of hydrocephalus, 101

Grafts, skin, permissibility, 248

Graham, Alexander J. P., address on euthanasia, 122

Greenhill, J. P., on necessary and unnecessary elective induction of labor, 145
on repeat cesarean section, 94
on usefulness of hypnosis in medicine, 29

Grinker, R. R., on narcosynthesis, 282

Group for Advancement of Psychiatry on value of electroshock treatments, 295

Guardian, consent of, requisite for experimentation, 261, 262

Guardians, consent of, 40
wishes, concerning use of extraordinary means, 136

Guide for Preparation of Medical Staff By-laws, 53

Guilt, assistance in illicit operations without incurring, 335

Guttentag, Otto E., on experimentation on sick, 264

Guttmacher, Alan F., on test of ideal donor for insemination, 237

H

Harmony, mutual, of husband and wife, danger to, by practice of rhythm, 170

Hawke, C. D., on castration of criminals, 187

Head, baptism conferred on, validity of, 301
presentation, baptism of fetus in, 301

Health, responsibility of individual to care for, 265

Healthy individuals, experimentation on, 263
organ, harmful effect on diseased organ, 202
removal, for disease of other organs, problem of, 202
for good of the whole, 11

Healy, Edwin F., on baptism of unrepentant p e r s o n, 313
on hysterectomy as direct sterilization, 216
on reason for permitting Catholic nurse to remain in state institution, 334
on routine circumcision, 259

Heffernan, Roy J., on status of therapeutic abortion, 77, 80

Helping the neighbor, principle, possible justification of organic transplantation, 245

Helpless, protection, 57

Hemorrhage, control by ergot, 84-89
in early pregnancy, 84-89
postpartum indication for hysterectomy, 210, 212
in unruptured tubal pregnancy, morality of operations for, 107

Hernia, castration for, in Middle Ages and Renaissance, 185

Heroism, continuous abstinence as, Pius XII on, 175

Heterologous insemination, 231-239

Hinman, Frank, on endocrine control of prostatic carcinoma, 200

Historical argument against euthanasia, 126
background of terms "ordinary" and "extraordinary" means, 131

History of euthanasia movement, Drinan on, 126

Holy Office (see Sacred Congregation of Holy Office)

Holy Scriptures, divine law revealed in, 3
quotations on killing of innocent persons, 118

Holy See (see also Sacred Congregation of Holy Office)
decrees concerning ectopic pregnancy, 107-110
explanation of natural law applied to medical problems, 31
pronouncements on therapeutic abortion, 69-71
teaching on euthanasia, 116-117

Homografts for good of both parties, justification, 248

Homologous insemination, 239-244

Hope of success in concept of means of preserving life, 133

Hospital, 305
protection from harmful effects of psychiatric treatment, 284
responsibility in disposing of amputated members, 331
and seminal analysis, 225-227

Hospitals, Accreditation, Joint Commission on, standard on consultation, 52

Howard, Frederick S., on treatment of prostatic cancer, 200

Huhner test for sterility, licitness, 225

Hull, Edgar, on elimination of indications for therapeutic abortion, 78

Human law, 2
laws made by Church, 31
life and bodily integrity, 5-6
inviolability, 62, 64, 65
sacredness, Judaeo-Christian tradition, 118
usefulness to others false measure, 119
value, and euthanasia, 116
nature, creation by God, 29
human propagation judged according to, 231
quality of major part of body, 328
soul, time of infusion into body, 66

Husband, attitude toward child born of donor insemination, 239

Hydrocephalus, aspiration for, 99-102
infant with, delivery, 96
intraventricular tap for, conformance with natural law, 104

Hypnoanalysis, narcoanalysis and, 282-287

Hypnoanesthesia as anesthetic or adjunct to chemoanesthesia, 290-293

Hypnosis as anesthesia, 288-293 moral status, 23

Hypophysectomy for palliation in cancer of breast, 203

Hysterectomy, 206-217
cesarean, indications and prohibitions, 213
controversial indications, 208
incidence in Catholic hospitals, 207
to induce sterility as method of contraception, 164
non-sterilizing, 214-215
routine, morality, 213
as treatment for prolapse, 209
unnecessary, 207

I

Ideal, Catholic, large family, 177
Christian, of family, 177

Illegitimacy of child conceived by artificial insemination outside marriage, 229

Illicit operations, cooperation in, 332
supervisor's duty concerning, 59

Illness, nature of, explanation to dying patient, 44
precise, obligation of informing patient, 48

Immersion, baptism by, of fetus in early stage, 300

Impediment of impotence, 240-241

Implications of principles, growing knowledge of, 19

Impotence, impediment, 240-241
resort to artificial insemination because of, condemnation, 229
result of castration, 187

Improvement after psychosurgery, definition in terms of morbid state, 276

Incontinence, danger of rhythm method, 170

Inconvenience, reasonable limits in preserving life, 132

Incurable cancer patient, 49

Incurability of mental disease as criterion for lobotomy, 276

Incurably ill patient, experimentation on, 263

Indications for psychosurgery, 272-274

Indifference, emotional, of mother toward child, danger of hypnosis, 288

Indifferent or morally good actions, 332

Indirect killing, 65-66

Individual as administrator of his life and bodily members, 265
inalienable rights superseding science or public welfare, 267
responsibility of, to care for health, 265
subordination to community, totalitarian a t t i t u d e, 266

Individualism, extreme, in granting consent to experimentation, 266

Individualization, requirement in elective induction of labor, 143

Induction of labor, early, medical indications only justification, 147
elective, 142-148

Infant, hydrocephalic, delivery, 96
operations on, in utero, 96-104

Infection, elimination of danger, in intrauterine baptism, 302
susceptibility to, indication for vasectomy, 192

Infertile period, reliability dependent upon individual factors, 180

Infertility (see also Sterility)
diagnostic procedures to determine cause, 218-227

examination of man, 219-225
of woman, 218
pills, condemnation of, 161
Information concerning rhythm, permissible, 180
Informing dying patient, 42-45
Injury, precautions against, in human experimentation, 268
Insemination, artificial, 228-244
outside marriage, condemnation, 229
in vitro, immorality and illicitness of, 230
assisted, permissibility, 240
donor, 231-239
objection to, 228
heterologous, 231-239
homologous, 239-244
without intercourse, condemnation, 243
of unmarried woman, 237
within marriage, 239-244
Instruction on baptism, 298-303
catechetical, before baptism, 305
modification for conscious dying person, 306
Integrity, bodily, human life and, 5-6
Intention of conferring baptism according to mind of Church, requirement for baptism, 299
probable, of joining Catholic Church, sign of wish for baptism, 310
requisite for baptism in conscious dying person, 306
Intercourse, abstinence, complete, indications for, 175
natural method of birth control, 169
conjugal, as marriage "debt," 170
homologous insemination without, condemnation, 243
substitutes, in homologous insemination, condemnation, 240

Interpretation of natural moral law, Church and, 31
Intrauterine baptism, 301
Intraventricular tap of hydrocephalic infant, 102
for hydrocephalus, conformance with natural law, 104
Intuitive nature of argument from finality against birth prevention, 158
Inviable fetus, baptism, 302
Inviolability of innocent human life, 62, 64, 65
Irradiation, of ovaries, hysterectomy after, 214
sterility result of, 161
to suppress ovarian function, 187

J

Jenkins, M. T., on indications for use of hypnoanesthesia, 292
Johnson, W.H., on use of military personnel for experimentation, 264
Joint Commission on Accreditation of Hospitals, standard on consultation, 52
Judaeo-Christian tradition on sacredness of human life, 118
Justification for acting against will of patient, 39
Justifications, possible, for elective induction of labor, 144

K

Kelly, Gerald, on defense of opinion allowing removal of damaged uterus, 216
Kenealy, William J., on natural integrity of marital act, 158
Kidd, Alexander, M., on legal aspects of experimentation on human beings, 264
Killing, direct, 62-65
indirect, 65-66

mercy (*see* Euthanasia)
unborn child, 63, 64

Kroger, William S., on selection of patients for hypnoanesthesia, 291

Kuehner, George F., on hypnosis in dentistry, 293

Kyneur, F. J., on favorable results of leucotomy, 277

L

Labor, elective induction, 142-148
hypnotism in, 291
short, argument for elective induction, 144, 146

Lambertini, Cardinal, repudiation of euphonic castration, 185

Last Sacraments, notification of condition in time for, 48

Lavely, Horace T., on lack of absolutes in pelvic surgery, 208

Law. affirmative, 4
civil, and consent of patient, 37
fulfillment contrary to natural law, 40
definition, 1
divine, 1-3, 30
positive, 2
ecclesiastical, on burial of Catholics, 331
human, 2
natural, 2, 28-30
affirmative, 4
application to medical cases, 30
cases of refusal of consent contrary to, 40
Catholic viewpoint, 31
a divine law, 30
equally applicable to Catholic and non-Catholic, 30
man's power to know, 150-153
moral, 30
negative, 4
part of truths of natural religion, 152

teaching of Church, necessity for knowledge of, 153
truths of ethics concerned with, 150
negative, 4

Lawmaking power of Church, 31

Laws, Church, human laws, 31

Lawsuits, protection of hospital from, by psychiatrist, 284

Legal advice on acting against wishes of doctor and relatives, 45
aspects of experimentation on human beings, 264
of informing cancer patient, 46

Lehmkuhl, A., on therapeutic abortion, 72

Leo XIII, approval of reply of Holy Office on burial of amputated members, 327
on direct abortion, 70

Leucotomy, term for prefrontal lobotomy, 271

Liberalism, crude, ingredient of false philosophy of life, 235

Liberty of human subject to terminate experiment, 268
of individual physician, undue interference, 58

Licitness, probable, of testing methods for male infertility, definition, 221

Life and bodily members, limitation of power to dispose of, 247
of child and life of mother, 63, 64
destruction or risk, 62-67
as gift of God, 119
human, and bodily integrity, 5
Judaeo-Christian tradition, 118
usefulness to others, false measure, 119
value, and euthanasia, 116
individual as administrator of, 265

preserving, 128-141
 extraordinary means, 135-141
 ordinary means, 128-134
 risk to, definition, 65
 of unborn child, value, 64
 value, measure of, 63, 64

Limbs as major parts of body, 328

Limits of duty of preserving life, 132

Literature, medical, on elective induction of labor, 144-146

Living wage, Catholic standards, 173

Lobotomy, moral justification, 270
 prefrontal, description, 271
 variations in technique, 271

Lock, Frank R., on indications for tubal ligation, 163

Lohkamp, Nicholas, on incidental appendectomy, 253
 on removal of damaged uterus, 216

Lynch, John J., on arguments favoring removal of damaged uterus, 216
 on ghost surgery, 254
 on infertility pills as contraceptive measure, 161
 summary of Pope Pius XII's address on corneal transplants, 250

Lynch, William A., on status of therapeutic abortion, 77, 80

Lynn and Nesbit, on incidence of epididymitis with prostatectomy, 193
 on vasectomy with transurethral resection, 193

M

McCarthy, J., on licitness of use of perforated condom to obtain semen specimen, 222

McCranie, E. James, on indications for use of hypno-anesthesia, 292

McFadden, Charles J., on treatment of enlarged prostate by ligature of *vasa deferentia*, 165

McGoldrick, Joseph L., on lack of necessity for therapeutic abortion, 79

McIntyre, Aurelia P., on anxiety as chief indication for psychosurgery, 274

McIntyre, Howard D., on anxiety as chief indication for pschosurgery, 274

McReavy, L. L., on administration of sacraments to dying non-Catholics, 314
 on arguments concerning removal of damaged uterus, 217

Maim, injury amounting to, person's own consent to, prohibition, 264

Malignancy, informing patient, 46
 of ovaries, hysterectomy after oophorectomy for, 214

Malignant ovarian tumors, radical surgery for, 214

Man and animal, distinction, basic to Western civilization, 125

Manic-depressive psychosis, indication for electro-shock therapy, 294

Man's power to know natural law, 150-153

Manuals of moral theology, references to disposal of amputated members in, 327

Markham, Raphael J., prayers for assistance of dying non-Catholics by, 306, 318

Marmer, Milton J., on use of hypnosis in anesthesiology, 293

Marquette University symposium on question of telling cancer patient, 46

Marriage, abuses, 154
artificial insemination in, 229
and castration, 187
Christian concept, 234
encyclical on, 153-155
donor insemination contrary to
divine plan, 231-234
fertile, Pope Pius XII on, 171
invalidation by impotence, 241
procreation of life the fruit,
229
purpose, mutual perfecting of
husband and wife, 178
secondary ends, 177
twofold purpose, 234
and virginity, distinct vocations,
175

Massage, expression of semen by,
for test specimen, 221

Masturbation, dependence of artificial insemination on,
235
hospital analysis of semen specimens obtained by, 226
as method of obtaining semen
for analysis, condemna-
tion, 219
prohibition, 183

Material cooperation, definition,
332

Materialism, cremation paving
way to, 326
underlying "proxy" father
propaganda, 235

Maternal death rates in hospitals
with and without prac-
tice of therapeutic abor-
tion, 76-78
instinct, thwarting by avoidance
of childbearing, 171

Matrimony, education of offspring
provided by, 232
unity, established by Creator,
233

Maturity of baby, criterion for
elective induction of la-
bor, 147

Mayfield, Frank H., on anxiety as
chief indication for psy-
chosurgery, 274

Measles, German, and therapeutic
abortion, 82

Medical examples of contraception and sterilization,
160-166
aspects of therapeutic abortion,
75-82
cases, application of natural
law to, 30
conclusions concerning elective
induction of labor, 147
consultation, 51-58
ethics, applicable to all human
beings, 153
some issues not clearly defined, 35
experimentation, risk to patient
involved in, 261
indications for cesarean section,
91
for electro-shock therapy,
294
for indirect sterilization, justification, 184
moral justification for psychosurgery, 277
for use of stilbestrol in
dysmenorrhea, 189
for suspension of duty of
childbearing, 172
judgment concerning castration
for abnormal sexual
urge, 186
justification for routine vasectomy with prostatec-
tomy, lack, 197
literature on elective induction
of labor, 144-146
and moral conclusions on elective induction of labor
the same, 148
morality, breach, disciplinary
action in, 61
opinion on hypnotism, status
and use in medicine,
290-293
personnel, duty to use extraordinary means of pre-
serving life, 135
problem, repeat cesarean section
as, 93
problems, natural law applied
to, 31

profession, abuses not in accord with published standards, 268
function, instruction concerning rhythm, 181
protection of reputation, ethical directives for, 28
questions, declarations of Holy See on, 33
research, importance in, of sound philosophical attitudes toward man, 266
moral limits, 10
reason for expectancy treatment of ectopic pregnancy, 107
societies, condemnation of euthanasia by, 121
staffs, Directives binding upon, 17

Medicine, good, conservatism as, 78
hypnosis in, 288-293
principle of double effect in, 14
of totality in practice, 10

Medico-moral codes, revision, 19

Membranes, fetus enclosed in, baptism of, 300
rupture, method of induction of labor, 146
ruptured, condition of, intrauterine baptism, 301

Menopause, irradiation, hysterectomy after, 214
natural, hysterectomy after, 214

Mental breakdown caused by abstention from intercourse, 182
deficiency, association with electro-shock therapy, 297
illness, indication for psychosurgery, 272
narcoanalysis and hypnoanalysis for, 282
treatment by cerebral surgery, 270

"Mercy killing," (see Euthanasia)

Merkelbach, Benedict, on man's right to use of his semen, 223

Metaphysical nature of argument from finality against birth prevention, 158

Method of elective induction of labor, proper care in choice, 143

Methods of induction of labor, 146-147

Military personnel, use for experimentation, 264

Minister, non-Catholic, calling, 320-324

Minogue, S. J., on general statement of indication for psychosurgery, 273

Mistakes, in emergency, avoidance of recurrence, 24

Monsters, baptism of, 302

Moore, Thomas Verner, on permissible cranial operations, 101

Moralists, Catholic, specialists in science of ethics, 34

Morbid state, not premorbid personality, measure of improvement after psychosurgery, 276

More, St. Thomas, on euthanasia, 125, 126

Mortality rate of brain surgery, 275

Mother and child, lives, 63, 64
physiological readiness, criterion for elective induction of labor, 147
safety, cesarean section necessary for, 91

Mother's desire for cesarean section, 92-93

Murder, euthanasia as, 116
one, against two deaths in therapeutic abortion, 75

Murders, mass, and euthanasia, 116

Muscular relaxation, result of hypnosis, 292

Mutilation, 6-8, 11, 12
cesarean section as, 92
cleidotomy and osteoclasis as, application of principle, 97

definition, 6-8
experiments involving, prohibition, 266
hysterectomy as, 206
particular problems, 245-260
by surgery or x-ray, 8
Mysteries, truths contained in supernatural revelation, 151

N

Narcoanalysis and hypnoanalysis, 282-287
Narcosynthesis, use of drugs in, 282
Natural birth control, abstinence, 169
  childbirth as hypnosis, 288
  finality, argument from, against contraception, 157
  law, 2, 28-30
    affirmative, 4
    application to medical cases, 30
    applied to medical problems, 31
    Catholic viewpoint, 31
    consent of patient required by, 37
    a divine law, 30
    equally applicable to Catholic and non-Catholic 30
    negative, 4
  moral law, 30
Nazi experimentation, example of totalitarian attitude, 266
Neary, James T., on euthanasia, 119
Negative law, 4
Neighbor, helping, possible justification for organic transplantation, 245
Neoplastic tissue, ovarian hormone favorable to growth, 204
Neuro-surgical relief of pain, 123
Neurosis as indication for psychosurgery, 272

Neurotic illness, psychiatric treatment of, 283
Non-Catholic minister, calling, 320-324
  patients, burial of amputated limbs, 327
  preparation for death, 43
  personnel, religious convictions, 27
Non-Catholics and Catholic codes, 26-35
  salvation of, 322
Non-sterilizing hysterectomy, 214-215
Norms for use of extraordinary means for patients, 130
Notions, basic, 1-16
Nuremberg trials, rules for experimentation on human beings used at, 268
Nurse, baptism by, 299, 301
  Catholic, calling of minister by, rulings on, 321
  spiritual ministrations to non-Catholic patients, 323
Nurses, Catholic, cooperation in illicit operations, permissibility, 332
  duty of informing dying patient, 44
  opportunity of spiritual ministry to conscious dying patients, 317
Nursing staffs, Directives binding upon, 17

O

Obligations, imposition, based on certainty, 21
O'Brien, Patrick, on removal of damaged uterus as illicit, 217
Obsolete material, elimination in codes, 21
Obstacles to knowledge of natural truths by human reason, 152
Obstetrical consultants on elective induction of labor, 142-144

Obstetrics, hypnosis as anesthetic in, 288
routine hysterectomy poor practice, 213

O'Connor, Cornelius T., on intraventricular tap in case of hydrocephalus, 101

O'Donnell, Thomas J., on affirmative view of removal of damaged uterus, 217
on choice of technique for lobotomy, 272

Office, Holy (see Sacred Congregation of Holy Office)

Ogino-Knaus discoveries, aspects to be stressed, 177

O'Malley, Austin, on mutilation, 6-7

Onan, sin, nature of, 159

Oophorectomy, advantages over x-ray in castration for breast carcinoma, 205
bilateral, in cancer of breast, 12-14, 164, 204
hysterectomy after, 214
to stop uterine bleeding, 188
unnecessary, immoral procedure, 164

Operation, illicit, supervisor's duty concerning, 59

Operations, cranial, on fetus, permissible, 101
to destroy and to preserve fetal life, distinction, 96
ectopic, morality of, 105
illicit, cooperation in, 332
on infant in utero, 96-104
to produce good effects, 13
psychosurgical, 271
which kill either mother or child, pronouncement on, 70

Opinion, differences, recognized in Directives, 22

Orchiectomy, palliation, in prostate cancer, 200
in prostate cancer, appropriate time for use, 202

in treatment of carcinoma of prostate, 165

Ordinary means of preserving life, 128-134

Organ, healthy, removal for disease of other organ, 202

Organic transplantation, moral implications, 20
possible justification, 245
subject of theological controversy, 247

Organs, maternal, affected by ectopic pregnancies, indispensability, 113

Orgasm, methods, of obtaining semen specimen not stimulating to, 223
outside coitus, contrary to nature, 221, 242

Osteoclasis on living fetus, morality, 97

Others, good of, experimentation for, 263-269
on mentally ill for, 279
mutilation and other procedures for, morality of, 246

Ovarian function, suppression, for palliation in cancer of breast, 203
by stilbestrol, 189
uterine bleeding and, 187-188
hormone, favorable to growth of neoplastic tissue, 204
tumors, malignant, radical surgery for, 214

Ovaries, diseased, removal of healthy uterus with, 214
endocrine function, suppression, in carcinoma of breast, 204
x-ray treatment for uterine bleeding, 188

Ovum, fertilized, treatment as human person, 67

Oxytocics, rupture of membranes by use, 146

361

P

Pain, fear and dread engendered by euthanasia movement, 119
  intractable, indication for psychosurgery, 272
    treatment by cerebral surgery, 270
  neuro-surgical relief, 123
  prevention, psychic, by hypnosis, 289
  reasonable limits in preserving life, 132
  sedatives for alleviation, 115

Palliation, first medical consideration in incurably ill patient, 263
  in prostate cancer through estrogens or orchiectomy, 199

Papal teaching concerning contraception and sterilization, reasons underlying, 157-160

Paquin, Jules, on permissibility of removal of damaged uterus, 217
  on routine circumcision, 259

Parenthood, chief glory of marriage, 171

Parents, consent of, 40
  marriage, necessary to well-being of child, 231

Part-for-the-whole, principle of, 9-11

Pastoral Psychology, Protestant views on euthanasia, 123, 124

Pathological condition, mutilation to avoid, 9
  procedures causing sterility permitted to cure or prevent, 183
  effect on fallopian tube of ectopic pregnancy, 109

Patient, cancer, curable, 49
  incurable, 49
  condition for reception of extreme unction, 43
  consent, 36-41
  damage, by deceit, 47

dying, informing, 42-45
  mentally ill, human dignity of, 278
  non-Catholic, calling of minister at request of, 320-324
  obligation to submit to extraordinary means of prolonging life, 135
    to use ordinary means of protecting life, 134
  primary concern of hospital, 17
  reaction to cancer, 47
  responsibility for burial of amputated limbs, 330

Patients, non-Catholic, preparation for death, 43
  protection of rights, ethical Directives for, 28
  religious care, provision for, 26
  selection, for hypnosis, 292
  wish concerning use of extraordinary means, 136

Payen, P. G., on presumption of patient's consent, 39

Pelvic surgery, lack of absolutes, 208

Penance, sacrament of, administration to unconscious dying patient, 314, 316

Pentothal sodium, use in narcoanalysis, 282

Permission for psychosurgery, 280

Perplexed conscience as justification for therapeutic abortion, 74
  solution by moralists, 24

Person, mentally ill patient as, 278

Personal dangers of r h y t h m method, 171

Personality changes resulting from psychosurgery, 275
  operations involving destruction, contrary to natural law, 281

Persons, doubtful number, of monstrosity, baptism of, 302

Pestilence, cremation permissible during, 326

Philosophy, anti-Christian, of euthanasia movement, 118
false, donor insemination product of, 231, 234
Physical danger of childbirth, outweighed by greater evils, 179
defectives, killing of, 116
evil, justification under some circumstances, 4
separation of husbands and wives, and resulting continence, 182
Physician (*see also* Doctor)
conference with chaplain on extreme unction, 44
duty of informing dying patient, 42
individual, undue interference with liberty, 58
point of view toward experimentation, 264
traditional role, conflict in, as experimenter and helper, 264
Physicians, awareness of moral values involved in rhythm, 180
conflicting views, recognized by Directives, 22
individual, condemnation of euthanasia by, 121
resident, ghost surgery by, morality of, 256
Physiological readiness of mother, criterion for elective induction of labor, 147
Pituitary extract in induction of labor, danger, 146
Pius XI, on artificial birth prevention, 109, 153
on direct abortion, 70
on education and upbringing of children, 232
encyclical on Christian marriage, 153-155
quotation from St. Augustine on prevention of conception, 159
Pius XII, on artificial birth prevention, 153

on challenges to Catholic physicians, 180
on Church as custodian of divine revelation, 152
on condemnation of totalitarian attitude toward individual, 266
on contraception as immoral act, 156
on corneal transplants, 249
on fertile marriage, 171
on heroism of complete abstinence, 175
on hypnosis in medicine, 288, 289
on instruction to married people, 181
on inviolability of innocent human life, 64, 66, 67
on judging value of life, 76
on killing of innocent persons, 117
on masturbation, 219
on moral problems of married life, 63
official teaching of Catholic Church on artificial insemination expressed by, 243
on power of human reason and divine revelation, 150
on principle of totality, 10-11
pronouncements on medical questions, 33
on removal of sex glands in prostate cancer, 202
on submitting to surgical procedures involving destruction of personality, 280
teaching on experimentation for good of others, 265-267
Placenta, detached, emptying uterus in case of, 85
Pope, pronouncements, 32
Portes, L., on elimination of indications for therapeutic abortion, 79
Posthypnotic suggestion, use in surgery, 293
Postmortem cesarean section, legality of, 302

Postpartum hemorrhage, use of ergot in, 88

Power, man's, to know natural law, 150-153

Prayers of nurse with and for patients, special ministry, 323

Precautionary regulations, 27

Precepts, imposition based on certainty, 21

Prefrontal lobotomy, description, 271

Pregnancy, abdominal, 111-114
    contrasted with tubal, with reference to double effect, 112
    danger, in breast carcinoma, 204
    ectopic, operations for, and contraception, stand of Church on, comparison, 109
    removal of fallopian tube in, 12-14
    effect of electro-shock therapy on, 297
    extrauterine, 105-114
    hemorrhage in, 84-89
    hypnotism in, 291
    interruption, moral acceptability, 53
    suspicion, "doubt of fact", 22
    termination before viability, morality, 112
    tubal, morality of operations for, 105-110

Pregnant patient, electro-shock therapy on, permissibility, 296-297

Premature delivery, rules applicable to abdominal pregnancy, 111

Prescribing of contraceptives, contrary to natural law, 160

Presenting part of fetus, conditional baptism, 301

Preservation of life, ordinary and extraordinary means, 23

Preserving life, 128-141

extraordinary means, 135-141
    ordinary means, 128-134

Press, secular, condemnations of euthanasia, 125

Presume good will, 60-61

Prick, J. J. G., on moral permissibility of leucotomy, 273

Priest as counselor concerning requirements for practice of rhythm, 173

Priests, articles on euthanasia by, 126
    baptism by others than, 298
    and physicians, sympathetic contacts helpful in treating Catholic patients, 287

Primary cesarean section, 90-92

Principle concerning treatment of hemorrhage, in pregnancy, 84-86
  of double effect, 12-16
    application to termination of abdominal pregnancy, 112
      to treatment of tubal pregnancy, 109
    practical applications, 15
  of totality, 8-11
  restatement, 246

Principles, applications, concrete, 19
  basic, 1-16
  Catholic, assertion by nurses in public institutions, 335
    observance in Catholic hospitals, 18
  formulation, striving for improvement, 19
  implications, growing knowledge of, 19
  moral, and practical applications, statements, 26
  unchanging, 19

Procedures prohibited by Directives, 17
  serious, patient's consent to, 38

Procreation and education of children, primary purpose of marriage, 178
of life according to will of Creator, harmony of, 230
fruit of marriage, 229
Professional standards on means of preserving life, 137-139
strict, 137-138
moderate, 138-139
Progenitors, donors as ideal, menace to welfare of society, 238
Prohibitions, imposition based on certainty, 21
Prolapse and other uterine pathology, hysterectomy for, 208-212
of uterus, hysterectomy permissible for, 206
Proportionate good, justification for mutilating procedure, 245
reason, condition for merely material assistance in evil action, 333
Prostate, carcinoma of, castration for, 12, 199-202
orchiectomy in, 165
enlarged, treatment by ligature of *vasa deferentia,* 165
as sexual organ, 200
Prostatectomy, radical, in early cases of carcinoma, 200
vasectomy with, 190-198
Protestants, unconscious dying, baptism of, 316
"Proxy" father propaganda for donor insemination, 235
Psychiatric aspects of informing cancer patient, 46
patient, treatment with narcosynthesis, 282
treatment of neurotic illness, 283
treatments, special problems with reference to patient's consent, 39
Psychiatrist, importance of conscientiousness in, 286

Psychic defectives, killing of, 116
Psychodynamics, training in, for successful use of hypnotic techniques, 291
Psychological factors in informing patient with curable cancer, 49
sanity of Catholic teaching on continuous continence, 182
Psycho-physical processes leading to orgasm, culmination in coitus, 236
Psychoses as indication for psychosurgery, 272
Psychosis, manic-depressive, indication for electro-shock therapy, 294
Psychosurgery, 270-281
procedure of last resort, 278
Psychotherapy, ideal treatment for mental illness and pain, 278
Public institutions, assertion of principles by nurses in, 333
welfare, supersedence of rights of individual, 267
Pujiula, James, on lack of necessity for therapeutic abortion, 79
Purposes of marriage, 178

Q

Quinlan, John T., on maternal death rate with and without practice of therapeutic abortion, 76

R

Rabbi, calling at request of patient, 320
Rabinowitch, I. M., on condemnation of euthanasia, 121
Rape and fertilized ovum, practical rule, 67
Read, Grantly Dick, method of natural childbirth, 288

365

Reason, age of, definition with reference to baptism, 304

human, inability to discover truths of supernatural revelation, 151

power, to know natural law, 150

patient's use of, prerequisite of giving consent to treatment, 283

sufficient, for avoiding childbirth, third requirement for practice of rhythm, 171

Reasons for suspension of duty of childbearing, 172

underlying papal teaching on contraception and sterilization, 157-160

Recompense, financial, for bequeathing body, morality of, 251

Reference material on adult baptism, 318

on contraception and sterilization, 166

on euthanasia, 119-127

Refused baptism, 313

Regulations, classes, of Directives and codes, 26

precautionary, 27

Reich, Walter J., on diagnosis and management of infertility, 219

Relatives of patient, advantages of moderate standard of preserving life, 139

request for minister by, granting of, 323

responsibility for burial of amputated limbs, 330

Relaxation, muscular, result of hypnosis, 292

Religious, calling of minister by, rulings on, 321

care of patients, provisions for, 26

convictions of non-Catholic personnel, 27

directives, 17-25

obligations in management of hospital, 17

Remedy, alternative, lack, indication for hysterectomy, 212

effective, precedence over experimental procedure, 262

Remedies, severe, obsolescence by new treatments, 21

Renal homotransplantation, morality of, 251

Repeat cesarean section, 93-95, 213

Reproductive and non-reproductive organs, distinction, 6

Research on cyclic variations in fertility, moral aspects, 180

medical, importance in, of sound philosophical attudes toward man, 266

moral limits, 10

scientific, hypnosis as serious subject of, 289

worker's point of view, 263

Resident physicians, surgery by, morality of, 256

Resignation in preference to assistance at illicit operations, 333

Respiratory depression, reduction by use of hypnosis as adjunctive anesthetic, 292

Responsibility of patient, family, and hospital in respect to burial of amputated members, 331

Resurrection, Christian burial profession of faith and hope in, 326

Revelation, argument from, against self-abuse, 236

divine, communication of truth to man by God, 151

and natural moral law, 31

in relation to divine laws, 2

teaching authority of Church concerning, 31

natural, communication of God by, 151

supernatural, mysteries contained in, 151

on time of infusion of soul lacking, 66

Revelations of psychiatric patient, inviolability, 285

Revision of medico-moral codes, 19

Rhythm, correct use, assistance by doctors in justifiable cases, 179

and doctor, 176-182

method, periodic abstinence, 169

morality, 168-175

omission of doing good, 169

practice of, ability of both parties, second requirement, 170

to restrict family to 4 or 5 children, 173

Right to be happy, false liberalism, 235

to consent to experimentation, limitations, 266

on self, limits, 264

Rights, inalienable, of individual, superseding science or public welfare, 267

of investigators and subjects equal as human beings, 264

of patient to refuse psychiatric treatment, 284

Riquet, Michael, on castration on many pretexts in Middle Ages, 185

Risk of elective induction of labor, 144

of experimental procedures, 261

of life, definition, 65

and results of experimentation, due proportion between, 268

unjustified, to patient, in psychiatric treatment, prohibition, 284

Roentgen castration for carcinoma of breast, 203

Roman Congregations, 33

Rubella and therapeutic abortion, 82

Rupture of fallopian tube, treatment of, 106

of membranes, method of induction of labor, 146

of uterus, danger, as indication for repeat cesarean section, 94

Russell, Keith P., on trend against therapeutic abortion, 81

S

Sacrament of baptism, 299-319

of extreme unction, condition of patient for reception, 43

Last, notification of condition in time for, 48

Sacred Congregation of Holy Office on artificial insemination (1897), 230

on craniotomy, 69

functions, 33

response to question on burial of amputated members, 326

on salvation of non-Catholics, 322

Sacrilege, baptism of unwilling adult, 315

Safety of elective induction of labor in selected patients, 147

Salpingectomy, hysterectomy after, 214

Salvation of non-Catholics, 322

principal truths necessary for, 306

sacrament of baptism ordinary means instituted by God, 310

Salvific will of God, basis for baptism of person who has rejected conversion, 315

Sander, Hermann, case of euthanasia by, survey of opinions, 120

Saving for future, part of living wage, 173

Scandal, analysis of semen specimen obtained illicitly, problem of, 226
avoidance, in baptism of unrepentant, 314, 315, 316, 317

Schizophrenia, indication for electro-shock therapy, 295

Science articles and papal teaching on experimentation for good of others, comparison, 265

Science, supersedence by rights of individual, 267

Scientific articles on experimentation on human beings, 263-265
competence of moral theologians, 34
experiments on human beings, 261-269
that entail harm, individual prohibited from, 266
research, hypnosis as serious subject of, 289
use of amputated parts, 328

Scientist, willingness to terminate experiment when continuation seems dangerous, 268

Scriptures, Holy, divine law revealed in, 3

Scrupulosity, patient's conscience in, influence of psychiatrist on, 286

Secondary ends of marriage, 177

Secrecy, patient's right, safeguard, in narcosis and hypnosis, 282
professional, rigid observance in psychiatric cases, 285

Section, cesarean (*see* Cesarean section)

Secular press, condemnation of euthanasia, 125

Sedation, preoperative, use of hypnosis for, 292, 293

Sedatives, use for alleviation of pain, 115

Selection of patients for hypnosis, 292

Self-abuse, condemnation by St. Paul, 236

Self-control required by rhythm, dangers associated with, 170

Self-preservation, patient's duty of, 38

Semen analysis, hospital and, 225-227
of illicitly obtained specimens prejudicial to good morals, 226
emission, after prostatectomy, 196
expression by massage, for test specimen, 221
methods of obtaining for analysis, morality of, 219
classification, 220
contrary to nature, 241
licit, 224
removal from testicles or epididymes by aspiration, 221
from wife to obtain test specimen, 221
specimen brought by patient for analysis, handling of, 227

Sex faculty, unnatural use, prohibition, 183, 219
glands, removal in prostate cancer, 202
hormone control of prostatic cancer, 200
perversion, natural basis of sex morality, 236

Sexual activities, individualistic use in masturbation, 235
ethics, basic principle, 242
sin, re-enactment under narcosis, 286
urge, abnormal, castration for, 186

Shimkin, Michael B., on problem of experimentation in human beings, 264

Shock therapy, 294-297

Sign of wish for baptism, interpretation, 309

Sin, discussion of, 168
grave, contraception as, 154
occasion of, in practices of ghost surgery, 255
of Onan, nature of, 160
sexual, re-enactment under narcosis, 286

Sins, acts of contrition for, before baptism, 299
of adult, 305

Size of family, restriction by rhythm method, 174

Skin banks, morality of, 251
grafts, permissibility, 248
water of baptism to flow on, 298

Smith, George D., translation of Pope Pius XII's address on moral problems of married life, 167

Smolik, Edmund A., on case of intractable pain treated by prefrontal lobotomy, 276

Social indications for suspension of duty of childbearing, 172
life, consequences of donor insemination on, 236-239
disastrous effects of donor insemination on, 231
reasons for family limitation, defects in society, 173

Society, Christian, right of husband and wife only to generate children, principle of, 232
donors as ideal progenitors a menace to, 238
individual not subordinated to, 267
social and economic reasons for family limitations, defects of, 173

Soul, human, time of infusion into body, 66
principle of life, 5

salvation, truths necessary to be believed for, 307

Sperm (see also Semen)
immoral procurement, 235-236
involved in donor insemination, 231

Spiegel, J. P., on narcosynthesis, 282

Spiritual counselor on avoidance of childbirth, 179
damage to patient by deceit, 47
good done by Catholic nurses in state institutions, 335
powers, highest value in human person, 279
liberation, aim of treatment of mentally ill, 279
preparation for death, 43

Spontaneous abortion, 84-89

Spoon, cervical, lawful use for insemination, 228
technique for aiding marital intercourse, 239
plastic, use to obtain semen specimen from vagina, 225

Staff, voluntary control of elective induction of labor, 148

Standard, double, not permitted in Catholic hospitals, 26

Standards, Catholic, of family living wage, 173
professional, of means of preserving life, 137-139

Stander, H. J., on osteoclasis and cleidotomy, 98

State institution, spiritual good done by Catholic nurse in, 334

Statistics, basis for surgical decisions, condemnation, 277
on maternal death rate in hospitals with and without practice of therapeutic abortion, 76-78

Sterility (see also infertility)
by-product of suppression of ovarian function in breast carcinoma, 204

of husband, usual cause for
d o n o r insemination,
237
indirect, induced by therapy of
prostate cancer, 201
no cause for invalidation of
marriage, 241
procedures causing, 183-189
after prostatectomy, 196
prostatectomy as cause, 194
result of hysterectomy, permissibility, 211
of suppression of ovarian
function, 188
temporary, induction by stilbestrol, 189
tests, conservative use of prohibitions concerning, 21
licit methods of obtaining semen specimen, 224
moral aspects, 218-227
vasectomy and, 194-196
Sterilization and castration, distinction, 205
Catholic teaching on, 149-167
direct, as contraceptive measure,
161
decree forbidding, 155
and indirect, 12
distinction, 162
unacceptable, 53
eugenic, condemnation of, 155
hysterectomy for, prohibition,
213
indirect, justification, 184
result of necessary therapeutic procedure, 161
moral problems concerning,
arising from consequen-
ces of cesarean section,
91
operations, morality, 53
Stilbestrol, dysmenorrhea and, 189
Subordination of individual to
community, totalitarian-
ism, 266
Substitute for intercourse, is any
justifiable, 242-243
Success, hope of, in concept of
means of preserving life,
133

Suffering, unchristian view, 118-
119
Suicide, experiments with possible
result of, prohibition,
266
neglect of ordinary means of
preserving life tanta-
mount to, 130
voluntary euthanasia, 116
Sulfa drugs, substitution for vasectomy, 190
Sullivan, Charles Leavitt, on repeat cesarean section,
93
Sullivan, Joseph V., on arguments
against euthanasia, 120
Sulphadiazine, use in transurethral prostatic resection,
193
Supernatural revelation, communication of God by, 151
Supervisor, doctor and, 59-61
duty, 59-60
Supervisors, duty of informing
dying patient, 44
Surgeon or referring physician,
duty to inform patient,
45
Surgery, cerebral, moral justification, 270
cosmetic, morality of, 259
ghost, 254-257
morally objectionable, 245
hypnosis as anesthetic in, 288
means of mutilation, 8
radical, for malignant ovarian
tumors, 214
unnecessary, appendectomy as,
254
morally objectionable, 245
result of ghost surgery, 255
Surgical castration for carcinoma
of breast, 203
procedures, death-dealing, on
mother and child, 70
effecting sterility, 161
risk to patient in ghost surgery,
255

Survey of articles on trend against therapeutic abortion, 76-82

Suspension of duty of childbearing, 172

Symposium on leucotomy held at University of Sydney, 274

Symposium on problem of experimentation on human beings, in *Science,* 263

Syms-Huhner test for sterility, licitness, 225

Syringe, use in intrauterine baptism, 301

T

Teaching authority of Church, 31
Catholic, on contraception and sterilization, 149-167
official, on artificial birth prevention, 153-157
by Church, methods, 32-35
necessity for knowledge of natural law, 153
official, on therapeutic abortion, 69-71
ordinary ways, 32
papal, concerning contraception and sterilization, reasons underlying, 157
solemn and extraordinary, 32

Temporal preparation for death, 43

Temptations, vehement, castration means of suppressing, 186

Ten Commandments, instructions concerning human nature, 29

Tension, emotional, chief good effect of psychosurgery, 274

Termination of pregnancy, before viability, morality, 112

Testicles, infection, vasectomy for, 190

Testicular biopsy, licit method of obtaining semen specimen, 225

tissue, use in artificial insemination, 242

Theologians, diversity of views, recognized by Directives, 22
moral, scientific competence, 33
objections to Catholic position on therapeutic abortion, 71-75
opinions, confusion with teaching of Church, 185
on morality of removal of badly damaged uterus, 215-217

Theological controversy over baptism of unconscious unknown person, 311
over desire of "good man" for baptism, 310
definition of ordinary and extraordinary means of preserving life, 129
manuals, method of teaching, 32
opinion on treatment of tubal pregnancy, 106-107

Therapeutic abortion, 68-83
medical aspects, 75-82
objections to Catholic position, 71-75
pretexts, castration on, in Middle Ages, 185
procedures, unnecessary, morally objectionable, 245

Therapy, electro-shock, 294-297

Thomas Aquinas, St., on morality of mutilating procedures, 8-9
on natural truths derived by human reason, 152
on necessity of supernatural revelation, 166
theory on time of infusion of soul into body, 66

Titus, Paul, on cleidotomy, 98

Tonsillectomy, routine, as unnecessary surgery, 260

Totalitarian attitude of subordination of individual, 266

state, philosophy, and euthanasia, 116

Totality, principle, 8-11
application to parts of natural body, 247
as justification of medical experimentation, evil of, 267
in relation to mutilating procedures, 8-11
restatement, 246

Tranquilizers, use of, elimination of shock therapy by, 296

Tranquilizing drugs, needless prescription, 258

Transfusions, blood, permissibility, 248
for good of others, 245

Transplantation, organic, moral implications, 20
possible justification, 245
subject of theological controversy, 247

Transplants, corneal, morality of, 249

Transurethral prostatic resection, vasectomy with, 193

Treatment, alternative, lack, justification of hysterectomy, 211, 212

Treatments of dubious efficacy, choice between, 262

Trend against therapeutic abortion, survey of articles showing, 76-82

Trent, Council of, declaration on marriage, 233

Tribunals, functions, 33

Truth, communication by divine revelation, 151

Truths, natural, difficulties of deriving, by human reason, 152

Tubal pregnancy, abdominal pregnancy contrasted, with reference to double effect, 112

morality of operations for, 105-110
unruptured, expectancy treatment, 106

Tuberculosis, indication for hysterectomy, 210, 212

Tubes (see fallopian tubes)

U

Unborn child, indications for killing, 63, 64
a person, 66-67

Unchristian view of suffering, 118-119

Unconscious adults, baptism of, 300
dying patient, baptism, 308
and unknown person, question of baptism, 311-313

Unction, extreme (see Extreme unction)

Understanding, mutual, between doctors and supervisors, 59

Unforeseen doubts, 22-25

Unity of matrimony established by Creator, 233

Unknown unconscious person, question of baptism, 311-313

Unmarried men, licit methods of testing fertility, 220
woman, insemination, 237

Unnecessary procedures, 257-260

Usefulness, criterion of means of preserving life, 133
to others, false measure of human life, 119

Uterine bleeding and ovarian function, 187-188
pathology, hysterectomy for, 208-212

Uterus, baptism within, 301
damaged, morality of removal, theologians' opinions, 215-217
removal, moral question concerning, 213, 215-217

healthy, removal with diseased ovaries, 214
operations on infant within, 96-104
pathology, hysterectomy permissible for, 206
rupture, danger, as indication for repeat cesarean section, 94

Utility as criterion of ordinary means of preserving life, 134

Utopia and euthanasia, consideration of, 126

Utopians and euthanasia, 125

V

Vaginal cup, use to obtain semen specimen, 225
delivery vs. cesarean section, safety, 91

Validity of baptism of unconscious unknown person, 315

Value of human life, euthanasia and, 116
of life, measure of, 63, 64
supreme, in terminal cases, 280

Values, hierarchy of, in human person, 279
law, observances, 265

VanderVeldt and Odenwald on value of electro-shock therapy, 295

Vanity, catering to, cosmetic surgery as, 260

Vas ligation, substitute for vasectomy in preventing epididymitis, 196

Vasa, continuity, effect of prostatectomy, 195
deferentia, resection or ligation, 165

Vasectomy with prostatectomy, 190-198
to suppress pathological conditions, 165

routine, current practice, 191
substitutes, in preventing epididymitis, 196
Vermeersch, Arthur, on baptism of unconscious dying adults, 316
on use of perforated condom to obtain semen specimen, 221

Viable fetus, delivery by cesarean section after mother's death, 302

Viability of fetus, definition, 111
termination of pregnancy before, morality, 112

Virginity and marriage, distinct vocations, 175

Vitality of Directives, 19-21

Voluntary control by staff of elective induction of labor, 148

W

Wage, living, Catholic standards, 173
saving, essential part of living wage, 173

Water on head, baptism by, 298

Welfare, public, supersedence by rights of individual, 267

Werts, Hilary R., on moral arguments against euthanasia, 119

White, J. C., on neurosurgery for relief of pain, 123

Whitelaw, M. James, on cervical cap method, substitute for intercourse, 239

Will of Creator, procreation of life according to, harmony of, 230

Will of God expressed in creation of human nature, 30
independent of written or oral formulation, 30
salvific, basis for baptism of person who has rejected conversion, 315

373

suffering experienced through, 118

Willingness of both parties, first requirement for licit use of rhythm, 170
of subject, requisite for valid baptism, 305

Willson, J. Robert, on justifiable indications for elective induction of labor, 146
on results of elective induction of labor, 145

Woywod, S., on burial of amputated limbs, 328

X-Y-Z

X-ray, advantages of oophorectomy, in castration for breast cancer, 205
castration for carcinoma of breast, 203
means of mutilation, 8
treatment of ovaries for uterine bleeding, 188

Year Book of Obstetrics and Gynecology, reference for current trends, 188

Zalba, M., on opinions concerning removal of damaged uterus, 217

Special Index of Directives

Forty-two of the sixty directives are quoted in this book. Since all of these are explained in the book and since some of them are referred to in chapters where they are not explained, readers may wish a guide for quick reference. In the following table, the bold-face number represents the directive, and the light-face number is the page on which the directive is quoted.

1, 17. **2**, 17. **3**, 17. **4**, 17. **5**, 26. **6**, 36.

7, 42. **8**, 51. **9**, 60. **12**, 62. **13**, 62. **14**, 62.

15, 69. **17**, 85. **18**, 90. **19**, 96. **20**, 105. **21**, 116.

22, 128. **23**, 115. **26**, 111. **27**, 22. **29**, 219. **30**, 168.

31, 183. **32**, 199. **33**, 176. **34**, 206. **35**, 206. **36**, 206.

38, 219. **39**, 228. **40**, 245. **41**, 245. **42**, 261. **43**, 245.

44, 270. **45**, 282. **47**, 294. **48**, 245. **58**, 320. **59**, 325.

Of the remaining eighteen directives, seven (**16, 24, 28**, which deal with indirect abortion, killing, or risk; and **49-52**, which concern baptism) are actually explained in my text, even though not quoted. Seven others (**37, 53-57, 60**) are practically self-explanatory. **10, 11, 25**, and **46** are partially explained in various parts of this book; and more complete explanations of them can be found in the references given in the present edition of the *Directives* or that will be given in subsequent editions.

3510-98-1